CONVERSION FACTORS

1 meter = 39.37 inches = 3.281 feet
1 kilometer = 0.6214 mile
1 light-year = 9.460×10^{15} meters
1 mile/hour = 0.447 meter/second
1 year = 3.156×10^{7} seconds
1 newton = 0.2248 pound of force
1 electron-volt = 1.602×10^{-19} joule
1 horsepower = 746 watts

VECTOR PRODUCTS

$$\mathbf{A} \cdot \mathbf{B} = AB \cos \theta = A_x B_x + A_y B_y + A_z B_z$$

$$\mathbf{A} \times \mathbf{B} = \hat{\imath}(A_y B_z - A_z B_y) + \hat{\jmath}(A_z B_x - A_x B_z) + \hat{k}(A_x B_y + A_y B_x)$$

$$= \begin{vmatrix} \hat{\imath} & \hat{\jmath} & \hat{k} \\ A_x & A_y & A_z \\ B_x & B_y & B_z \end{vmatrix}$$

$$|\mathbf{A} \times \mathbf{B}| = AB \sin \theta$$

PREFIXES

deci	$(=10^{-1})$	d			
centi	$(=10^{-2})$	c			
milli	$(=10^{-3})$	m	kilo	$(=10^{3})$	k
micro	$(=10^{-6})$	μ	mega	$(=10^{6})$	M
nano	$(=10^{-9})$	n	giga	$(=10^{9})$	G
pico	$(=10^{-12})$	p	tera	$(=10^{12})$	T
femto	$(=10^{-15})$	f			
atto	$(=10^{-18})$	a			

INTRODUCTORY MECHANICS

INTRODUCTORY MECHANICS

Edwin F. Taylor, *Wesleyan University*

John Wiley & Sons, Inc., New York · London

Library of Congress Catalog Card Number: 63–11454
Printed in the United States of America

to Helen

Preface

This book presents an attempt to develop the fundamental field of mechanics with a degree of care, rigor, and sophistication not yet typical of introductory treatments of the subject. Physics is now too big an enterprise, too subtle and mathematical a discipline, to "cover" meaningfully in one year. I feel that the subject matter for an introductory college physics course for students expecting to major in science and engineering should be selected from a very short list of the fields of physics most used as tools in research and technology. This subject matter can then be treated with exceptional thoroughness. A list of such fields will include at least classical and relativistic mechanics, electromagnetic theory, and quantum mechanics. Perhaps the subjects on even so short a list cannot all be introduced with care in one year. Of these subjects, mechanics has traditionally been taught first. There are good reasons for this choice. Mechanics lies near the surface of common experience, and the mathematics used in mechanics is both less advanced than, and fundamental to, the mathematics used in electromagnetic theory and quantum mechanics.

Preliminary versions of this book have been used at Wesleyan University in the first semester of a freshman physics course composed of a small number of students carefully selected for their high aptitudes, good mathematics background, and motivation in science. The second semester is devoted to electromagnetic theory.

A casual examination of the text will show two devices which deserve comment. A series of questions is embedded in the text. These *text questions* have several purposes: to allow the student to test his understanding of the material; to encourage him to fill in missing steps and to carry out simple extensions of the development presented in the text;

and to probe more deeply into the logical foundations underlying the definitions and results. The instructor may wish to assign some of these questions as exercises in addition to those at the end of the chapters, but this assignment should not be presented in such a way as to imply that questions not assigned are unimportant. Some questions carry such profound implications that a careful and comprehensive answer would be suitable for submission to a learned journal. Such questions are labeled *class discussion questions.* Inevitably some students will find the text questions distracting. Such students should be encouraged to read first through the text itself without stopping to answer the questions, and to use the questions as a tool for deeper study and review on subsequent readings.

A second device is the so-called *project.* There are several applications of mechanics which are so important in themselves (such as the motion of a projectile or the Bohr atom) or so important for later study in physics (such as the harmonic oscillator or Rutherford scattering) or of so much current interest (such as the vertical ascent of a rocket or the stabilization of an orbiting astronomical observatory) that they are important parts of an introductory textbook in mechanics. At the same time these applications involve little new fundamental material. I have chosen to place these applications in a series of projects which the student works through for himself with appropriate guidance from the text. The use of projects results in some economy of space in the text, but, more important, it gives the student practice in working out significant material for himself. The instructor will select projects to be assigned as exercises or outside examinations according to the time available and his own tastes and convictions concerning their significance.

Chapter 4 on the mathematics of mechanics includes simple derivations in differential and integral calculus along with an introduction to vectors. Even though physical examples are useful in introducing calculus, it is hard to justify the inclusion of calculus in this text. Calculus is included because first year college mathematics appears from the outside to be in even greater flux than first year college physics. The physics instructor can select, summarize, and omit sections of this material to compensate for the current state of mind of his colleagues in mathematics.

Four chapters on the theory of relativity conclude the text. This material should not be omitted from an introductory course in mechanics. Not only is relativistic mechanics in everyday use by physicists, but also in some very real sense a student cannot be said to have a thorough grasp of classical mechanics unless he understands the limits of its validity. If this understanding does not come early in his career, he will have many preconceived notions which will be difficult to overcome later.

Probably the instructor will find that there is too much material in the text to cover in one semester. This gives him some latitude of choice. It should not mean the omission of all the material on relativity. Although the first three chapters are intended to be rigorous enough not to lead the student into later difficulties, it is probably wasteful of time to follow every philosophical trail that leads from this material, at least until the student has been through the relativity section once. The following sections can be omitted without loss of continuity with the rest of the text: Section 6.9 to the end of Chapter 6; Section 9.3 or 9.4 to the end of Chapter 9. In addition, Sections 7.5 and 7.6 can be shortened by deriving expressions for torque, angular momentum, and kinetic energy with respect to the center of mass instead of with respect to an arbitrary moving point; and Section 8.10 can be shortened by deriving expressions for components of torque and angular momentum along an axis which moves parallel to itself and passes through the center of mass. Project X makes a conceptually complete stopping place if there is not time for the last chapter of the book.

Although this book was designed and used initially for an introductory course, there is no reason why it cannot be adapted for use in more advanced courses wherever the material is relevant. Such adaptation might involve a summary of the first four or five chapters and use of some of the later material for which there may not be time in one semester of an introductory course.

As used earlier in this preface the term *classical mechanics* will be taken to refer to non-relativistic non-quantum mechanics, that is, to the description of the motion of macroscopic particles moving with speeds very much less than the speed of light. According to this convention, relativistic mechanics is not part of classical mechanics.

I have had the suggestions and advice of nearly twenty reviewers on the unfinished manuscript. The chances for penetrating comment and correction have been among the most pleasant surprises encountered in this work. Many of these reviewers have remained anonymous to me, but I am particularly grateful to Professor Bruce Hawkins of Smith College and Professor Stanley Deser of Brandeis University whose thoughtful and extensive suggestions have had an important influence on the rigor and clarity of the final draft.

Some obligations cannot adequately be paid or acknowledged. I owe such obligations to Mrs. Clara May Corley and to Miss Constance Carpentiere for their swift competence and good humor through many mimeographed drafts. Much of the emotional burden of writing has been shared by my wife with strength, cheerfulness, and forbearance. To her this book is dedicated.

EDWIN F. TAYLOR

Middletown, Connecticut
January 1963

To the Student

Physics has the reputation of being a difficult subject. Perhaps this is because the laws of physics are expressed and manipulated through mathematical forms and because physics is a cumulative discipline—an understanding of each part of physics depends on an understanding of much of the material that has gone before.

In another sense physics is the simplest of disciplines. It deals with the simplest possible physical problems. This course begins by considering a single particle at rest in interstellar space. There is no physical system simpler than this. We shall carry out experiments on this particle and express the results of these experiments in a form which is both simple and concise.

Do not be fooled by the apparent simplicity of some of the experiments we carry out in this region of space. These experiments are simple in order that the assumptions and the results will be clearly outlined. Once the results derived from these experiments are thoroughly understood, we can move out from these results in two different directions. One of these directions is toward more complicated and hence more realistic problems and applications. The other of these directions is toward a more profound study of the assumptions which underlie classical mechanics. Travel along both of these paths will be richly rewarding not only in the developing ability to solve significant problems in mechanics but also in the insight into one of the fields of intellectual endeavor where the foundations can be probed most deeply with substantial agreement among professionals in the field.

Contents

. . . the wise man looks into space,
and does not regard the small as too little,
nor the great as too big;
for he knows that there is
no limit to dimensions.

Lao-tse

chapter 1

Particle at rest

1.1 INTRODUCTION

Consider a particle at rest in interstellar space.

This particle can be a bit of cosmic dust or a chunk of rock blasted loose in an ancient collision of stars or an empty tin can thrown out of a passing space ship. In order to organize our thoughts, let us suppose that this particle is large enough that it would be visible to our unaided eyes if we happened to be nearby but not so large that we would have any difficulty in describing its exact location. If someone asked us where the particle is, we could point our finger toward a *single* point and say "Right there." In earth-terms this particle is something we might hold in our hand. We shall call it *particle one*. (See Fig. 1-1.)

Particle one is in interstellar space. There are many regions in the universe which are situated vast distances from our sun and from any other star. Particle one is in such a region. We cannot say yet whether or not the presence of even distant stars will have any kind of effect on particle one. But since the stars are so distant and so numerous, it seems reasonable to suppose that whatever effect they have on particle one will be some kind of average effect due to many stars. For this reason the results of any experiments we carry out on particle one should not depend on the *detailed* arrangement of distant stars. Thus the same experiments should give the same results in many such regions of interstellar space.

In the immediate region surrounding particle one there will almost certainly be a few atomic particles (mostly protons and electrons), perhaps a small magnetic field, and some light from the stars and from the lamps we shall use to observe particle one during our experiments. None of these should have any measurable effect on the experiments we carry out with a particle large enough to be visible to the naked eye.

Fig. 1-1. Particle one.

Question

1-1 In the first paragraph of this section, what assumption about the propagation of light is implied in the words "we could point our finger toward a single point and say 'Right there.' "?

Class Discussion Question

1-2 What sort of procedure would you use to verify the statement made in the last sentence of the last paragraph above? How would you verify that the observer, his equipment, and his methods of measurement can be arranged to have negligible effect on experiments with particle one?

1.2 ESTABLISHING A REFERENCE POINT. We say that particle one is *at rest* in interstellar space. What can we mean by the phrase "at rest"? There is no firm ground on which we can stand and watch the particle to see if it moves past us or stays fixed, no laboratory walls from which to measure the position of the particle so that we can time its motion if it moves about. On earth we measure motion *with respect to something* which we consider fixed. What can be considered fixed in interstellar space?

This question has perplexed scientists for a hundred years and more. A great deal of time and energy has gone into the search for a "frame of reference" which can be considered stationary in space independently of the motion of the earth or the sun or the galaxy. According to our best current knowledge, the answer to the question "What can be considered fixed in interstellar space?" is "Nothing." There is *no unique* point in all the universe that scientists can point to and say "That point is at rest: the position of all particles, stars, and galaxies may be measured with respect to that point."

Since there is no universal fixed point, we shall have to do the best we can in setting up a point of our own from which to measure the position of particle one.

As a point of reference, let us simply use a second particle. We shall call this second particle the *reference particle.* We shall attempt to place the reference particle near particle one in such a way that the two particles do not move with respect to one another as far as we can tell with our unaided eyes. It turns out to be a difficult feat in empty space to place the reference particle near particle one so that particle one does not move with respect to the reference particle. Almost invariably a small push will be given to the reference particle as it is released, so that the two particles appear to move apart or else collide with each other. After sufficient practice, however, we develop enough skill to complete the following procedure.

Procedure for Determining a Point of Reference in Interstellar Space

1. Obtain a reference particle which is easily visible but is not very much larger than particle one.

2. Place the reference particle near particle one but not touching it.

Fig. 1-2. Particle one at rest.

3. Release the reference particle and watch to see if it appears to move nearer to or farther from particle one.

4. If the reference particle *does* appear to move nearer to or farther from particle one, repeat steps 2, 3, and 4. If it *does not* appear to move in this way, proceed to step 5.

5. If the reference particle does not appear to move nearer to or farther from particle one, then the position of the reference particle may be taken as a reference point and particle one is said to be "at rest with respect to the reference particle."*

* This definition of "at rest" includes the case in which both particles remain at constant separation from one another but revolve about each other with respect to the "fixed stars," as is required if the gravitational attraction between the particles cannot be neglected. If particle one is nearer to the reference particle than the accuracy with which we choose to measure distance, then this revolution involves negligible displacement and particle one is sensibly at rest. This stopgap measure will allow us to ignore the "fixed stars" until after the inertial reference frame is defined in Sec. 4.15.

Questions

1-3 For what experimental reasons is the reference particle not allowed to touch particle one?

1-4 Would we be wrong in taking the first "particle at rest in interstellar space" to be the reference particle and calling the second particle we position near it "particle one"?

1-5 Suppose that you set up a reference point according to the foregoing procedure so that your particle one is at rest with respect to the reference particle. Suppose that your roommate executes the same procedure on a nearby "particle two," using his own reference particle. Suppose that these two reference particles are moving with respect to one another so that his reference particle moves away from yours and disappears in the distance. Is your particle one at rest or is his particle two at rest? Are both at rest or is neither at rest?

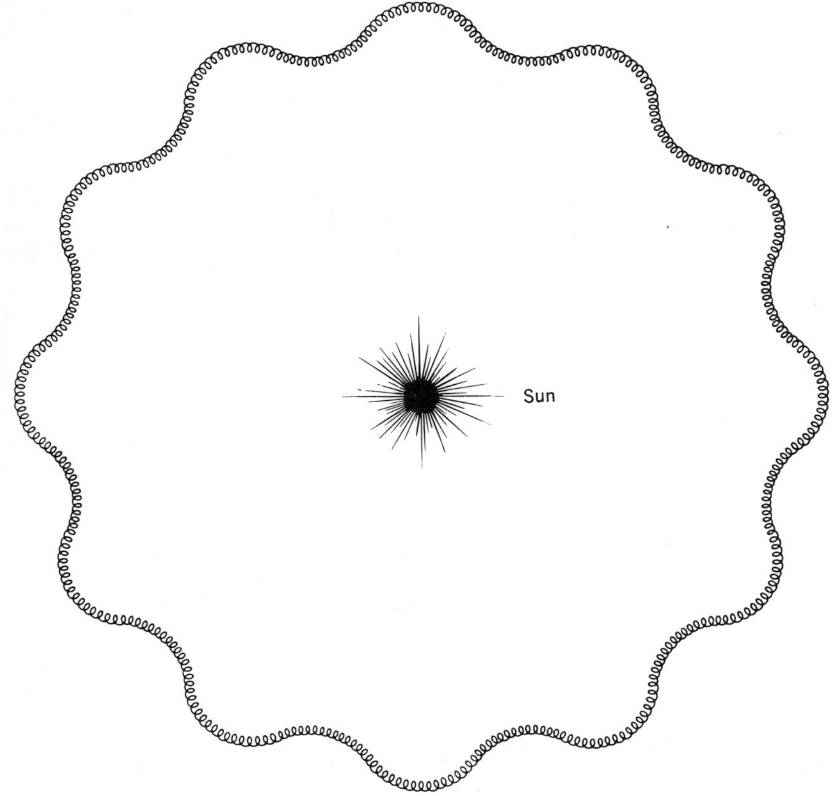

Fig. 1-3. Picture of the motion of a point fixed on the surface of the earth during one year. Not to scale.

1.3 WHY BOTHER? Why is it worthwhile to begin the study of physics by setting up a reference point in interstellar space when there are comfortable laboratories on earth with fixed walls and tables on which experiments can be carried out much more simply?

First of all, of course, there is no place on earth where a particle can be said to be free of forces. Even if drafts of air, vibration, and friction can be effectively eliminated, the "force of gravity"—whatever that really means—is always present. Furthermore, can a point on the surface of the earth be said to be "fixed"? The common view of the motion of the earth is that it rotates on its axis approximately once a day. This means that a point on the surface of the earth follows a circular path around the axis of the earth. The common view of the motion of the earth and moon is that they revolve about one another as they follow a path around the sun. Figure 1-3, not drawn to scale, gives a picture of the resultant motion of a point on the surface of the earth during one year according to this common view. In this picture the sun remains at rest. Yet in the opinion of astronomers the sun is not at rest but moves in a path around the center of our galaxy which we see as the Milky Way. Is the center of our galaxy at rest? This is the same question we hoped to avoid by choosing a point on the earth as our "fixed point"!

It is true that for many experiments on earth these relative motions may be neglected. However, they cannot be neglected in studying many geological occurrences, the motion of air masses over the surface of the earth, long range rockets, earth satellites, the motions of planets, stars, and space ships. We cannot have much confidence in a science of mechanics which is not able to describe these phenomena.

chapter 2

The uniform motion of a particle

2.1 MOTION IN A STRAIGHT LINE. Suppose that we have followed the "Procedure for determining a point of reference in interstellar space" so that particle one is near but not touching the reference particle and sensibly at rest with respect to it.

Now let us give particle one a whack with a golf club, making sure that the golf club does not touch the reference particle. What happens to particle one? We are not yet able to describe the motion of particle one while the golf club is in contact with it. But, *after it leaves the golf club, particle one moves in a straight line.* This is an *experimental result.* There is no way to predict ahead of time how the particle will move after leaving the golf club without trying the experiment to find out.

But what is meant by the term "a straight line"? This is a problem in mathematics rather than physics, but a simple physical straightedge might

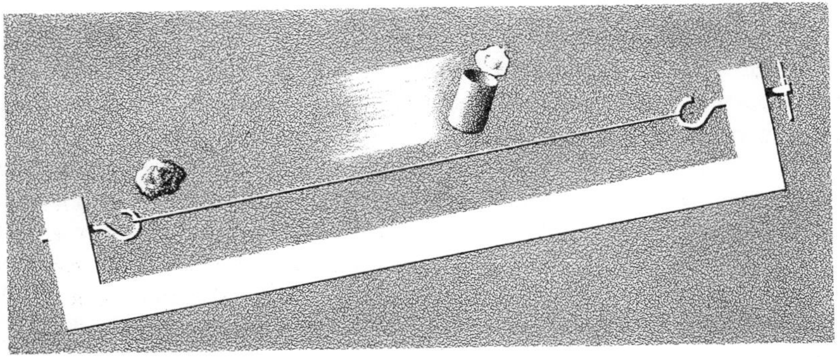

Fig. 2-1. Particle one moving in a straight line.

be made of a rigid U-shaped frame across which a flexible wire is stretched under tension. The stretched wire can be made to be a very good approximation to a mathematical straight line. This straightedge can be laid alongside the path of particle one to verify that this path is a straight line.

Class Discussion Question

2-1 In order to use this straightedge it must be positioned so that it is also at rest with respect to the reference particle. How can you make sure that after this positioning the straightedge is not rotating like an airplane propeller? Show that instead of the statement, "Particle one moves in a straight line," a more careful statement would be, "A straightedge can be positioned in a way such that every point on the straightedge is at rest with respect to the reference particle and such that particle one moves along the straightedge with the minimum distance from particle one to straightedge neither increasing nor decreasing."

Another observation we make is that after particle one leaves the golf club it moves with constant speed. Before we can give quantitative meaning to the word "speed," it is necessary to define carefully what is meant by the terms "length," "distance," and "time."

2.2 LENGTH, DISTANCE, AND TIME. Length and time are central concepts of physics. Together with mass and electrical charge they form the basis for the description of every event studied by the natural sciences. The fact that all of us have an intuitive concept of length and time from childhood tends to obscure the fact that these concepts require very precise definitions in physics. The Theory of Relativity which Einstein developed at the turn of the century came from a careful re-examination of the meaning of these terms. Many physicists predict that a complete understanding of the atomic nucleus will come only after reinterpretation of the meaning of length on the minute scale of the nucleus.

Length. The definition of length always involves a *unit length*, and the process of measuring the length of an object always involves comparing the object with the unit length.

We may take any object to be a *unit length*. However, it is convenient if the object taken as the unit length is as rigid as possible (not the diameter of a balloon filled with water) and, to start with at least, not too long or too short to be easily manipulated (not the diameter of the sun). Suppose that we take as our unit of length a particular wooden matchstick. We expect that such a matchstick will not change length very much and is easy to carry about and use in the following experiments.

To measure the length of an object we compare the object with the unit length. A simple procedure for doing this is to place the head of the matchstick next to one end of the object to be measured, make a mark on the object near the other end of the matchstick, then move the matchstick along its own length with respect to the object until the head of the matchstick coincides with the mark on the object. Then another mark is made on the object at the other end of the matchstick, the matchstick is moved along its own length again until the head of the matchstick coincides with the second mark on the object. This operation is repeated until the other end of the object is reached. The "length" of the object is defined as the number of times the unit length has been laid along the object in the course of this procedure. The mathematics of measuring length is thus reduced to counting.

Questions

2-2 Given a matchstick as a unit of length, how would you divide it into ten equal parts? (There are several ways to do this.) Modify the procedure above for measuring length to include objects whose dimensions are less than a unit length and also objects whose dimensions are not an integral number of unit lengths.

2-3 Does the object whose length is measured using the above procedure have to be straight in the dimension being measured? How curved can it be and still use the matchstick as a unit length? How would you measure the thickness of an irregular body in terms of the unit length?

Class Discussion Question

2-4 How do we know that our matchstick which is taken as the unit length is not continually stretching or shrinking in length, that is, getting "longer" or "shorter"?

The foregoing procedure is the basis of the measurement of the length of an object. In addition to measuring the lengths of objects, however, we shall want to measure the distance from the reference particle to particle one.

Class Discussion Question

2-5 Show that the procedure for measuring the length of an object cannot be used to measure a distance greater than one unit length between two particles in space because some of the instructions (e.g., "make a mark on the object" and "move the matchstick along its own length with respect to the object") cannot be translated to have a unique meaning when applied to the measurement of a distance in space.

The measurement of the distance between two particles in space can be carried out using a measuring rod. A *measuring rod* is simply a straight

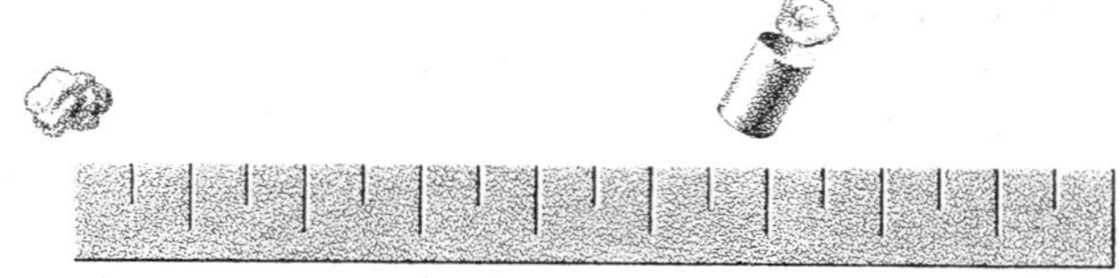

Fig. 2-2. Measuring the distance between the reference particle and particle one using a measuring rod.

rod along whose length has been marked a number of unit lengths (usually subdivided into fractions). The distance of particle one from the reference particle can be measured by using the following procedure. Place the measuring rod so that one end is at rest near but not touching the reference particle and any other point on the rod is near but not touching particle one. Count the number of unit lengths (and fractions) from the end of the rod near the reference particle to the point on the rod adjacent to particle one. *This number of unit lengths is defined as the distance between the reference particle and particle one.*

The measuring rod can also be used to measure the length of an object. In fact, the matchstick will not be used very often once the measuring rod is constructed. Nevertheless the matchstick used as a unit length remains very important both conceptually and in practice. The matchstick remains the *standard of length.* After it has been used to lay off unit lengths on the measuring rod, the matchstick can be laid aside in some safe place (such as the National Bureau of Standards) to be used only for making more measuring rods or checking the accuracy of old ones.

Questions

2-6 Suppose that the distance from the reference particle to particle one is measured several times and is found to remain constant. If now the measuring rod is reversed and the distance from particle one to the reference particle is measured, will this measurement give the same result? Is it *obvious* that the result will be the same? Does this conclusion follow from the preceding argument, or must it be verified by experiment?

2-7 Suppose that any large object can be considered to be made up of smaller particles which are held together in some way. Show that the concept of "length of the object" can be reduced to the concept of the distance between certain of these particles. Does this reduce the conceptual difficulties involved in measuring the lengths of curved objects?

Time. Just as length is measured in terms of an object (a matchstick) taken to be the unit of length, so time is measured in terms of a mechanism which produces repeatedly the unit of time. An ordinary clock is such a mechanism. Until recently the time it takes the earth to rotate once on its axis was the basis of our time scale and all other units of time were defined in terms of this unit. The unit of time could just as well be defined in terms of the period of rotation of any other planet or other object rotating on its axis. A very good clock for our experiments in interstellar space might be a large object with a spot painted on it. The object could be set in rotation in such a way that the painted spot would be on its "equator" and the unit of time would be the interval between reappearances of the spot. Since there would be no frictional forces of bearings or air drag, such a clock would not run down. Our later study will show that such a clock would be perfectly satisfactory as long as it remained rigid once it was set in rotation. Alternatively we could use an ordinary spring clock or stopwatch (why not a pendulum clock?). The spring clock might run at a different rate in interstellar space than on earth because of the absence of air drag and weight of parts, but this does not concern us. All such mechanisms will be given the general label "clock."

Questions

2-8 Given a clock consisting of a rotating particle with a spot on it, how would you construct and set in operation a second clock which indicates the same unit of time? How would you construct and set in operation a clock which gives units of time $\frac{1}{10}$ as long as the first clock?

2-9 How would you establish whether or not a spring clock runs at a different rate in interstellar space than it does on earth?

2-10 How can you show that any given clock runs uniformly, that is, reproduces repeatedly the *same* unit of time?

In defining a unit length or a unit of time we make use of the intuitive ideas of length and time which we all share. The measurement of length or time using such definitions can be criticized as being based on circular logic. We use an intuitive concept of the length of an object to define a unit length which we then use to measure the length of another object. Definitions in physics are often based on such refinements of intuitive concepts. Most physicists do not worry much about the logical looseness of such a procedure and defend it by pointing to the agreement between the results of such an analysis and the results of further experiments. Nevertheless this logical looseness of definitions is a matter of great interest to those who study the philosophical foundations of science.

We shall assume in the experiments which follow that all clocks and measuring rods are at rest with respect to our reference particle. If clocks and measuring rods are not at rest with respect to our reference particle, the analysis becomes more complicated. This case will be treated in Chapter 12.

2.3 AN EXPERIMENT. With a measuring rod and a clock we can carry out some quantitative experiments on particle one after it has been hit with a golf club. It has already been established that particle one moves in a straight line. The measuring rod can thus be laid along the path of the particle with one end of the measuring rod very close to but not touching the reference particle. By keeping an eye on both particle one and the clock it is possible to record the position of particle one along the measuring rod at, for example, the end of each unit of time. The distance that particle one has moved along the rod from its initial position we shall call *displacement*. A record of the displacement of particle one at the end of each interval might look as follows.

Units of Time	Displacement (Units of Distance)
0	Struck by golf club
1	Still in contact with golf club
2	1.5
3	3.0
4	4.5
5	6.0
6	7.5
7	9.0
8	10.5

Physicists, as professionals, would prefer to look at graphs rather than tables. The reason for this preference is simple and appealing: physicists are lazy like everyone else, and it is easier and quicker to look at a graph. The graph in Fig. 2-4 shows a plot of these numbers.

Fig. 2-3. Timing the motion of particle one.

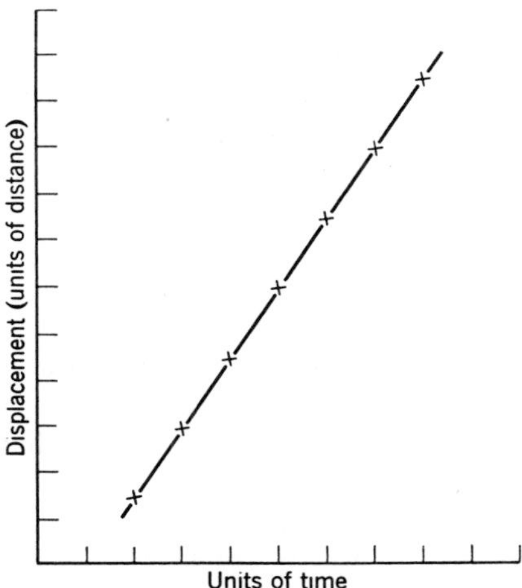

Fig. 2-4. Displacement vs time curve for particle one hit by a golf club.

Question

2-11 What can be said about the motion of the particle before 2 units of time or after 8 units of time have elapsed?

In the graph the crosses represent the observations. They appear to lie on a straight line, and the straight line is drawn through them. Any continuous curve drawn through points representing observations on a displacement vs time graph is called a *displacement vs time curve* or a *world line*.

The continuous line is drawn through the experimental points of Fig. 2-4 in order to make it possible to use the tools of analytic geometry to analyze the motion of the particle represented by this curve. Drawing a continuous curve through experimental points raises one of the most involved and subtle problems of physics—that of *continuity*. What is meant physically by drawing a *continuous* curve (in this case a straight line) through a set of *discrete* points which result from an experiment? The physical meaning might be that, if we should make displacement vs time determinations as closely spaced in time as we are able to, then all the resulting points in the displacement vs time graph will still lie on this continuous curve (within the limits of experimental error). But no matter how rapidly we take readings, we shall never be able to verify *every* point on the continuous curve because mathematically there are an *infinite* number of points on any segment of a continuous curve. Hence the *mathematical* justification for drawing a continuous curve through a set of experimental points is not a rigorous one. As usual, the physicist justifies his mathematical liberties by pointing to the fact that later results of the analysis of such continuous curves can be used to predict correctly the results of more complicated experiments. Such a justification defers rather than solves the problem of continuity.

Questions

2-12 Even though *every* point on the world line cannot be verified experimentally, can *any given* point be so verified?

2-13 Discuss to what extent the problem of continuity is a serious one for "particles," defined as objects which are large enough to be seen by the unaided human eye. In the study of the motion of what other objects will the problem be a more serious one?

2.4 SPEED. Now we are able to see exactly what is meant by saying that particle one moves with constant speed after it leaves the golf club. The table in the preceding section shows that particle one moved 1.5 units of distance during the third interval of time. The same distance was traveled in the fourth interval of time. In fact, in this experiment particle one moved 1.5 units of distance in each unit of time after leaving the golf club.

The *speed* of a particle is defined as the number of units of distance the particle travels per unit of time. Thus in the experiment above particle one has a speed of 1.5 units of distance per unit of time. Since this speed is the same for all units of time measured, particle one is said to have a *constant* speed.

Questions

2-14 In a repetition of the experiment conducted above the particle is again found to travel with constant speed. However, after leaving the golf club it moves through four units of distance in five units of time. What is its speed?

2-15 The reference particle is not mentioned in the definition of speed. In what way is the presence of the reference particle necessary to this definition?

In a graph like that of Fig. 2-4 the *mathematical slope* of a straight line is defined as the change in the vertical coordinate for a portion of the line divided by the change in the horizontal coordinate for the same portion of the line. Equivalently it can be defined as the tangent of the angle (θ in Fig. 2-5) which the straight line makes with the horizontal axis. Since the tangent of an angle is unitless, the mathematical slope has no

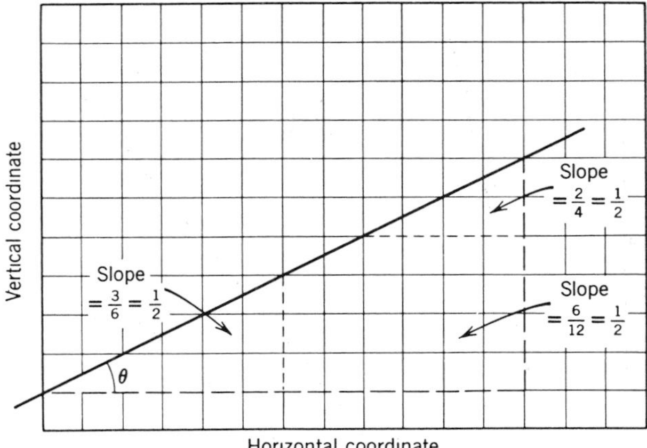

Fig. 2-5. Measuring the slope of a straight line.

units. The calculation of this slope is shown graphically in Fig. 2-5. Notice that, no matter where on the straight line we calculate the slope or how large or small a portion of the straight line is used in the calculation, the calculated slope is the same for each of these determinations.

The *physical slope* of a straight world line is defined as the change in the position of the particle together with the units of distance for any portion of the line, divided by the time interval together with the units of time for the same portion of the line. Graphically the determination of physical slope proceeds the same as the determination of mathematical slope. From the definition of speed it can be seen that the physical slope of a straight world line is numerically equal to the speed of the particle and has the units of speed as well. The fact that the physical slope of a straight world line is everywhere the same is a reflection of the fact that the particle subject to no forces moves with constant speed.

Questions

2-16 Show that the mathematical slope of a straight world line depends on the relative *scale* to which the displacement and time plots are made, while the physical slope of this line is independent of scale.

2-17 While particle one was still at rest with respect to the reference particle, was it moving with constant speed? How does the world line look for this case?

Now suppose we repeat this experiment several times, retrieving particle one each time, placing it at rest with respect to the reference particle,

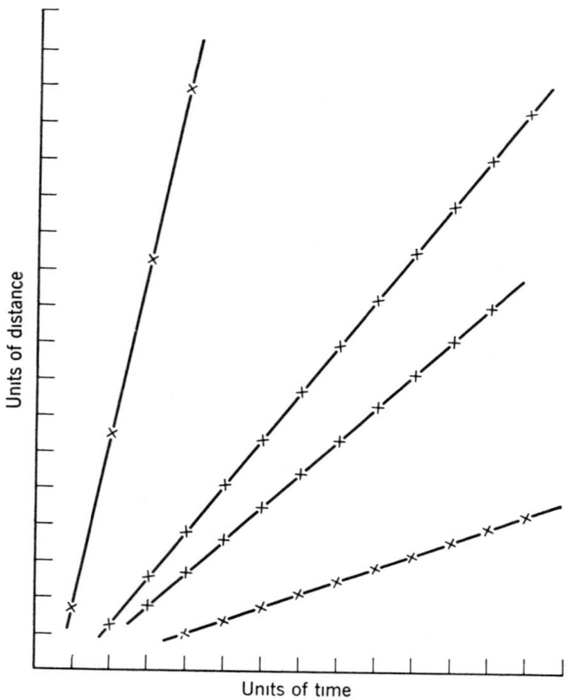

Fig. 2-6. Possible set of displacement vs time curves for particle one hit repeatedly from rest by a golf club.

hitting particle one with the golf club, and drawing its world line through a graph of experimental points determined with the measuring rod and clock. A possible set of results is plotted in Fig. 2-6. Notice that no two experimental straight lines have the same slope. This means that, although the speed of particle one is constant for each experiment, this speed can be different for different repetitions of the experiment. In the next chapter we shall investigate the reason for these different speeds.

What is the greatest speed that has ever been measured? A flash of light moves with a great speed. Let the phrase "the speed of light" refer to the speed of such a flash of light. Experiments show that the speed of light is different in different materials. For instance, light moves more slowly in glass than in the earth's atmosphere. It is found that light travels faster in space (i.e., in a vacuum) than it travels in any material medium.

Question

2-18 Design an experiment to measure the speed of a flash of light in space. Although the experiment may require simple materials, it should be designed to measure very great speeds. (A flash of light travels a distance equal to the circumference of the earth in less than one-seventh of a second.) How could this experiment be modified to measure the speed of light in another material such as air or glass?

No particle has been observed to move faster than the speed of light in space. There is nothing in what we have said thus far which would explain *why* greater speeds are not possible. For the present we shall simply accept this as an experimental fact.*

Question

2-19 Some atomic particles have been observed to move in the atmosphere of the earth at speeds greater than the speed of light in the atmosphere. How can this be possible if the preceding statements about a maximum speed are true?

Class Discussion Question

2-20 Consider the following paradox: Observer A sees particle one move past his reference particle with a speed of four-fifths the speed of light. Observer B, riding with particle one, sees a second particle—"particle two"—move past him with a speed four-fifths the speed of light. If these two speeds lie in the same direction, will not particle two move past observer A with a speed greater than the speed of light? You should be confused by this paradox. Show that the assumptions made at the end of Sec. 2.2 have been violated and that we might expect trouble.

2.5 STANDARDS OF LENGTH AND TIME. Suppose that a second experimenter watches your experiments and takes readings of displacement vs time with his own clock and measuring rod. Will his results be the same as yours? There is no other way of answering this question than to try an experiment to find out. Experiment shows that, if the clocks and measuring rods used by the second experimenter are also at rest with respect to your reference particle, the world lines which he derives for particle one will be the same as yours. This is fortunate, because the usefulness of natural science depends on the fact that two or more observers can agree on the results of an experiment. Of course it would be necessary to compare measuring rods and units of time. The second experimenter may have chosen a matchstick of different length as his unit of length and a clock which runs faster or slower than yours. Such comparison is not difficult and would be the result of an auxiliary experiment.

* See Milton A. Rothman, "Things that Go Faster than Light," *Scientific American*, July 1960, p. 142.

Question

2-21 Obtain two pencils of unequal length. Suppose that each is a unit of length for two different experimenters. Compare their length quantitatively, using no other ruler or measuring instrument.

No law of physics is violated if each experimenter has his own units of length and time. The exchange of experimental results between experimenters is helped, however, if all experimenters use the same units of length and time. If a single *primary standard of length* is chosen and placed in a central location, then any number of measuring rods (*secondary standards of length*) may be made using this primary standard. Similarly a primary standard of time would consist of a carefully regulated clock with which other clocks can be compared.

The most popular and convenient unit of length used in science is the *meter*. The meter is a little over a yard in length (exactly 39.37 inches). Until 1960 the meter was defined as the distance between two scratches on a platinum-iridium bar called the *international prototype meter* kept in Sèvres, France. Techniques of measurement have become refined to the point that the width of these scratches introduce measurable uncertainty in the unit of length. For this reason the 11th General Conference on Weights and Measures defined the meter in terms of a multiple of the wavelength of the orange-red light given off by one of the isotopes of the element krypton when excited in an electric discharge. According to this definition the meter is equal to 1,650,763.73 wavelengths of the orange-red light of krypton 86. Optical methods allow measuring devices to be calibrated in terms of this wavelength with very high accuracy.* An important advantage of this definition of the meter is that it is possible for any well-equipped laboratory to use the primary unit of length.

For very small or very large distances the meter may not be a convenient unit of length. For this reason fractions and multiples of the meter are often used as follows:

one kilometer (km) $= 10^3$ meters
one centimeter (cm) $= 10^{-2}$ meter
one millimeter (mm) $= 10^{-3}$ meter
one micron (μ) $= 10^{-6}$ meter (approximate size of a bacterium)
one angstrom (Å) $= 10^{-10}$ meter (approximate size of an atom)
one fermi (F) $= 10^{-15}$ meter (approximate size of a nucleus)

Notice that all these units differ from the meter by factors of ten. This makes it easy to convert from one unit to another by simply moving the

* David Halliday and Robert Resnick, *Physics for Students of Science and Engineering*, Part II, John Wiley and Sons, Inc., New York, 1962, p. 998.

decimal point. The so-called English system of units, which has 5280 feet per mile, 12 inches per foot, and inches subdivided by powers of two, is very cumbersome and is rarely used in scientific work. Appendix II presents definitions of English units of length.

The unit of time used in science is the *second.* Until 1960 the second was defined in terms of the rotation of the earth on its axis. However, it was discovered that this rotation was slowing down by a small but measureable amount with the passage of time. For this reason the 11th General Conference on Weights and Measures redefined the standard second in terms of the revolution of the earth about the sun. According to this definition the *ephemeris second* is defined as 1/31,556,925.9747 of the tropical year starting at midnight December 31-January 1 of the year 1900. A more complete explanation of this standard of time is given in Appendix I. It is necessary to choose a particular year in setting a standard because the length of the tropical year changes from year to year. This change is predictable to a high order of accuracy, so that clocks can be set from present astronomical observation even though the year 1900 is not accessible for direct measurement.

The ephemeris second is unambiguously defined in this way. However, the actual calibration of a clock in terms of this standard is a lengthy and complicated procedure involving numerous corrections and many subtle concepts exasperating to impatient physicists. So called "atomic clocks" are now being developed which use the properties of certain atoms to measure time with great uniformity and accuracy.* Many physicists regard the present definition of the second as a provisional one which will be superseded as soon as the atomic clocks are sufficiently developed. With such a definition of the second any well-equipped laboratory could use the primary unit of time. Even now time signals derived from the present standard are broadcast on several radio frequencies for use by the scientific community.

Question

2-22 During the period when the second was *defined* in terms of the rotation of the earth on its axis, how was it possible to detect a slowing down of this rotation?

For very small or very large intervals of time the second may not be a convenient unit. For this reason fractions and multiples of a second are often used, as shown at top of page 20.

The speed of a particle has been defined as the number of units of distance a particle travels per unit of time. Using the meter as the unit of

* See Harold Lyons, "Atomic Clocks," *Scientific American*, February 1957, p. 71.

one year (yr)	= (approx.) 31.56×10^6 sec
one ephemeris day	= 86,400 sec
one hour (h)	= 3,600 sec
one minute (min)	= 60 sec
one millisecond (msec)	= 10^{-3} sec
one microsecond (μsec)	= 10^{-6} sec
one nanosecond (nsec)	= 10^{-9} sec

length and the second as the unit of time, speed has the units of meters per second, sometimes written meters/second (or m/sec).

Questions

2-23 A particle moves with constant speed in a straight line. The particle covers a distance of 1 km in 5 msec. What is its speed in meters per second?

2-24 A flash of light travels approximately 30 cm in 1 nsec. What is its speed in meters per second?

Class Discussion Question

2-25 It has been argued that time has no meaning of its own but is merely a shorthand method of relating occurrences to each other. This relating of occurrences to each other can be done by relating each of them to some common occurrence such as the angle of rotation of the earth. For instance, the statement "Particle one has a speed of one meter per second" could be replaced by the statement "Particle one is displaced one meter when the earth has performed an additional 1/86,400 part of its rotation." Evaluate this argument. Criticize the use of the word "when" in the alternative statement. Can the kind of analysis we have been undertaking be carried out without at least the notion of simultaneity?

The speed of a flash of light in space has been measured to be 2.9979×10^8 meters/second. Light can be used to measure distance indirectly. By measuring the time it takes for a flash of light which is emitted at one point to be observed at a second point, the distance between the two points may be calculated. A convenient unit of length in astronomy is the light-year. One light-year is defined as the distance traveled by a flash of light in one year.

Questions

2-26 A flash of light from the sun takes about 500 sec to reach the earth. Approximately how far is the earth from the sun?

2-27 Calculate the length of a light-year in meters. (*Answer:* 9.46×10^{15} meters).

chapter 3

The motion of a particle subject to a constant force

3.1 INTRODUCTION. We have seen that after being hit by a golf club particle one moves with respect to the reference particle in the following manner:

1. Particle one moves in a straight line.
2. Particle one moves with constant speed.
3. Repetitions of the experiment can give different constant speeds of particle one for each try.

A whole new area of inquiry opens up for us if we refuse to be satisfied with the third result as it stands. What causes particle one to have a different speed after each repetition of the experiment? Very likely it has something to do with how "hard" we hit particle one with the golf club. This is easily verified: If we repeat the experiment several times, hitting particle one alternately "very hard" and "very lightly," then, although the resulting speeds of particle one may be different for every repetition of the experiment, every one of the group of speeds which result from hitting the particle "very hard" is much greater than every one of the group of speeds which result from hitting the particle "very lightly." A possible set of such results is represented by the bar graph of Fig. 3-1. The conclusion, then, is that the different speeds of particle one in repetitions of the experiment are due to the fact that particle one is hit "harder" or "more lightly" by the golf club. But suppose that we go back a step and ask the question: What exactly is the difference between hitting a particle "hard" and hitting it "lightly"? This question is deceptively simple because we all have an intuitive—even muscular—sense of what is involved in hitting a

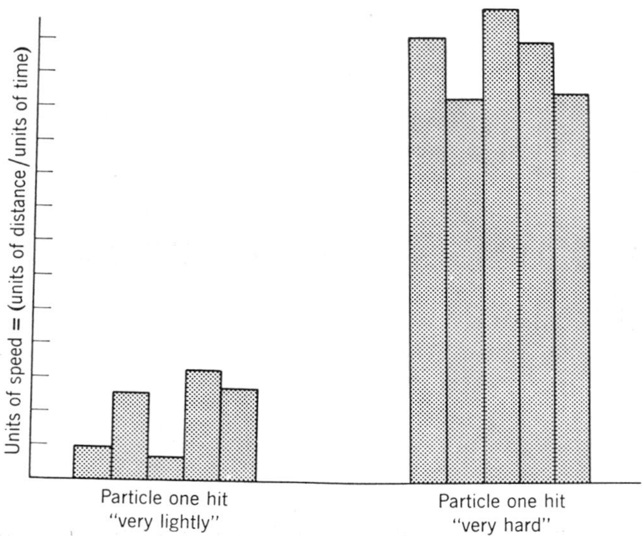

Fig. 3-1. Various speeds which might result from hitting particle one "very lightly" and "very hard" with a golf club.

"particle" (golf ball, baseball, boxing opponent) "hard" or "lightly." The question, however, does *not* say "Demonstrate how to hit a particle 'hard' or 'lightly'." Rather it asks what goes on in detail when the golf club comes into contact with particle one. The details of this collision can be exceedingly complex. A high speed movie of the impact might show that the first contact of the golf club with particle one causes slight deformation of both bodies; then both bodies deform more; particle one picks up speed as the golf club slows down; fragments of particle one (or of the golf club!) may break off under the blow and fly off in several directions; finally, what is left of particle one loses contact with the golf club and moves from there on at a constant speed.

Such an analysis does not tell us much more about the collision than we knew before. All that is clear is that somehow the golf club "pushes" particle one or exerts a "force" on it. Since this *push* or *force* appears to be crucial to the process, perhaps we should take a simpler case in which the forces do not change so rapidly with time. The simpler case should be chosen so that the term *force* can be made to have a clear meaning.

3.2 FORCE. How shall we define force? *Length* is defined in terms of a physical standard of length and a procedure by which length is measured using this standard. *Time* is defined in terms of a mechanism which reproduces repeatedly the unit of time. In the same way *force* is to be defined in terms of a mechanism which measures force and a procedure ("operation") by which this mechanism is used to measure force.

As a force-measuring mechanism, let us use an old-fashioned spring balance (Fig. 3-2). The spring balance consists of a spring with a hook at each end. At one end of the spring is fastened a pointer. This pointer indicates the amount of extension of the spring on a scale which is attached to the opposite end of the spring from the pointer. We shall make the spring of such a material and shall be careful to stretch it little enough so that it always returns to the same original length when released. When the spring is at this original length, let us mark the pointer position on the scale and label it "zero." Now let us extend the spring an arbitrary amount and mark the pointer position once again, this time labeling it "one." This "one" indicates the position of the pointer when the pointer end of the spring is exerting "one unit of force." You can see that the magnitude of the standard unit of force can be chosen just as arbitrarily as the magnitude of the unit length was chosen originally.

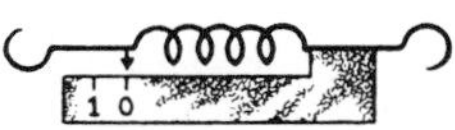

Fig. 3-2. Spring balance.

In defining force in this way we make use of intuitive ideas of force which we all share. There are many hidden assumptions in these intuitive ideas, such as the assumption that a given stretch of the spring corresponds to a given force regardless of other conditions such as the time on a clock, the age of the spring balance, or the speed of the spring balance with respect to the reference particle. This is the same kind of logical looseness which was remarked in the definitions of length and time. As in those cases, such a definition is justified in the eyes of the physicist if it is simple, proves convenient, leads to no contradictions, and can be used to predict correctly the results of later experiments. Other possible definitions of force would satisfy all these criteria. We shall see in Chapter 5 that not all forces can be measured with a spring balance. Later we shall develop methods for measuring such forces. For the present we shall limit ourselves to forces which can be applied to particle one by means of spring balances. One important reason for beginning our study of mechanics in interstellar space is that the concept of force can be introduced using spring balances alone.

3.3 SOME EXPERIMENTS WITH A CONSTANT LINEAR FORCE. Now we can study the behavior of particle one when acted on by one unit of force (Fig. 3-3). The results are simplified if particle one is initially at rest with respect to the reference particle. A fine thread is used to attach particle one to the pointer end of the spring balance. Then by hand or by rocket the other end of the spring balance is pulled along in a straight line

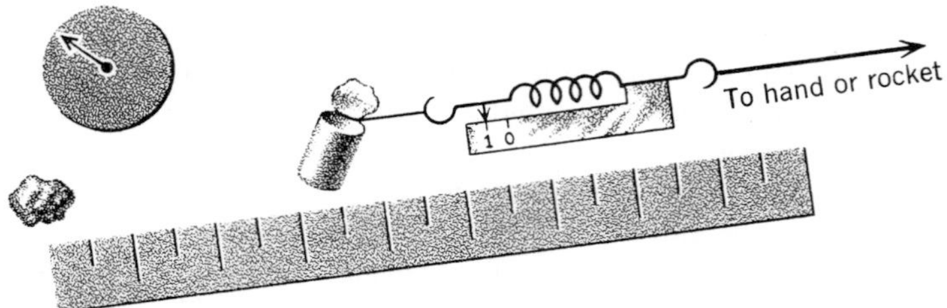

Fig. 3-3. Particle one acted on by one unit of force.

in such a way that the pointer indicates "one" on the spring balance scale. It will require some skill to keep the pointer on the "one" mark. Particle one is then said to be subject to a force of one unit magnitude. If the particle subject to this force moves from rest in a straight line, the force is said to be *linear*. Thus under these circumstances particle one is subject to a *constant linear force of one unit magnitude.*

Question

3-1 If a rocket is used to pull the spring balance, what precautions should be used regarding the rocket exhaust blast? Devise a simple mechanism which could be used to control the rocket so that the force exerted on particle one will not vary from one unit magnitude by more than a predetermined amount during the experiment.

Now once again let us use the clock and measuring rod to determine the displacement of particle one at the end of each unit of time. We

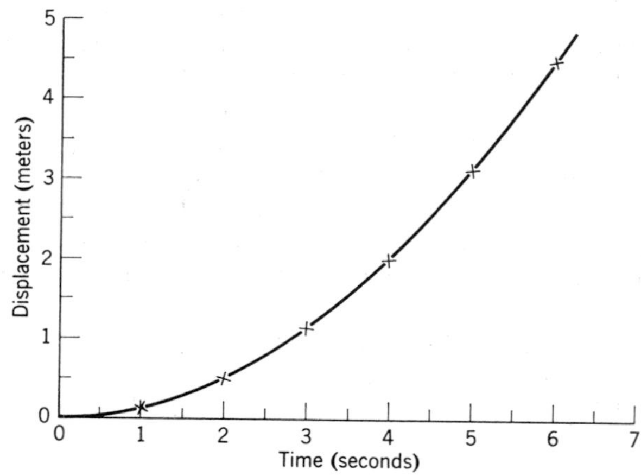

Fig. 3-4. World line of particle one subject to a unit force starting from rest.

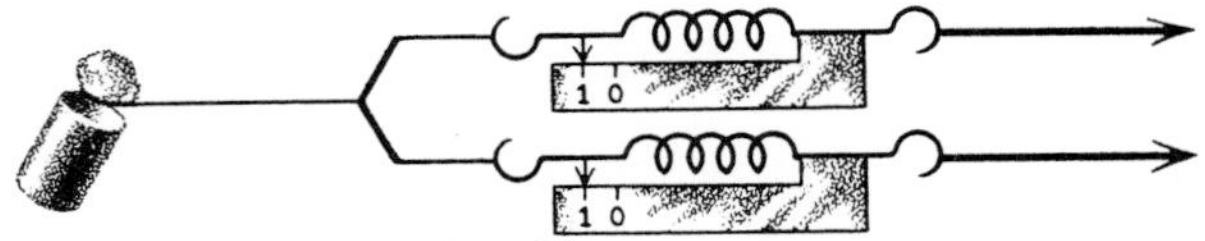

Fig. 3-5. Particle one acted on by two identical spring balances.

measure displacement in meters and time in seconds. A graph of one possible set of results is given in Fig. 3-4. Here again the crosses represent the experimental points. Clearly, a single straight line cannot be drawn through all these points. Experiment shows that a *parabola* can be drawn through the experimental points, and the smooth curve in the figure is a parabola. This is an important *experimental result.* There is no way to predict the form of this curve without trying the experiment to find out.

What will happen if particle one is acted on by *two* units of force instead of one? How can we exert exactly two units of force on particle one? One way to do this is to make a second spring balance identical with the first one, with the "zero" and "one" marks at the same places on the scale as on the scale of the first spring balance. Now one end of both spring balances can be attached to particle one at the same time, and the other end of both spring balances can be pulled along in such a way that each indicates one unit of force (see Fig. 3-5). Then *by definition* there are two units of force acting on particle one, one exerted by each spring balance.

Question

3-2 If you were not sure that the second spring balance were identical with the first one, how could you check that it was properly calibrated to exert one unit of force?

It is found by experiment that, if particle one is initially at rest and is acted on by two units of force in this way, the world line will be a different parabola from that produced by one unit of force, as shown in Fig. 3-6.

Now the first spring balance may be calibrated to give two units of force in the following manner: Attach only the first spring balance to particle one and repeat the preceding experiment several times, using different extensions of the spring until an extension of the spring is found at which the displacement vs time curve is the same as that produced by two units of force. The pointer position on the scale may then be marked "two" for this extension of the spring.

Questions

3-3 Describe how the first spring balance may be calibrated to exert

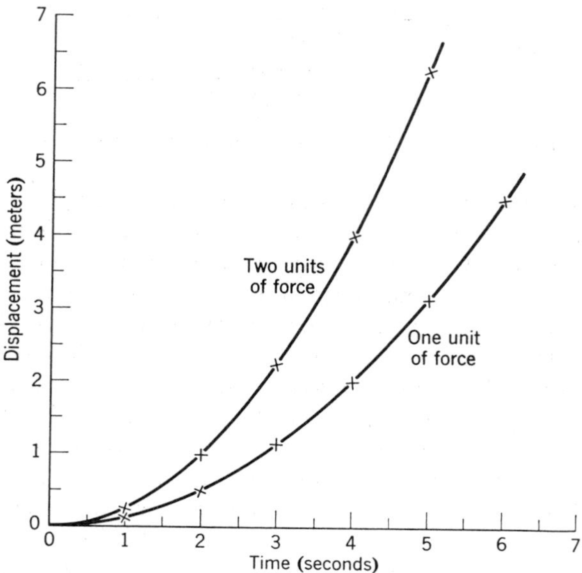

Fig. 3-6. World lines for particle one starting from rest acted on by one and by two units of force.

three, four, etc., units of force. Use for this calibration no more than two spring balances.

3-4 How may the first spring balance be calibrated to exert one-half unit of force? any fractional part of a unit of force? one and one-half units of force?

3-5 In the procedures above is it assumed that the distance from the "zero" mark to the "one" mark on the spring balance scale is the same as the distance from the "one" mark to the "two" mark?

What is the relation between the two parabolas which represent the motion of particle one under the influence of one unit of force and two units of force? Before we can answer this question, we must analyze more closely the parabolic shape of the world line in both cases to see what else this shape can tell us about the motion of particle one subject to a constant linear force.

3.4 INSTANTANEOUS SPEED. Suppose we ask the question: What is the speed of a particle subject to a constant linear force? In Chapter 2 we found that a particle subject to no forces either remained at rest or moved in a straight line at a constant speed. The world line in this case was a straight line, and the speed was shown to be numerically equal to the physical slope of that straight line. Since the world line of a particle subject to a unit force is *not* a straight line but rather a parabola, the *speed of the particle under these conditions is not constant* but is continually changing.

How is speed measured when this speed is continually changing? Let us repeat the experiment with a unit force acting on particle one, but this time with the following change: at the end of a particular time interval, say the third, remove the force from particle one by cutting the thread which connects particle one to the spring balance. The way the world line for this experiment looks is shown in Fig. 3-7. The dashed curve is the parabola which represents the motion of particle one in the last experiment in which the force was *not* removed. Experiment shows that after the force is removed the world line becomes a straight line. This means that after the force is removed the particle moves with constant speed. Again, this is an *experimental result* and an interesting one, although not unexpected. This experiment, supported by many similar experiments, shows that *whenever particle one is subject to no forces it either remains at rest or moves with constant speed in a straight line.* This is called *Newton's First Law of Motion.* The similar result in Chapter 2 dealt only with the motion of particle one after being struck from rest by a golf club.

When does particle one begin to move with constant speed? At the instant the force is removed. It seems reasonable to say that the speed which the unit force has given particle one in three seconds is the constant

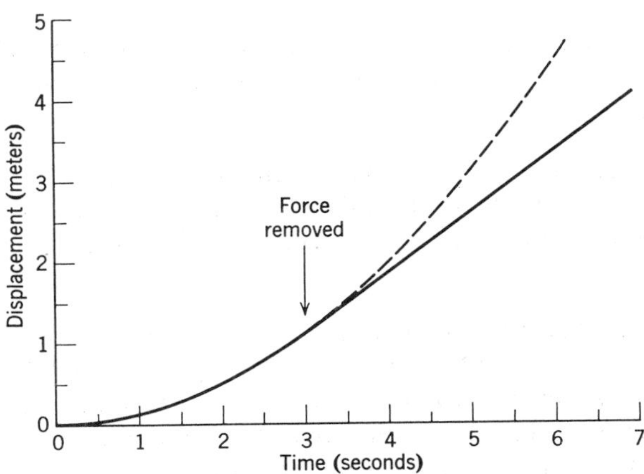

Fig. 3-7. World line for particle one acted on by one unit of force until $t = 3$ seconds and by zero force after $t = 3$ seconds.

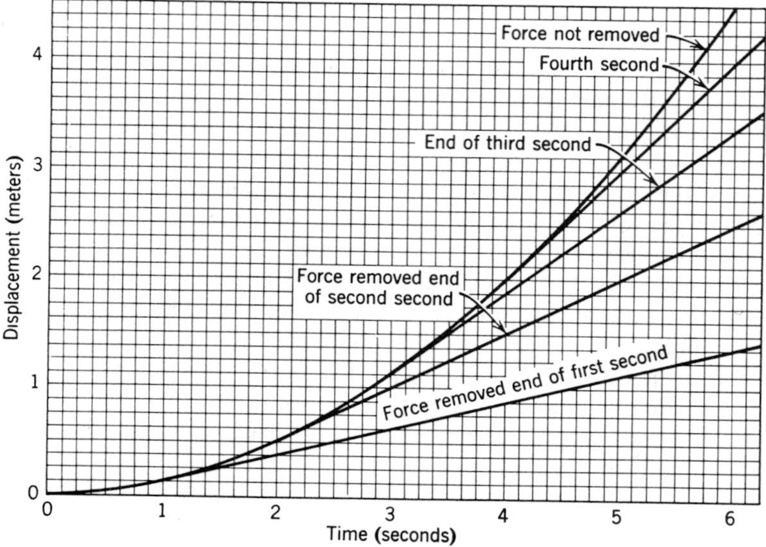

Fig. 3-8. Superimposed world lines for particle one accelerated from rest by one unit of force for various time intervals.

speed which particle one would have if the force were removed at the end of three seconds. In general, we may say that *the speed of a particle at any instant is the constant speed which that particle will assume if all forces are removed from the particle at that instant.*

Question

3-6 Does it follow from this definition that the speed of particle one at the end of the third second is the same whether or not the force is removed then?

Now we can repeat the experiment over and over again, each time cutting particle one away from the spring balance at the end of a different interval of time. The superimposed results of this series are shown in Fig. 3-8.

Question

3-7 It is essential that you understand every aspect of Fig. 3-8. Why do so many curves represent the motion of a single particle? What is the justification for superimposing these curves? Where would the curve lie if particle one were released from the force after one and one-half seconds? Measure the slope of each of the straight lines. What physical quantity have you measured? What is the speed at time $t = 0$ sec? How do you know?

By measuring the slopes of the straight lines in our diagram we can calculate and then plot the instantaneous speed of particle one at the end of every second. This is shown in Fig. 3-9. Notice that these points lie on a straight line, which is drawn through them.

Questions

3-8 Suppose a particle initially at rest with respect to the reference particle is subject to zero force. What is its speed vs time curve? Is it a straight line? What is the speed vs time curve for a particle moving with constant speed?

3-9 Particle one is initially at rest and is thereafter acted upon by a constant *negative* force. Draw the world line and the speed vs time curve.

3-10 The straight line of Fig. 3-9 would seem to imply that, if a constant force were applied to particle one for a sufficiently long time, any speed could be attained, even a speed greater than that of light in a vacuum. Is this inconsistent with any experimental results discussed in the preceding chapter?

Experiments show that the points on a graph obtained in the same way as in Fig. 3-9 will deviate significantly from a straight line if the final speed is greater than one-tenth the speed of light (i.e., greater than about 30 million meters per second). At one-tenth the speed of light the deviation is about 1 percent. It will be assumed in all the experiments which follow that the speeds of all particles with respect to the reference particle are less than one-tenth the speed of light in a vacuum.

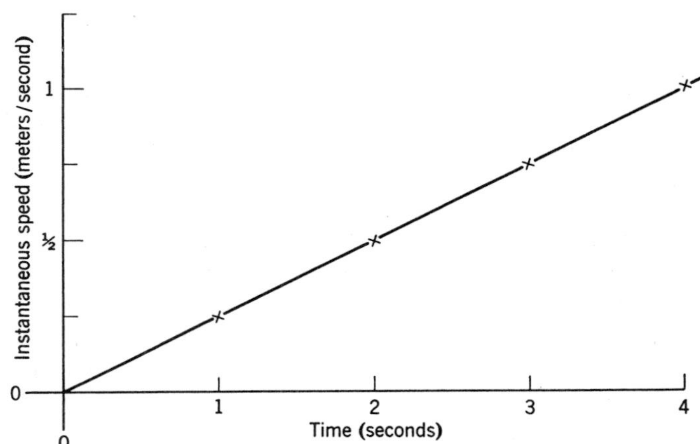

Fig. 3-9. Instantaneous speed vs time curve for particle one accelerated from rest by one unit of force.

3.5 TANGENT TO A CURVE. The preceding series of experiments is a cumbersome way to derive the velocity vs time curve for a particle subject to a constant force. We can save considerable time by using two other devices to derive this curve. First of all, look closely at the superimposed curves and straight lines of Fig. 3-8. What relation do all the straight lines have to the parabola? They are *tangents* to the parabola. A tangent to a curve at any point is defined as that straight line of infinite length which touches the curve at that point without crossing the curve at that point. There are a number of exceptional points on some curves to which this definition does not apply,* but it will be satisfactory for the present.

Notice that the fact that the straight lines of Fig. 3-8 are all tangent to the parabola is an *experimental result.* There is no *mathematical* reason why this should be so, but experiment shows it to be the case.

Using this information, it is possible to measure the instantaneous speed of a particle subject to a constant force at any time without conducting a separate experiment for each such speed. This can be done by drawing a tangent to the displacement vs time curve at the point corresponding to the time at which it is desired to measure the speed. The instantaneous speed is then simply the magnitude of the physical slope of this tangent.

Question

3-11 On a piece of graph paper draw any continuous curly-cue curve. Draw tangents at several points. How would you measure the slopes of these tangents? Could some of these tangents have *negative* slopes? Can you draw curves at some points of which the definition of tangent above does not apply?

If we can find an equation for the parabola which represents the displacement vs time curve, we can use an even simpler mathematical device which will give us directly a formula for velocity at any point. The name of this mathematical device is the *derivative.*

3.6 DERIVATIVE OF A PARABOLA. The problem is to find a formula for the slope of the tangent to a curve at any point. The curve we have been dealing with is the parabola. If the displacement is given the symbol x (measured in meters) and the time is given the symbol t (measured in seconds), then the general formula for the parabolas with which we have been dealing is

$$x = Kt^2 \qquad (3\text{-}1)$$

* For example, points of discontinuity, points of discontinuous first derivative, inflection points.

In this expression K is some constant. The constant K will have a different value for each different parabola (see Fig. 3-6). The mathematical argument involved in finding the slope of the tangent runs as follows. Consider any point (x_1, t_1) on the curve in Fig. 3-10. Suppose we consider another point on the curve which has the t value $(t_1 + \Delta t)$, where Δ is the capital Greek letter "delta" and Δt means "a small addition to t." What is the value of x corresponding to $t_1 + \Delta t$? Call this new value $x_1 + \Delta x$. Then from the formula

$$x_1 + \Delta x = K(t_1 + \Delta t)^2$$

or

$$\Delta x = K(t_1 + \Delta t)^2 - x_1 = K(t_1 + \Delta t)^2 - Kt_1^2 \tag{3-2}$$

Now consider a straight line drawn through the two points (dashed line in Fig. 3-10). If these two points are near each other on the curve, this straight line is not a bad approximation of the tangent to the curve at the point (x_1, t_1). What is the *slope* of this straight line? From the figure the slope is seen to be given by $\Delta x/\Delta t$. We can find a formula for this slope by dividing both sides of Eq. (3-2) by Δt.

$$\frac{\Delta x}{\Delta t} = \frac{K(t_1 + \Delta t)^2 - Kt_1^2}{\Delta t}$$

Expanding the term in parentheses, we have

$$\frac{\Delta x}{\Delta t} = \frac{K[t_1^2 + 2t_1 \Delta t + (\Delta t)^2] - Kt_1^2}{\Delta t}$$

The two Kt_1^2 terms cancel to give

$$\frac{\Delta x}{\Delta t} = \frac{K[2t_1 \Delta t + (\Delta t)^2]}{\Delta t} = K(2t_1 + \Delta t) \tag{3-3}$$

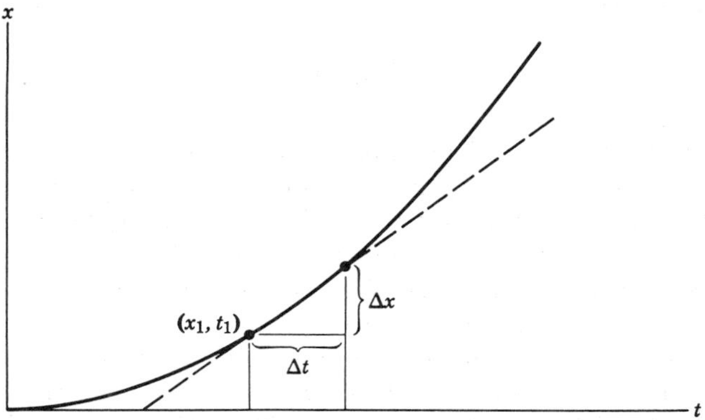

Fig. 3-10. Finding the derivative of a parabola.

This is a mathematical expression for the slope of a straight line drawn through two points near each other on a parabola. Because of the second term in the parentheses this slope depends on the value of Δt. But look again at Fig. 3-10. If the two points were made to come nearer and nearer to each other while both still lie on the curve, then the straight line determined by the two points would be a better and better approximation to the tangent to the curve at that point. In fact, the tangent to a curve at this point is *defined* as this straight line as the two points approach each other. This definition is more precise than the definition of tangent given in the preceding section. Mathematically the two points on the curve are made to get nearer and nearer by letting Δt get smaller and smaller. The slope of the tangent is found by taking "the limit of $\Delta x/\Delta t$ as Δt goes to zero." Symbolically this is written

$$\lim_{\Delta t \to 0} \frac{\Delta x}{\Delta t} = \lim_{\Delta t \to 0} (2Kt_1 + K\,\Delta t) = 2Kt_1 \tag{3-4}$$

Question

3-12 Using the curve of Fig. 3-10, explain why it is necessary to take the limit as Δt goes to zero instead of simply setting Δt equal to zero.

If this limit exists, it is called the "derivative of x with respect to t" and is written symbolically

$$\frac{dx}{dt} = \lim_{\Delta t \to 0} \frac{\Delta x}{\Delta t} \tag{3-5}$$

and for a parabola

$$\frac{dx}{dt} = 2Kt_1$$

Since this is true of any t_1, we can omit the subscript and write simply

$$\frac{dx}{dt} = 2Kt \tag{3-6}$$

It is important that as the limit is taken both points which determine the slope remain on the curve. This is assured by the way Δx is found in Eq. (3-2). This is the reason why the limit is taken by letting Δt go to zero. Nothing is said about Δx (even though it also goes to zero in the limit) because it is implied that Δx follows Δt in such a way that $(x_1 + \Delta x, t_1 + \Delta t)$ is always a point on the curve.

In the last section we saw that the instantaneous speed of a particle at any point on a world line is equal to the magnitude of the physical slope of the tangent of the world line at that point. This slope is equal to the derivative of the world line. Hence, for the parabolic world line of a particle which is initially at rest and is acted upon by a constant force, this speed has the value

$$\text{Speed} = \text{magnitude of } \frac{dx}{dt} = 2Kt \tag{3-7}$$

In the next section we shall introduce the concept of velocity which will help to simplify the form of this equation.

Questions

3-13 Consider the case treated in Chapter 2 in which particle one is hit by a golf club and is thereafter free of forces. In that case the world line is a straight line. A straight line in these coordinates has the equation $x = bt + c$ where b and c are constants for any given straight line. Using the foregoing mathematical procedure, find the derivative of this straight line. Why is the derivative independent of t?

3-14 Suppose that some displacement vs time curve were of the form $x = qt^3$, where q is a constant. Using the procedure above, find the derivative of this curve.

3-15 Can you derive the general form for the derivative of the function $x = Kt^n$, where K is a constant and n is any positive integer? (*Hint:* Use the first few terms of the binomial expansion. *Answer:* $dx/dt = nKt^{n-1}$.) What if $n = 0$? Is it necessary that n be positive? For what special cases have you already proved the formula?

3-16 Can you draw a curve for which the limit-taking process involved in finding a derivative does not lead to a unique answer at some points on the curve? There are several kinds of such curves.

3.7 INSTANTANEOUS VELOCITY. We define the *instantaneous velocity* v of a particle moving along a straight line path to be equal to the derivative of x with respect to t, where x is the displacement of the particle along the straight line path.

$$v = \frac{dx}{dt} \quad \text{by definition} \tag{3-8}$$

This definition holds for any motion of the particle along a straight line path, not only for the case of a parabolic world line treated in the last section. Suppose, for example, that particle one is *approaching* the reference particle. In this case the displacement x of the particle decreases with time so that dx is negative and dx/dt, which is equal to the velocity v, is also negative.

Now the *speed* of a particle is defined as the distance it moves divided by the time interval for this motion. Since distance is always taken to be a positive quantity, the speed is a positive quantity no matter which direction the particle is moving along the straight line path. From Eq. (3-7) we see that the speed of a particle is equal to the magnitude of the velocity of that particle.

The definition of velocity given here is true only for motion in a straight line. In Chapter 4 we shall derive a more general definition of velocity for motion in three dimensions.

Question

3-17 Consider an infinitely long straight line which passes through the reference particle. Particle one moves along this straight line. Suppose that one direction of this line from the reference particle is taken arbitrarily to be the direction of positive displacements of particle one and the opposite direction to be the direction of negative displacements. Show that if particle one has a negative velocity it will be moving in the same direction on both the positive and the negative portions of this straight line.

In the special case of a particle initially at rest acted on by a constant force, the velocity can be found from Eqs. (3-6) and (3-8).

$$v = \frac{dx}{dt} = 2Kt \tag{3-9}$$

3.8 ACCELERATION. With one more extension of the concept of derivative we can complete the mathematics involved in the study of a single particle subject to a constant linear force. The instantaneous speed vs time curve is a straight line. See Fig. 3-9. This means that the slope of the velocity vs time curve is constant. Therefore the derivative of the velocity vs time curve must also be constant. This is shown as follows (starting with Eq. 3-9) (see Question 3-13).

$$\begin{aligned} v &= 2Kt \\ v + \Delta v &= 2K(t + \Delta t) \\ \Delta v &= 2K(t + \Delta t) - v = 2K(t + \Delta t) - 2Kt \\ &= 2K\,\Delta t \end{aligned}$$

whence

$$\frac{\Delta v}{\Delta t} = 2K$$

so that

$$\frac{dv}{dt} = \lim_{t \to 0} \frac{\Delta v}{\Delta t} = \lim_{\Delta t \to 0} 2K = 2K$$

Therefore

$$\frac{dv}{dt} = 2K \tag{3-10}$$

independent of t.

Here at last is a physical quantity which is constant when a constant force acts on a particle initially at rest. What is the physical meaning of this quantity called dv/dt? It is the derivative or slope of the velocity vs time curve. As such, it represents the rate at which velocity changes with time. This quantity is so important in physics that it is given a special name. It is called the *acceleration* and is given the symbol a.

$$a = \frac{dv}{dt} \quad \text{by definition} \tag{3-11}$$

If the unit of displacement is the meter and the unit of time is the second, then the units of acceleration are (meters/sec)/sec = meters/sec^2. If the unit of displacement is the centimeter, then the units of acceleration are centimeters/sec^2.

For a particle accelerated from rest by a constant force we have from Eq. (3-10)

$$a = 2K = \text{constant}$$

From Eq. (3-9)

$$v = at \tag{3-12}$$

and from Eq. (3-1)

$$x = \tfrac{1}{2}at^2 \tag{3-13}$$

This formula gives displacement as a function of time for a particle moving from rest with a constant acceleration. Equation (3-12) is the equation of a curve like that of Fig. 3-9. Hence the physical slope of the straight line in Fig. 3-9 is equal to the acceleration experienced by the particle.

Question

3-18 From Eqs. (3-12) and (3-13) find an expression which relates velocity to displacement.

Another symbol for acceleration is used in mechanics. Remember that by definition $a = dv/dt$, but also by definition $v = dx/dt$, so that

$$a = \frac{d(dx/dt)}{dt}$$

Hence a is the derivative with respect to t of a derivative of x with respect to t. This is called a second derivative with respect to t and is usually written as follows.

$$a = \frac{d^2x}{dt^2}$$

Question

3-19 If $x = qt^3$, what is d^2x/dt^2? If $x = kt^n$, what is the *third* derivative of x with respect to t? The third derivative is written d^3x/dt^3.

What have we learned about the motion of a particle accelerated from rest by a constant force? First of all, experimental points for this motion lie on a world line which has the shape of a parabola. Secondly, experiment shows that the instantaneous velocity of the particle at any time is given by the physical slope of the tangent to the world line at the point corresponding to that time. Finally, if the acceleration of a particle is defined as the first derivative of the velocity vs time curve, which is the same as the second derivative of the world line, then experiment shows that for a particle accelerated from rest by a constant force *the acceleration is constant.*

3.9 FORCE AND ACCELERATION. In Sec. 3.3 we plotted the two displacement vs time parabolas for particle one accelerated from rest by one unit of force and by two units of force respectively. The question was asked then what the relation was between these two parabolas. Now we are able to answer this question. From Eq. (3-13) each of these parabolas has the formula $x = \frac{1}{2}at^2$, where a is the acceleration, which is constant for each parabola but different for different parabolas. By fitting this formula to the two parabolas two different values of the acceleration may be found.

Question

3-20 Carry out the process of finding the constants a for the parabolas of Fig. 3-6. (*Hint:* It is easiest to replot the graphs as x vs t^2. Then they will become straight lines whose slope is $\frac{1}{2}a$.)

It must be emphasized that Fig. 3-6 is derived from an experiment. The *experimental result* is that the acceleration of particle one acted upon by two units of force is *twice* as great as the acceleration of particle one acted upon by one unit of force. By repeating the experiment for three, four, five, etc., units of force and analyzing the resulting displacement vs time parabolas it is found that for particle one *the acceleration is proportional to the force.* This is symbolized by the equation

$$a \propto F \tag{3-14}$$

where the symbol $\propto$ means "is proportional to." This expression can be written in the form of an equation by introducing a constant b.

$$a = bF \tag{3-15}$$

where b is called the "constant of proportionality."

Question

3-21 If F has the value one unit of force and a has the value $\frac{1}{4}$ meter/sec^2, what is the value of b? What are the units of b? If F is now increased to four units of force, what value does a have?

If the same set of experiments is carried out on different particles, the results for each particle can be expressed in the same form as Eq. (3-15). However, the experimental value of the constant b will sometimes be different for different particles. We shall discuss this difference between particles in the next section.

3.10 MASS. Suppose that the same force is used to accelerate two different particles from rest separately. Will the acceleration be the same in both cases? When this is tried, it is found that for most pairs of particles the acceleration of one particle will be different from the acceleration of the other particle when each is acted on by a force of the same magnitude.

Question

3-22 Does the result above contradict Eq. (3-14)? Explain carefully why it does or does not.

What is different about particles which are accelerated at different rates by the same force? Perhaps the difference is due to the *size* of the particle. Perhaps *bigger* particles accelerate less than *smaller* particles. Yet a series of experiments shows that this is not necessarily true. The same force may give an empty tin can a greater acceleration than it gives a rock half the size. A large kitchen sponge may be accelerated more than a small piece of lead acted upon by the same force.

Yet a curious result *does* emerge. If the two particles being compared are solid pieces of the same substance, then the particle with the larger volume will be accelerated less than the particle with the smaller volume. In fact, careful measurements show that, if the volume of the second particle is *twice* the volume of the first particle and if both are solid pieces of the same substance, the acceleration of the larger particle is *half* that of the smaller particle acted upon by the same force. This is true no matter what the force is as long as it is constant and is the same for both particles.

Question

3-23 Particle one is a solid piece of Muenster cheese of volume 0.00040 cubic meter (m^3). When acted upon by a constant force of four units magnitude its acceleration is 1 meter/sec^2. Particle two is a solid piece of the same Muenster cheese of volume 0.00010 m^3. What will be the acceleration of particle two when acted on by a constant force of four units magnitude? What will be the acceleration of particle two when acted upon by a constant force of one unit magnitude?

Consider two solid particles of the same volume and made of the same substance. If these two particles are glued together to make a single particle, it seems reasonable to say that there is "twice as much material" in the glued particle as there was in either of the two particles from which it was made (if the "material in the glue" can be neglected). Experimentally a given constant force will produce only half the acceleration in the glued particle that it produces in either of the two original particles. Perhaps the acceleration produced by a given constant force is related in some way to the "amount of material" in the particle being acted on by the force. The greater the "amount of material" in a given particle, the smaller will be its acceleration under any given force. In fact, we find that this is an inverse proportion for any given substance. (Twice the amount of material means half the acceleration, etc.)

At one time physicists called the "amount of material" *mass*. The symbol for mass is m or M. Comparing particles made of the same substance, we have found that for any given constant force the acceleration is inversely proportional to the "amount of material" and thus inversely proportional to the mass. This inverse proportion can be written symbolically as

$$a \propto \frac{1}{m}$$

For any particle, acceleration is also directly proportional to the force (Eq. 3-14). The expression above may be rewritten

$$a \propto \frac{F}{m} \tag{3-16}$$

If both sides of (3-16) are multiplied by m, we have

$$F \propto ma \tag{3-17}$$

This proportion can be changed to an equation by introducing a constant of proportionality k.

$$F = kma \tag{3-18}$$

$k =$ constant for all particles made of the same substance. Equation (3-18) has been derived for all particles made of the same substance. Any particle of this substance may be chosen as the *unit mass*. The mass of any other particle made of the same substance can be compared to this unit mass by comparing the accelerations of the two particles when acted upon by the same constant force. The procedure for comparing masses might be as follows.

Procedure for Comparing Masses

Suppose that the mass of particle two is to be compared to the mass of particle one. Call the mass of particle one m_1. Call the unknown mass of particle two m_2.

1. Let a constant force act on particle one. Measure the acceleration of particle one due to this force. Call this acceleration a_1.
2. Let a constant force of the same magnitude act on particle two. Measure the acceleration due to this force. Call this acceleration a_2.
3. Since the two forces are equal, Eq. (3-18) tells us that

$$km_2a_2 = km_1a_1$$

and, if k has the same value for both particles, the equation will read

$$m_2a_2 = m_1a_1$$

or

$$\frac{m_2}{m_1} = \frac{a_1}{a_2} \tag{3-19}$$

This equation says that under the conditions described above the ratio of the masses is inversely proportional to the ratio of the accelerations. Since the accelerations have been measured, the ratio of the masses can be calculated. In this way the mass of m_2 can be compared to the unit mass m_1. *This comparison is what we mean by the expression "measuring the mass of particle two."*

Question

3-24 You are given three particles of unknown masses, m_1, m_2, m_3 respectively, all made of the same substance. Suppose that you compare the masses m_1 and m_2 by the procedure above, then you compare the masses m_2 and m_3 using the same force. Will the results of these two experiments give the same comparison between m_1 and m_3 as a direct experimental comparison will give?

The foregoing procedure may be used for particles made of the same substance. How can the mass of particles be compared if the particles are made of *different* substances? The concept of "amount of material" which led to the definition of mass does not have the same clear meaning when applied to particles made of different substances. If two solid particles with the same volume but made of different substances are glued together, it seems that nothing can be said about the "amount of material" in the glued particle. There appears to be no independent way to determine the "amount of material" in particles made of different substances in order to determine the relationship between their masses.

However, if we look closely at the expression "amount of material," we see that it has no meaning independent of the concept of mass. Since we now have a perfectly clear procedure for measuring mass, we can discard the concept of "amount of material" as an unnecessary and somewhat inexact synonym for mass. Physicists *define* the mass of *any* particle by means of the procedure outlined above without regard to the substance or substances of which the particle is made. This amounts to defining the constant k in Eq. (3-18) to be the same for particles made of any substance.

$$F = kma \tag{3-20}$$

where $k =$ constant for *all* particles. Once the units of force, mass, and acceleration have been chosen, the value of k can be found for all particles.

Question

3-25 Particle one is defined as the unit mass. When acted on by one unit of force its acceleration is $\frac{1}{4}$ meter/sec^2. Particle two has an acceleration of $\frac{1}{8}$ meter/sec^2 when acted upon by the same force. What is the mass of particle two? Does it matter if particle one is a tin can and particle two is an apple? If particle three has an acceleration of 2 meters/sec^2 when acted upon by *six* units of force, what is the mass of particle three?

There is one more apparently trivial experimental result which has profound consequences for the laws of motion which we shall derive later. *If two particles are joined together, they behave as if their total mass were the sum of their individual masses.* This is called the *additive property of mass.* We assumed this additive property of mass in developing the concept of mass for particles made of the same material. Experiment shows that this additive property of mass holds also for particles made of different materials.

Question

3-26 Design an experiment to test the additive property of mass. Write specific instructions for carrying out this experiment. Does a series of such experiments prove this property for all particles?

Although the unit of mass may be chosen arbitrarily, it is convenient if all experimenters agree upon the same unit of mass. The unit of mass agreed upon for scientific work is the *kilogram*. The standard kilogram is called the International Prototype Kilogram. It is a block of platinum-irridium alloy kept at the International Bureau of Weights and Measures in Sèvres, France. Other masses are compared with it and are used as "secondary standards" of mass in scientific laboratories. A cube of water 10 centimeters on an edge has a mass of approximately 1 kilogram. The abbreviation kg stands for kilogram. For very small masses the kilogram may not be a convenient unit of mass. For this reason, fractions of a kilogram are often used as follows:

one gram (g) $= 10^{-3}$ kilogram
one milligram (mg) $= 10^{-3}$ gram $= 10^{-6}$ kilogram
one microgram (μg) $= 10^{-6}$ gram $= 10^{-9}$ kilogram

In earthbound laboratories the procedure for comparing masses outlined above is not so accurate as other methods because of the presence of gravity, friction, vibration, and air resistance. The actual comparison of masses on earth is usually carried out using an *equal-arm balance*. In Sec. 8.9 we shall describe this method in detail and show that the equal-arm balance gives the same comparison between masses as the method outlined above.

3.11 STANDARD UNITS OF FORCE. If units of force, mass, and acceleration are chosen, the value of k in the equation $F = kma$ can be found once and for all time. What is done in practice is more shrewd than this. Since no common unit of force has yet been chosen there are really two symbols, F and k, in the equation which have not yet been completely defined. *One* of them may be chosen arbitrarily. What is done is to *choose k to have the numerical value one and to have no units*. Then the equation $F = ma$ is used to *define* the magnitude of the standard unit of force. A standard unit of force is defined as that constant force necessary to accelerate one unit of mass with an acceleration of one unit magnitude.

If the unit of mass is the kilogram and the unit of acceleration is one meter per second squared, then the standard unit of force will be that constant force which will accelerate a mass of one kilogram with an acceleration of one meter per second squared. This unit force is given the name one *newton* (abbreviation: N). Since the constant $k = 1$ has no units, the units of the newton are kilogram-meters per second squared.

If the unit of mass is the gram and the unit of acceleration is one centimeter per second squared, then the standard unit of force will be that constant force which will accelerate a mass of one gram with an acceleration of one centimeter per second squared. This unit force is given the name one *dyne* (abbreviation: dyn). The units of the dyne are gram-centimeters per second squared.

Questions

3-27 How many dynes of force are equal to one newton? (*Answer:* one newton = 10^5 dynes.)

3-28 Suppose that you are given in interstellar space a standard kilogram, a standard meter bar, a standard clock which reads seconds, and an uncalibrated spring balance. How would you calibrate the spring balance to read "one newton" correctly? How would you proceed to calibrate the spring balance from 0 to 10 newtons in intervals of tenths of a newton?

3-29 Suppose that particle one has a mass of 10 grams. When accelerated from rest by a constant force its speed vs time curve is given by Fig. 3-9. What is the force acting on particle one? Express in newtons the magnitude of the "unit of force" used in Sec. 3.4.

The expression $F = ma$ is called the *Law of Motion* or *Newton's Second Law*. It is the central formula of classical mechanics. The next six chapters will deal with some of the implications of this formula.

The pound mass and the slug, the English units of mass, together with the pound force, the English unit of force, are defined in Appendix II at the end of this book.

3.12 SUMMARY. In these first three chapters we have done quite a few experiments on "particle one" and have made quite a few statements about its motion in one dimension. Below is a summary of the statements and experimental results. The items in the summary are labeled in such a way as to make as explicit as possible which statements are definitions and which statements represent the results of experiments. It is assumed that the operational definitions of length, time, speed, and acceleration are already understood.

Summary for the Motion of a Particle in One Dimension

1. *Definition.* A *particle* is a material body which is visible to the unaided human eye and whose position in space is accurately enough described by a geometrical point.

2. *Experimental observations.* There exist regions of the universe in which the amount of matter and radiation is so small as to have a negligible effect upon experiments carried out in these regions on particles visible

to the unaided human eye. Some of these regions exist at sufficient distances from the nearest stars that any effect of these distant stars upon experiments carried out in these regions will be an average one, essentially the same for many such regions. The observer, his equipment, and his methods of measurement can be arranged so that their presence and use have negligible effect on experiments with particles.

3. *Definition.* To say that a particle is "at rest" is simply to define a frame of reference. For the study of motion of a particle in one dimension, a second particle may be used as a reference point. This second particle is called the *reference particle.*

4. *Limiting assumptions.* Only those experiments will be considered which satisfy all the following conditions.

(*a*) The experiments are carried out on particles as defined in 1 above.

(*b*) The experiments take place in the regions and under the circumstances described in 2.

(*c*) All measurements of position are made with measuring rods which are at rest with respect to the reference particle, and all measurements of time are made with clocks which are also at rest with respect to the same reference particle.

5. *Experimental observation.* If a particle initially at rest with respect to the reference particle suffers a collision with another body, then after the collision the particle will move in a straight line and at constant speed with respect to the reference particle.

6. *Limiting assumptions.*

(*d*) Only those straight line paths will be considered which, if extended, would pass through the reference particle.

(*e*) The speed of light is assumed to be the same in all directions.

(*f*) Only those experiments will be considered in which no particle involved in the experiment attains a speed with respect to the reference particle greater than one-tenth of the speed of light.

7. *Experimental observations.* No particle has been observed to travel at a speed greater than the speed of light in a vacuum. This speed has the value 2.9979×10^8 meters/sec. No contradiction results from assuming that the speed of light is the same in all directions. If the conditions of 6*f* are satisfied, the results of actual experiments will differ by less than 1 percent from the results derived below.

8. *Definition.* The concept of force and its magnitude and direction may be defined operationally using a spring balance. The unit of force so defined can be of arbitrary magnitude (but see 13 below). A linear force is one whose *direction* always lies along the same straight line.

9. *Experimental observation.* A particle acted upon by a constant linear force will undergo a constant acceleration in the direction of the force.

10. *Experimental observation.* The constant acceleration of different particles will usually be different when they are acted on separately by a constant linear force of the same magnitude.

11. *Definition.* The mass ratio of any two particles is the inverse of the ratio of the accelerations induced by a given constant linear force acting on the two particles separately. One particle may be chosen to have the unit mass, and the mass of other particles may be measured by comparison with this unit mass using this definition of mass ratio.

12. *Experimental observations.* The mass ratio of two particles does not depend on the magnitude of the constant linear force used in carrying out the procedure of the preceding definition. If two particles are joined together, their total mass is equal to the sum of their individual masses.

13. *Definition.* The magnitude of the standard unit of force is defined as the magnitude of that constant linear force necessary to accelerate the particle taken to be the unit of mass with an acceleration of one unit magnitude.

It is interesting to see what happens when any of the assumptions in the summary are violated. Assumptions (*b*) and (*d*) are simplifying assumptions which will be removed as our study of mechanics proceeds. Assumption (*a*) can be violated in two ways: the bodies involved in experiments can be either too large or too small to be called particles. Bodies too large to be called particles are treated in Chapters 7 and 8. Bodies which are too small to be called particles, i.e., bodies too small to be visible to the unaided human eye, appear to follow the same laws of motion down to sizes comparable to that of a molecule. For objects this small and smaller, the laws of motion take on a quite different form because the methods of measurement cannot be assumed to have a negligible effect on the results of experiments with objects this small. The study of motion of molecules, atoms, and so-called "elementary particles" is called *quantum mechanics.*

If assumptions (*c*) and (*f*) are violated, some difficulties arise with the operational definitions of length and time. Resolution of these difficulties leads to the study of *relativity*, which will be undertaken in Chapters 10 through 13. There is no physical way to demonstrate that assumption (*e*) is violated.

Questions

3-30 Why is the second sentence in step 12 an experimental observation rather than a logical result of the preceding definition?

3-31 What considerations would be involved in determining whether or not the position of a material body were *accurately enough* determined by a geometrical point to justify calling it a particle?

Class Discussion Question

3-32 If, contrary to experimental observation 7, directional differences were detected in the speed of light, show that it might be possible to distinguish from all others a particular group of reference particles which could be defined as "absolutely at rest."

COMMENTS ON THE EXERCISES

The purpose of the exercises and projects at the ends of chapters is to help you to build bridges between the idealized world in which the laws of mechanics are developed and the real world in which problems in mechanics are solved. For this reason the exercises and projects often deal with concrete situations which you might expect to encounter either in everyday life or in scientific pursuits.

1. Because problems encountered in everyday life do not come attached to a chapter of material on a given topic, the exercises at the end of any chapter may make use of material in any preceding chapter as well.
2. Because problems in applied physics usually do not deal with the same idealizations that are used in the construction of the theory, you will have to decide for yourself what approximations must be made in order to apply an idealized physical result to the solution of a real problem.
3. In solving problems in applied physics the physicist or engineer has to decide what information is relevant to his solution. For this reason you will have to introduce your own symbols in solving the exercises. Each solution should be accompanied by a key to the meaning of the symbols used in it.

Just as quickly as possible, you should learn to respond to the question: Does this answer seem *reasonable*? To help yourself gain this insight you may wish to estimate all numerical answers without carrying out the calculations in detail. More careful work in employing the correct number of significant figures may be left to the laboratory. One simple way to check your answer to any problem is to see whether or not the units are the same on both sides of the final equation. For this reason it is best to solve a problem completely using symbols and then substitute numerical values, *including their units*. If both sides of the final equation do not have the same units, the error can sometimes be found by checking the units in the equations leading to the answer. To be sure, your answer can still be wrong if the units are correct; but it is not likely to be correct if the units are wrong!

Students sometimes encounter difficulty with the *conversion of units.* This difficulty is unnecessary. The conversion of units is based on the fact that any quantity may be multiplied by the number one without changing its value. For instance,

$$10^3 \text{ meters} = 1 \text{ kilometer}$$

therefore

$$10^3 \text{ meters}/1 \text{ kilometer} = 1$$

where the number 1 on the right of this equation has no units. Therefore if it is desired, for instance, to change 3 kilometers to meters the conversion proceeds as follows:

$$3 \text{ kilometers} = 3 \text{ kilometers} \times 1 = 3\,\cancel{\text{kilometers}} \times \frac{10^3 \text{ meters}}{1\,\cancel{\text{kilometer}}}$$
$$= 3 \times 10^3 \text{ meters}$$

Notice that the same units in the numerator and denominator may be cancelled. The conversion factor must be written so that this cancellation can take place.

This procedure may be repeated as often as desired. For instance,

$$1 \text{ fermi} = 10^{-15} \text{ meter}$$

therefore

$$3 \text{ kilometers} = 3\,\cancel{\text{kilometers}} \times \frac{10^3\,\cancel{\text{meters}}}{1\,\cancel{\text{kilometer}}} \times \frac{1 \text{ fermi}}{10^{-15}\,\cancel{\text{meter}}}$$
$$= 3 \times 10^{+18} \text{ fermis}$$

Once you have completed a problem to your satisfaction, you can double or triple its benefit to you by the expenditure of very little additional effort. Try working the problem backward: given the result, find one of the pieces of information in the statement of the problem. Make up a new problem of the same or a different kind. If the problem has been about automobiles, try one about billiard balls. One's own problems are much more stimulating than those devised by others.

EXERCISES

3-1 My Voomflauten X-100 sports car will accelerate from 0 to 60 miles per hour (0 to 26.8 meters per second) in 7 seconds. If the horizontal accleration is constant, what is this acceleration? If the car and driver together have a mass of 1400 kilograms, what horizontal force must the road exert on the car in order to provide this acceleration? If the driver has a mass of 70 kilograms, what horizontal force must the seat exert on him in order to keep him in the car during the acceleration?

3-2 The barrel of a rifle is 1 meter long. The bullet has a mass of 10 grams. The speed of the bullet as it leaves the barrel is 800 meters per second. Assuming that its acceleration is constant, how long a time is the bullet in the barrel after firing? What is the average acceleration of the bullet in the barrel? If the rifle is fired horizontally, what is the average net horizontal force on the bullet while it is in the barrel?

3-3 A car going 60 miles per hour (26.8 meters per second) crashes into a concrete bridge abutment. If the car is brought to rest in 38 milliseconds, what is the average deceleration during that time? How far does the car move during this deceleration? If the car plus occupants has a mass of 1600 kilograms, what average force must the concrete abutment exert on the car in order to cause this deceleration? If each passenger is strapped to his seat and has a mass of 70 kilograms, what average force do the seat belts exert on him during the deceleration? If a 70-kilogram man weighs 686 newtons at the surface of the earth, how many times this weight must the seat belts exert during the collision? What happens to the passengers if they are not strapped to the seats? Do you still feel like going for a joyride?

3-4 As train A rounds a curve at 30 miles per hour (13.4 meters per second) the engineer slams on the brakes because he sees train B standing with its last car 150 meters ahead along the same track. If train A decelerates at a rate of $\frac{1}{2}$ meter per second squared, will there be a collision? If so, what is the speed of train A at impact? If not, how far short of train B will train A come to rest?

3-5 The engineer of train B in the previous problem sees train A at the same instant the engineer of train A sees train B. If train B immediately accelerates from rest at a rate of 0.2 meter per second squared (about 27 miles/hour/min), will there be a collision? If so, what is the relative velocity of the two trains at impact? If not, what is the minimum distance between them?

3-6 Particles released near the surface of the earth are observed to fall with an acceleration of approximately 9.8 meters per second squared. An acceleration of this magnitude is referred to as "one g." Show that the force of gravity exerted on a particle of mass m near the surface of the earth has the magnitude mg. This is called the *weight* of the particle. If a particle in interstellar space is accelerated from rest with a linear acceleration of 1 g, how long will it take to reach a speed equal to one-tenth the speed of light? What distance will the particle cover in this time? Express this distance in light-years.

3-7 Suppose that during vertical takeoff from the earth an astronaut is able to sustain a total force equal to eight times his normal weight mg. How long will it take for the rocket to rise a distance of 20 kilometers?

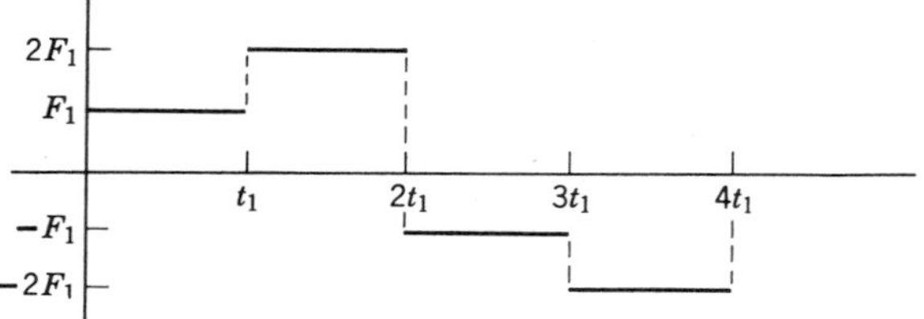

Fig. 3-11.

Assume g has the value 9.8 meters per second squared, and neglect any change of g with altitude. How would you calculate the force exerted on the astronaut by the rocket engines?

3-8 On a windless day I drop a rock over the edge of a high cliff and 10 seconds later hear the sound of the rock striking bottom. How high is the cliff? Assume that sound travels at a speed of 344 meters per second and neglect air resistance. What will my error be if I assume that the sound travels instantaneously from the bottom to the top of the cliff?

3-9 In interstellar space you are given a reference particle, a standard kilogram, a standard spring balance calibrated in newtons, a clock which reads seconds, and an unmarked straight rod. Describe how you would use these materials to measure a length of one meter along the straight rod.

3-10 In interstellar space you are given a reference particle, a standard kilogram, a standard meter bar, a standard spring balance calibrated in newtons, and a clock which is designed to read seconds but is out of adjustment. Describe how you would use these materials to enable you to adjust the clock to read seconds correctly.

3-11 Particle one is at rest next to the reference particle at time $t = 0$. Particle one experiences a sequence of linear forces given by the graph in Fig. 3-11. Positive forces act toward the right, negative forces act toward the left. Draw roughly the acceleration vs time curve, the speed vs time curve, and the displacement vs time curve (world line) for the motion of particle one. Give the values of as many points and slopes on these curves as you can in terms of the force unit F_1, the time unit t_1, and the mass of the particle.

3-12 Figure 3-12, between $t = 0$ and $t = t_6$, is a displacement vs time curve (world line) for a particle moving in a straight line. Describe qualitatively in detail the position, velocity, and acceleration of the particle between $t = 0$ and $t = t_6$. Pay special attention to the direction of these quantities. Describe the direction of the net force on the particle as a function of time during this interval. Explain carefully the physical reasons why the curve after $t = t_6$ is not a possible world line for such a particle.

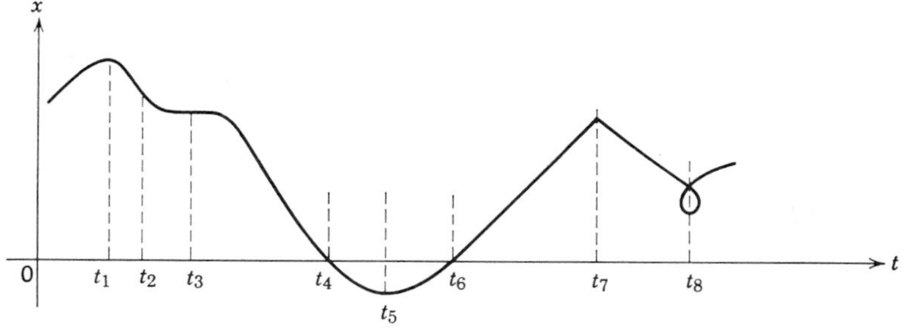

Fig. 3-12.

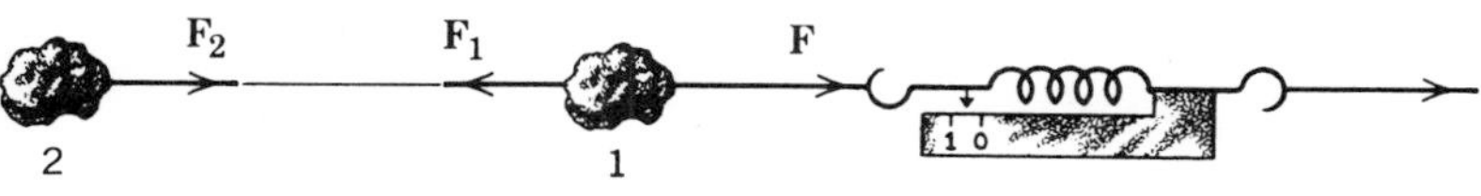

Fig. 3-13.

3-13 Some physicists believe that a given particle may have a different mass when accelerated in one direction (with respect to the fixed stars) than when accelerated in some other direction. It is expected that the difference in mass would be the same fraction of the total mass for every particle. Would it be possible in interstellar space to demonstrate experimentally the truth or falsity of this belief? If it is possible to demonstrate the truth or falsity of this belief, describe an experiment which could in principle be carried out to accomplish this demonstration. Be explicit. What significant assumptions are implied in your method? If it is not possible to demonstrate the truth or falsity of this belief, explain explicitly and in detail what experimental difficulties make it impossible.

3-14 Consider two particles numbered one and two which are connected by an inextensible string of negligible mass (Fig. 3-13). A spring balance is connected to particle one and a force F is applied to this particle by the spring balance. All motion takes place and all forces are directed along the same straight line. The symbol F_2 represents the force exerted on particle two by particle one via the string. The symbol F_1 represents the force exerted on particle one by particle two via the string. No other forces exist between the two particles. Show that F_1 is equal in magnitude and opposite in direction to F_2. You may use the equation $F = ma$, the additive property of mass, and the law of superposition of forces in one dimension which says that, if two linear forces act simultaneously on a particle along the same line, the resultant force is equal to the sum (or difference) of these forces with due regard to sign. Since you are demonstrating the law of action and reaction (sometimes called Newton's Third Law of Motion), you may not use this law in the demonstration.

chapter 4

The mathematics of mechanics

4.1 INTRODUCTION. We have outlined in a simplified form the laws of mechanics for the motion of a particle along a straight line under the action of a constant force or zero force. The experiments dealt with in this analysis are simple ones and are not necessarily the most interesting, the most useful, or the most general. In order to generalize the laws of mechanics we must take account of the following facts.

1. The force on a particle may not be constant in time.
2. Motion can take place in more than one direction. A particle may move on paths which can be described only in three dimensions.
3. Force may change direction as well as magnitude with time, and it need not lie along the direction of motion of the particle.
4. More than one force may act on a particle at one time.
5. A mechanical system may consist of more than one particle.

Before we can study these generalizations fruitfully, it is necessary to develop more mathematical tools. The *derivative* and the *integral* will allow us to take account of item 1 above. These together with the analysis of vectors will allow us to take account of items, 2, 3, and 4. A consideration of item 5 is postponed until Chapter 7.

4.2 THE DERIVATIVE. Let us generalize the work done in Sec. 3.6. Suppose that the world line of a particle moving along a straight line path is given by the formula $x = f(t)$, where $f(t)$ is some function of t. The time t is called the *argument* of the function $f(t)$. If the force on the particle is not constant (or zero), then the $f(t)$ vs t curve will not be a parabola (or a straight line). Consider some point (x_1, t_1) on this curve (see Fig. 4-1). Then $x_1 = f(t_1)$. Suppose that another point on the curve is

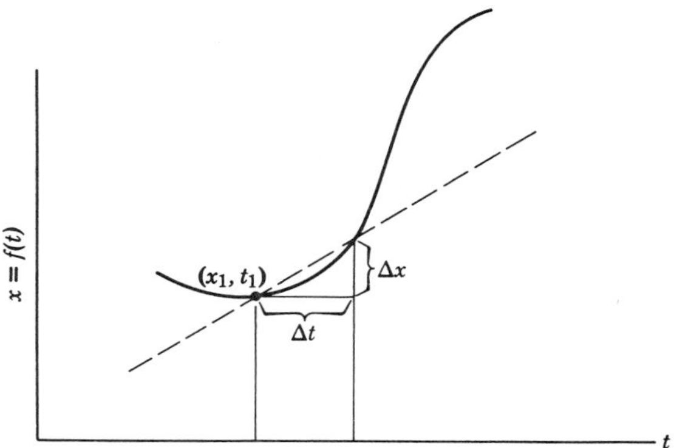

Fig. 4-1. Finding the derivative of a function $f(t)$.

chosen with the value of t given by $t = t_1 + \Delta t$. Then the value of x of this new point on the curve is $x = x_1 + \Delta x = f(t_1 + \Delta t)$. This equation may be rearranged to give a value for Δx.

$$\Delta x = f(t_1 + \Delta t) - x_1 = f(t_1 + \Delta t) - f(t_1) \tag{4-1}$$

The slope of the straight line connecting these two points is given by

$$\frac{\Delta x}{\Delta t} = \frac{f(t_1 + \Delta t) - f(t_1)}{\Delta t} \tag{4-2}$$

The *derivative* of x with respect to t is defined as the limit of this expression as Δt goes to zero if this limit exists.

$$\frac{dx}{dt} = \lim_{\Delta t \to 0} \frac{\Delta x}{\Delta t} = \lim_{\Delta t \to 0} \frac{f(t_1 + \Delta t) - f(t_1)}{\Delta t}$$

Since t_1 is *any* point on the curve, the subscript may be omitted.

$$\frac{dx}{dt} = \lim_{\Delta t \to 0} \frac{\Delta x}{\Delta t} = \lim_{\Delta t \to 0} \frac{f(t + \Delta t) - f(t)}{\Delta t} \tag{4-3}$$

From this definition of derivative the following result has already been found (Question 3-15). If

$$x = t^n$$

then

$$\frac{dx}{dt} = nt^{n-1} \tag{4-4}$$

Questions

4-1 Using the definition above, demonstrate that

$$\frac{d(Kx)}{dt} = K\frac{dx}{dt}$$

where K is a constant.

4-2 Suppose that x is equal to the sum of two functions of $t, f(t)$ and $g(t)$. Using the definition, demonstrate that

$$\frac{dx}{dt} = \frac{d[f(t)]}{dt} + \frac{d[g(t)]}{dt}$$

What is the derivative of $x = f(t) - g(t)$?

Suppose that x is equal to the *product* of two functions $x = f(t) \cdot g(t)$, where $f(t)$ and $g(t)$ are functions of t. What is the derivative of x? If the argument increases from t to $t + \Delta t$, then the value of x will change. Call this new value $x + \Delta x$. Then

$$x + \Delta x = f(t + \Delta t) \cdot g(t + \Delta t)$$

Now, because of a change in its argument, $f(t + \Delta t)$ will, in general, have a value different from $f(t)$. Let this difference have the symbol Δf so that $f(t + \Delta t) = f(t) + \Delta f$. Similarly, let $g(t + \Delta t) = g(t) + \Delta g$. Then we may write

$$x + \Delta x = [f(t) + \Delta f][g(t) + \Delta g]$$

therefore

$$\begin{aligned}\Delta x &= [f(t) + \Delta f][g(t) + \Delta g] - x \\ &= [f(t) + \Delta f][g(t) + \Delta g] - f(t) \cdot g(t)\end{aligned}$$

and, expanding,

$$\Delta x = \cancel{f(t) \cdot g(t)} + g(t) \cdot \Delta f + f(t) \cdot \Delta g + \Delta f \, \Delta g - \cancel{f(t) \cdot g(t)}$$

or

$$\frac{\Delta x}{\Delta t} = g(t)\frac{\Delta f}{\Delta t} + f(t)\frac{\Delta g}{\Delta t} + \Delta g\frac{\Delta f}{\Delta t}$$

Taking the limit,

$$\frac{dx}{dt} = \lim_{t \to 0}\left[g(t)\frac{\Delta f}{\Delta t} + f(t)\frac{\Delta g}{\Delta t} + \Delta g\frac{\Delta f}{\Delta t}\right]$$

Here Δf is by definition $f(t + \Delta t) - f(t)$, so that when the limit of $\Delta f/\Delta t$ is taken we get the derivative df/dt by the definition in Eq. (4-3). The same is true of $\Delta g/\Delta t$.

$$\frac{dx}{dt} = g(t)\frac{df}{dt} + f(t)\frac{dg}{dt} + \frac{df}{dt}\lim_{\Delta t \to 0}\Delta g$$

Now $\Delta g \to 0$ as $\Delta t \to 0$, so the result is

$$\frac{dx}{dt} = \frac{d(fg)}{dt} = g(t)\frac{df}{dt} + f(t)\frac{dg}{dt} \tag{4-5}$$

This is the formula for the derivative of a product of two functions of t.

Suppose x is equal to a function taken to some power. For instance,

$$x = [f(t)]^n$$

where n is any number, positive or negative, except zero. Using the same procedure as before,

$$x + \Delta x = [f(t) + \Delta f]^n$$

or

$$\Delta x = [f(t) + \Delta f]^n - x = [f(t) + \Delta f]^n - f^n(t)$$

Expanding the terms in brackets, using the binomial expansion:

$$\Delta x = f^n(t) + nf^{n-1}(t)\,\Delta f + \frac{n(n-1)}{2!}f^{n-2}(t)\,(\Delta f)^2$$

$$+ \text{(terms involving higher powers of } \Delta f) - f^n(t)$$

$$\frac{\Delta x}{\Delta t} = nf^{n-1}(t)\frac{\Delta f}{\Delta t} + \frac{n(n-1)}{2!}f^{n-2}(t)\left(\frac{\Delta f}{\Delta t}\right)\Delta f + \cdots$$

$$\frac{dx}{dt} = \lim_{t\to 0}\left[nf^{n-1}(t)\frac{\Delta f}{\Delta t} + \frac{n(n-1)}{2!}f^{n-2}(t)\frac{\Delta f}{\Delta t}\Delta f + \cdots\right]$$

$$\frac{dx}{dt} = nf^{n-1}(t)\frac{df}{dt} \tag{4-6}$$

All terms in the series except the first have a factor Δf to some positive power, which goes to zero as Δt goes to zero. Notice that n does not have to be an integer.

Question

4-3 Suppose $x = g(t)/f(t)$, what is dx/dt? *Hint:* Let

$$\frac{1}{f(t)} = [f(t)]^{-1}$$

and use the rule for the derivative of the product of two functions. *Answer:*

$$\frac{dx}{dt} = \frac{1}{f(t)}\frac{dg}{dt} - \frac{g(t)}{f^2(t)}\frac{df}{dt} \tag{4-7}$$

A word on notation. A derivative is often symbolized by putting a prime over the function whose derivative is to be taken; if

$$x = f(t)$$

then

$$\frac{dx}{dt} = f'(t) \tag{4-8}$$

Alternatively a dot is used to symbolize a derivative with respect to time:

$$\frac{dx}{dt} = \dot{x}$$

In this way the velocity of a particle moving in a straight line may be written

$$v = \dot{x}$$

4.3 HIGHER DERIVATIVES. The *second derivative* is simply the derivative of the first derivative. The second derivative is given the symbol d^2x/dt^2. If $f'(t)$ is the first derivative of x with respect to t, then the second derivative is defined by the following limit if this limit exists.

$$\frac{d^2x}{dt^2} = \lim_{\Delta t \to 0} \frac{f'(t + \Delta t) - f'(t)}{\Delta t} \tag{4-9}$$

In practice one finds the second derivative by taking the derivative of the first derivative. For instance, if $x = t^3$, then the first derivative is $dx/dt = 3t^2$ and the second derivative is

$$\frac{d^2x}{dt^2} = \frac{d\left(\dfrac{dx}{dt}\right)}{dt} = 6t$$

A second derivative is sometimes symbolized by a double prime over the function whose second derivative is to be taken. If $x = f(t)$, then

$$\frac{d^2x}{dt^2} = f''(t)$$

Alternatively a double dot is used to symbolize a second derivative with respect to time:

$$\frac{d^2x}{dt^2} = \ddot{x}$$

Third, fourth, fifth, and higher derivatives may be defined by simple extensions of the previous definitions.

Questions

4-4 Write a definition of the third derivative by analogy to Eq. (4-9).

4-5 What is the third derivative of $x = t^3$? What is the fourth derivative of this function? the fifth derivative?

4.4 THE DERIVATIVE IN MECHANICS. How is the derivative applied to problems in mechanics? Suppose that the displacement of a particle along a straight line is known as a function of time: $x = f(t)$. From this expression the instantaneous velocity at any time is found by differentiating both sides of the equation with respect to time: $\dot{x} = v = f'(t)$. From the expression for velocity, instantaneous acceleration can be found by differentiating a second time: $\ddot{x} = \dot{v} = a = f''(t)$. If the mass of this particle is known, the instantaneous force on it can be found.

$$F = ma = mf''(t)$$

Notice that this force may be a constant one or may change with time.

Questions

4-6 The world line for a particle of mass m moving in a straight line path is given by the equation $x = bt^2 - ct^3$, where b and c are constants. What are the instantaneous velocity and acceleration as functions of time? What is the instantaneous force on the particle as a function of time?

4-7 The displacement vs time curve for a particle of mass m moving in a straight line is given by $x = bt^2 + ct + e$, where b, c, and e are constants. What is the force on the particle? How does this case differ from the one treated in Chapter 3? (See Eq. 3-1.) Write the equation for the world line, replacing the constants b, c, and e with the constants a for acceleration, v_1 for velocity at $t = 0$, and x_1 for displacement at $t = 0$.

4.5 THE INTEGRAL. As the last section shows, the *derivative* may be used to solve mechanics problems of the following form: given the mass of a particle and a mathematical formula for its displacement as a function of time, find its instantaneous velocity and acceleration and the force acting on it as functions of time. However, many of the most interesting problems in mechanics run in the opposite direction, so to speak: given the mass of a particle and the force acting on it as a function of time, find the instantaneous velocity and displacement of the particle as functions of time. We can begin the solution of the latter problem in the following way. If the mass of the particle and the force acting on it are known, the instantaneous acceleration can be found by dividing force by mass: $a = F/m$. Now we need a mathematical tool that can use such an expression for acceleration to find velocity, and which can use the resulting

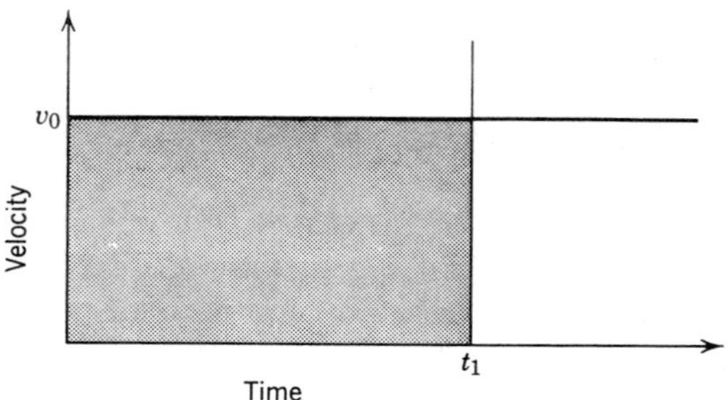

Fig. 4-2. Velocity vs time curve for a particle moving with constant speed v_0.

expression for velocity to find displacement. The tool we are looking for will act like the inverse of differentiation. This tool is called *integration.*

Suppose that we wish to find the displacement of a particle if its velocity is known as a function of time. In order to get a grasp on the problem let us consider the simplest possible case, that of a particle moving with a constant velocity v_0 with respect to the reference particle. Figure 4-2 shows how the velocity vs time curve for this particle looks. The question we wish to answer is: How far does the particle move between time $t = 0$ and any later time $t = t_1$? Since the velocity is constant, we already know the answer to be that the distance x_1 traveled in this time is $x_1 = v_0 t_1$. This result follows from the definition of constant velocity. Now, returning to Fig. 4-2, let us draw a vertical line representing the time t_1, as shown, and ask what is the area of the shaded region bounded by the lines $v = 0$, $v = v_0$, $t = 0$, and $t = t_1$. This area is the area of a rectangle and is given by $v_0 t$. But this has the same value as x_1, the displacement of the particle in a time t_1 as calculated above. Thus, in this case, the displacement of the particle between the times $t = 0$ and $t = t_1$ is equal to the area under the velocity vs time curve between the lines $t = 0$ and $t = t_1$.

Question

4-8 Be sure you understand every aspect of the preceding analysis. How can an area be equal to a length (displacement)? Show that the displacement calculated from the area of Fig. 4-2 will be independent of the *scale* of the diagram. Show how to find the further displacement of the particle between the time t_1 and a later time t_2, using first the definition of velocity and then the graphical method.

Will the same method for finding displacement work if the velocity changes with time? The simplest such case would be a constant rate of change of velocity, i.e., a constant acceleration. This is the case treated in

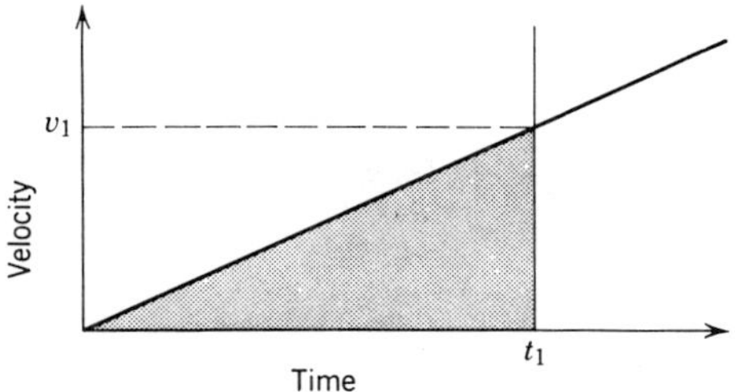

Fig. 4-3. Velocity vs time curve for constant acceleration.

Chapter 3. Figure 3-9 is reproduced in Fig. 4-3. What is the displacement of the particle between the times $t = 0$ and $t = t_1$? As before, draw a vertical line at $t = t_1$. We wish to find the area under the curve between $t = 0$ and $t = t_1$. From Eq. (3-12) we know that the equation for the curve is $v = at$, where a is the constant acceleration. Thus at $t = t_1$ the velocity v_1 will have the value $v_1 = at_1$. This is just the height of the shaded right triangle in the figure. The base of the triangle is t_1. The area of the shaded triangle is one-half the base times the height.

$$\text{Area} = \tfrac{1}{2}(t_1)(at_1) = \tfrac{1}{2}at_1^{\,2}$$

But Eq. (3-13) says that this is also the displacement of the particle in this time. Hence, once again, the displacement of the particle between the times $t = 0$ and $t = t_1$ is numerically equal to the area under the velocity vs time curve between the vertical lines $t = 0$ and $t = t_1$.

Question

4-9 Using your knowledge of the area of simple geometrical figures, find the additional displacement of the particle between the time t_1 and a later time t_2. Express the total displacement from $t = t_1$ to $t = t_2$ in terms of the acceleration a, the displacement x_1 at $t = t_1$, the velocity v_1 at $t = t_1$, and the time interval $(t_2 - t_1)$. Compare this expression to the one you derived in Question 4-7.

It is not difficult to demonstrate that, *no matter how the velocity changes with time*, the displacement of a particle in any time interval $t_2 - t_1$ is simply the area under the velocity vs time curve* between the vertical lines $t = t_1$ and $t = t_2$. Consider the velocity vs time curve given in Fig. 4-4. This curve gives velocity as a function of time: $v = v(t)$. Suppose that

* There are certain mathematical restrictions on the shape of such a curve, but these restrictions are more than amply satisfied by the velocity vs time curve of a particle in classical mechanics.

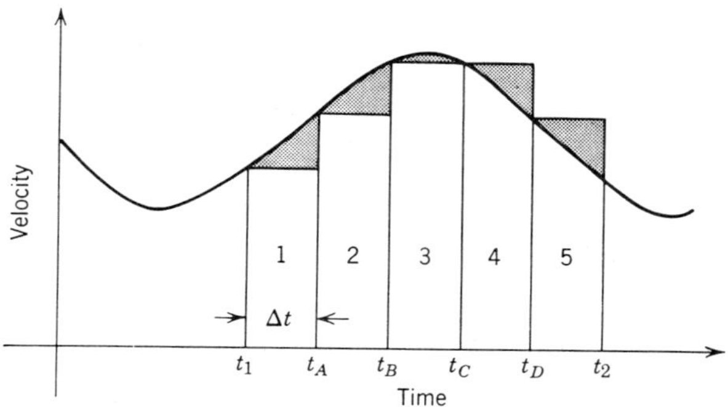

Fig. 4-4. Approximation of the area under the velocity vs time curve.

our problem is to find the displacement of the particle in the time interval $t_2 - t_1$. We wish to show that this displacement is numerically equal to the area under the curve between the vertical lines $t = t_1$ and $t = t_2$.

Draw a series of long narrow boxes with vertical sides, as shown in the figure, so that they fill the interval $t_2 - t_1$. Make the boxes of equal width and call this width Δt. Make the height of each box equal to the height of the velocity curve at the upper left corner of each box.

Now consider the box labeled 1. This box has a width Δt and a height given by $v(t_1)$. Hence its area is $v(t_1)\,\Delta t$. From the previous work with a particle moving at constant velocity we see that the area of box 1 is numerically equal to the displacement of a particle moving with constant velocity $v(t_1)$ in a time Δt. In actuality, of course, the velocity of the particle increases during the first interval Δt from the value $v(t_1)$ at the beginning of the interval to the value $v(t_A)$ at the end of the interval. In other words, the area of box 1 is only approximately equal numerically to the displacement of the particle in the first time interval Δt. How to improve this approximation will be shown below.

Suppose that we add together the areas of all the boxes which fill the time axis from t_1 to t_2. Mathematically the sum of all these areas has the form

$$v(t_1)\,\Delta t + v(t_A)\,\Delta t + v(t_B)\,\Delta t + v(t_C)\,\Delta t + v(t_D)\,\Delta t \qquad (4\text{-}10)$$

The area of each box is approximately equal to the displacement of the particle during that interval. Thus the total area enclosed by all the boxes is approximately equal to the total displacement of the particle in the interval $t_2 - t_1$. How can we improve this approximation? Notice that the total area enclosed by all the boxes is also approximately equal to the area under the velocity vs time curve in the interval $t_2 - t_1$. The small shaded areas in the figure are the areas for which the region covered by the boxes fails to coincide with the region under the curve. Now if Δt were made smaller it would take more boxes to fill in the region between t_1 and t_2 because each box would be narrower, but the *total* shaded area would be reduced as shown in Fig. 4-5.

We can repeat the previous analysis for each box in Fig. 4-5. The area of each box is a closer approximation to the displacement of the particle during that interval than before, because the velocity of the particle changes by a smaller percentage in the shorter time Δt. Thus, as we add together the area of each box, the total area enclosed by all boxes will be numerically more nearly equal to the total displacement of the particle in the interval $t_2 - t_1$. The total area enclosed by all boxes will also be more nearly equal to the total area under the curve in the interval $t_2 - t_1$.

If the number of boxes becomes very large and the width of each box becomes very small, the numerical value of the area enclosed by all the boxes can be made to approach as near as desired to the value of the actual displacement of the particle in the interval $t_2 - t_1$. In the same process the area enclosed by all the boxes approaches as near as desired to area under the curve. In this way we have shown that the displacement of a particle in the interval $t_2 - t_1$ is equal to the area under the velocity vs time curve between the vertical lines $t = t_1$ and $t = t_2$.

As the number of boxes increases, the sum corresponding to Eq. (4-10), which gives the total area of all the boxes, will have very many terms. In the limit as Δt becomes infinitesimally small and the number of boxes becomes infinitely large, the width Δt is written dt and the sum of terms is symbolized by the elongated letter S of the integral:

$$x_2 - x_1 = \int_{t_1}^{t_2} v(t)\, dt \tag{4-11}$$

In this equation, x_1 is the displacement of the particle at t_1 and x_2 is the displacement of the particle at t_2 so that the net displacement in the

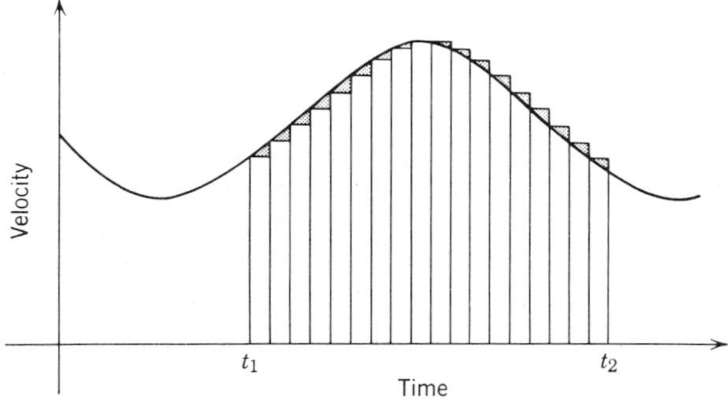

Fig. 4-5. Better approximation of the area under the velocity vs time curve using smaller time intervals.

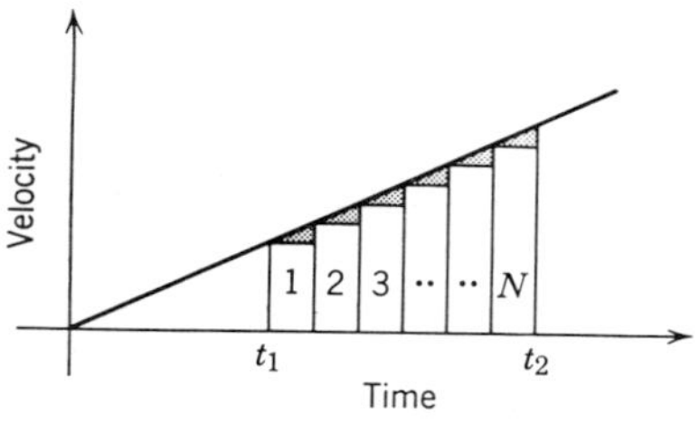

Fig. 4-6.

interval $t_2 - t_1$ is equal to $x_2 - x_1$. The symbols t_1 and t_2 written at the bottom and top of the summation integral are called the "limits of integration" and represent the vertical lines between which the area under the curve is to be found.

Questions

4-10 Demonstrate that

$$\int_{t_1}^{t_3} v(t)\,dt = \int_{t_1}^{t_2} v(t)\,dt + \int_{t_2}^{t_3} v(t)\,dt$$

4-11 Consider the velocity vs time curve in Fig. 4-6. The equation of this curve is $v = at$, where a is the constant acceleration. The space between t_1 and t_2 is filled with N boxes of equal width Δt as described above. Calculate the *total* area of the shaded triangles in the figure in terms of N, a, and Δt. This is the difference between the area under the curve and the total area of the N boxes. Find an expression which relates N to Δt. Show that as the number of boxes, N, becomes large (or as Δt becomes small) the total area of the shaded triangles can be made to be as small as desired.

Given the velocity vs time curve of a particle moving in a straight line, we are now able to find the displacement of the particle during any time interval by measuring an appropriate area under the velocity vs time curve. Using the same method, it is possible to find the change of *velocity* of a particle in any time interval if the acceleration is known as a function of time. Consider the graph of acceleration vs time for a particle moving with constant acceleration a (Fig. 4-7). The area under this curve in the time interval 0 to t_1 is given by at_1. But this is simply the change in velocity in this time interval, since by the definition of constant acceleration

$$v_1 - v_0 = at_1$$

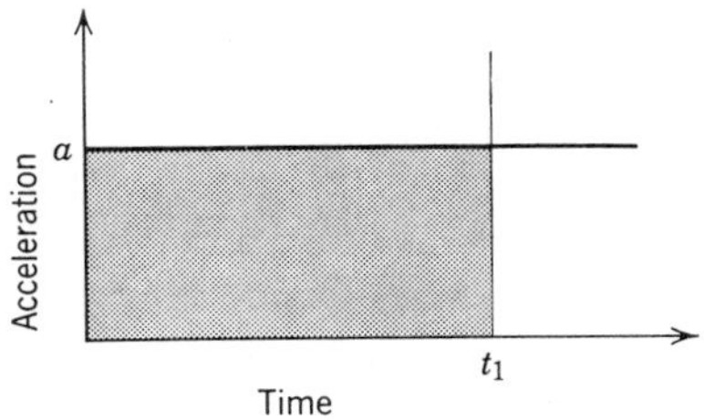

Fig. 4-7. Acceleration vs time curve for a particle moving with constant acceleration a.

Thus in this case the change of *velocity* of the particle in the time interval 0 to t_1 is numerically equal to the area under the *acceleration* vs time curve. Note the similarity between this case and the first case treated in this section.

Using the same method as before, it is easy to show that the change in velocity during any time interval is numerically equal to the area under the acceleration vs time curve between the vertical lines representing the beginning and end of that interval.

Question

4-12 Carry out arguments similar to those concerning velocity for the cases of uniformly increasing acceleration and for the case of an arbitrary acceleration vs time curve.

The demonstration of the general case will lead to the following expression for the change in velocity in the arbitrary time interval $t_2 - t_1$.

$$v_2 - v_1 = \int_{t_1}^{t_2} a(t)\, dt \tag{4-12}$$

where $a(t)$ is the function which gives the acceleration as a function of time.

4.6 THE INTEGRAL IN MECHANICS. We now have a method which can be used to find the change in velocity and change of position of a particle of known mass when it is acted on by a known linear force. This method proceeds as follows. First divide the force by the mass. This gives an expression for acceleration as a function of time. Then plot this acceleration vs time curve. The area under this curve between the vertical lines representing the beginning and end of any time interval will be numerically equal to the change of velocity of the particle during this time interval. Notice that this procedure gives only the *change* in velocity during this interval. If it is desired to know the final total velocity at the end of the time interval, the initial velocity at the beginning of this interval must be be given as part of the statement of the problem.

Assuming that the velocity is now known as a function of time, a curve of this velocity is plotted vs time. The change of displacement during any time interval is the area under this velocity vs time curve between the two lines representing this time interval. Once again, this procedure only gives the *change* of displacement during this time interval. If it desired to know the final displacement at the end of the time interval, the initial displacement at the beginning of the interval must be given as part of the statement of the problem.

Question

4-13 Carry out the foregoing procedure, starting with the acceleration vs time curve of Fig. 4-7. Assume that the constant acceleration is 1 m/sec^2 the initial velocity at $t = 0$ is 2 m/sec, and the initial displacement at $t = 0$ is 6 m from the reference particle. Find the velocity and displacement of the particle at $t = 10$ sec.

Plotting graphs and measuring areas is a somewhat cumbersome way to solve mechanics problems. If a mathematical expression can be found for the force on the particle as a function of time, then sometimes (but not always) it is possible to derive other expressions which give velocity and displacement directly. This amounts to solving the integrals (4-12) and (4-11) without plotting graphs.

The method of solving integrals directly arises from considering the fact that integration is the inverse of differentiation. We already know how to take derivatives, and this should help us to evaluate integrals. As an example, suppose we know that $dx/dt = v(t) = at$, where a is the constant acceleration, and that $x = 0$ at $t = 0$, Then Eq. (4-11) becomes

$$x - 0 = \int_0^t at\,dt$$

But we already *know* that the answer is $x = \frac{1}{2}at^2$ from Eq. (3-12), so that

$$x - 0 = \int_0^t at\,dt = \tfrac{1}{2}at^2$$

Since

$$\int_{t_1}^{t_2} v(t)\,dt = \int_0^{t_2} v(t)\,dt - \int_0^{t_1} v(t)\,dt$$

from Question 4-10 in the preceding section, a general expression for the integral of this type would be

$$\begin{aligned} x_2 - x_1 = \int_{t_1}^{t_2} at\,dt &= \int_0^{t_2} at\,dt - \int_0^{t_1} at\,dt \\ &= \tfrac{1}{2}at_2^{\,2} - \tfrac{1}{2}at_1^{\,2} \end{aligned}$$

where x_1 is the displacement of the particle at $t = t_1$. The usual way to find an expression for the value of an integral is to employ the swindle used above: namely, to take only the integrals of those expressions which are the results of previous differentiations. For instance, since

$$\frac{d(t^n)}{dt} = nt^{n-1} \qquad n \neq 0$$

therefore

$$\int_{t_1}^{t_2} nt^{n-1}\, dt = t_2{}^n - t_1{}^n \qquad n \neq 0 \tag{4-13}$$

This is the basic limitation of the integral. A derivative can be found for any function if the appropriate limits exist, but it is not always possible to solve the integral for any given function, even if the integral exists, unless the function is the derivative of another function already known.

Questions

4-14 Do the following integration.

$$\int_{t=2}^{t=6} t^2\, dt$$

4-15 Do the following integration symbolically.

$$\int_{t_1}^{t_2} \left[f(t)\frac{dg(t)}{dt} + g(t)\frac{df(t)}{dt} \right] dt$$

4-16 Do the following integral symbolically.

$$\int_{t_1}^{t_2} \frac{d[f^2(t)]}{dt}\, dt$$

4-17 If f and g are two functions of t, show that

$$\int_{t_1}^{t_2} (f + g)\, dt = \int_{t_1}^{t_2} f\, dt + \int_{t_1}^{t_2} g\, dt$$

Equation (4-13) does not cover the case

$$\int_{t_1}^{t_2} \frac{dt}{t}$$

since the equation is not defined for $n = 0$. Later on it will be necessary to evaluate an integral of this form. The answer will be given here. The following derivative can be found.

$$\frac{d[\ln t]}{dt} = \frac{1}{t} \tag{4-14}$$

where $\ln t$ is the logarithm of t taken to the base $e = 2.7182818\ldots$. This derivative is found by using the same limit-taking process used previously, but the mathematics is omitted here because some of the limits are difficult to evaluate.* From the derivative above it follows that

$$\int_{t_1}^{t_2} \frac{dt}{t} = \ln t_2 - \ln t_1 = \ln \frac{t_2}{t_1} \tag{4-15}$$

Since the values of all the foregoing integrals depend only on the values at the endpoints t_2 and t_1, the usual practice is to tabulate the solutions to integrations in the form of *indefinite integrals.* Indefinite integrals are written without the limits of integration. As an example,

$$\int at\, dt = \tfrac{1}{2}at^2$$

Then, when the endpoints are known, they are simply inserted in the integral and the correct expression on the right is the difference of the expressions when the two endpoints are inserted.

$$\int_{t_1}^{t_2} at\, dt = \tfrac{1}{2}a{t_2}^2 - \tfrac{1}{2}a{t_1}^2$$

The usual mathematical symbol for the insertion of endpoints is a vertical line after the indefinite integral, with the endpoints placed at the top and bottom of the vertical line; thus:

$$\int_{t_1}^{t_2} at\, dt = \tfrac{1}{2}at^2 \Big|_{t_1}^{t_2} = \tfrac{1}{2}a{t_2}^2 - \tfrac{1}{2}a{t_1}^2 \tag{4-16}$$

Question

4-18 Demonstrate that

$$\int_{t_1}^{t_2} f(t)\, dt = -\int_{t_2}^{t_1} f(t)\, dt$$

A summary of the indefinite integrals derived thus far follows.

$$\int K\, dt = Kt \qquad K = \text{constant} \tag{4-17}$$

$$\int Kf(t)\, dt = K\int f(t)\, dt \qquad K = \text{constant} \tag{4-18}$$

$$\int t^n\, dt = \frac{1}{(n+1)}\, t^{n+1} \qquad n \neq -1 \tag{4-19}$$

$$\int t^{-1}\, dt = \int \frac{dt}{t} = \ln t \tag{4-20}$$

$$\int \frac{df}{dt}\, dt = f \tag{4-21}$$

* See, for instance, R. E. Johnson and F. L. Kiokemeister, *Calculus with Analytic Geometry*, Allyn and Bacon, Inc., Boston, 1960.

where f is any function of t.

$$\int (f + g)\,dt = \int f\,dt + \int g\,dt \tag{4-22}$$

where f and g are any two functions of t.

$$\int \left(f\frac{dg}{dt} + g\frac{df}{dt}\right) dt = fg \tag{4-23}$$

where f and g are any two functions of t.

4.7 EXAMPLE: UNIFORMLY ACCELERATED MOTION. Let us now apply this new tool—the integral—to the physical problem of a particle acted on by a constant force. In this case $F = ma$ and, since F is a constant, a must also be constant. Given the force and the mass, we can solve for a.

$$a = F/m$$

But a is also the derivative of velocity with respect to time. Since the derivative of the velocity vs time curve is known, we can find the curve itself by integration.

$$v_2 - v_1 = \int_{t_1}^{t_2} \frac{dv}{dt}\,dt = \int_{t_1}^{t_2} a\,dt = a\int_{t_1}^{t_2} dt = at_2 - at_1$$

since a is a constant. What are t_2 and t_1? t_1 is some initial time and t_2 is *any* later time. Since t_2 represents any time, why not simply call it t? Call the velocity at this later time v. Then

$$v = v_1 + a(t - t_1) \tag{4-24}$$

Velocity is known as a function of time (if v_1 and t_1 are given). But velocity is the derivative of the displacement vs time curve. Since we know the derivative of this curve, we can find the curve itself by using the integral a second time.

$$x_2 - x_1 = \int_{t_1}^{t_2} \frac{dx}{dt}\,dt = \int_{t_1}^{t_2} [v_1 + a(t - t_1)]\,dt$$

$$= \int_{t_1}^{t_2} v_1\,dt + \int_{t_1}^{t_2} at\,dt - \int_{t_1}^{t_2} at_1\,dt$$

But a, v_1, and t_1 are constants, so

$$x_2 - x_1 = v_1\int_{t_1}^{t_2} dt + a\int_{t_1}^{t_2} t\,dt - at_1\int_{t_1}^{t_2} dt$$

$$= v_1t_2 - v_1t_1 + \tfrac{1}{2}at_2^{\,2} - \tfrac{1}{2}at_1^{\,2} - at_1t_2 + at_1^{\,2}$$

$$x_2 - x_1 = v_1(t_2 - t_1) + \tfrac{1}{2}a(t_2 - t_1)^2$$

Once again, t_1 is an initial time and t_2 is *any* later time. x_2 is the displacement at this later time. Set $t_2 = t$ and $x_2 = x$.

$$x = x_1 + v_1(t - t_1) + \tfrac{1}{2}a(t - t_1)^2 \tag{4-25}$$

The quantity t_1 is simply the time when the experiment began. If the clock is started from zero at the beginning of the experiment, $t_1 = 0$ and the three equations of motion become

$$a = \text{constant}$$

$$v = v_1 + at \tag{4-26}$$

$$x = x_1 + v_1 t + \tfrac{1}{2}at^2 \tag{4-27}$$

Question

4-19 For the special case of zero initial velocity and zero initial displacement ($v_1 = 0$, $x_1 = 0$) show that the displacement vs time curves have the same shape as those studied in Chapter 3. Show that, if $x_1 \neq 0$ but $v_1 = 0$, the displacement vs time curves is still a parabola, with the parabola vertex on the $t = 0$ axis. If $x_1 \neq 0$ and $v_1 \neq 0$, show that the displacement vs time curve is still a parabola opening upward but with its vertex off the $t = 0$ axis. What is the experimental difference between the cases in which the vertex of the parabola is to the left and to the right of the $t = 0$ axis? What physical meaning can be given to times less than zero?

From Eq. (4-26)

$$t = \frac{v - v_1}{a}$$

Substituting this expression for t into Eq. (4-27), expanding, and canceling, we have

$$x = x_1 + \frac{1}{2}\frac{(v^2 - v_1^{\,2})}{a}$$

or

$$v^2 = v_1^{\,2} + 2a(x - x_1) \tag{4-28}$$

Formulas (4-26), (4-27), and (4-28) are equations for constantly accelerated motion in one dimension.

Question

4-20 A particle of mass m starts from rest at $t = 0$ and is acted on by a force which increases with time according to the formula $F = bt$, where b is a constant. Find expressions for the velocity and for the displacement of the particle as a function of time. From these equations find an expression for the velocity as a function of displacement.

4.8 OTHER VARIABLES. Up to this point in the discussion of derivatives and integrals, time has been the independent variable plotted along the horizontal axis and displacement or velocity has been the dependent variable plotted on the vertical axis. One of the strengths of mathematics is that the same analysis can hold when different symbols are used. Any physical relationship that can be plotted as a continuous curve can be analyzed by means of the same mathematical procedures. Thus, in a rocket, *mass* changes with time because fuel is being expelled from the rear; in the impact of a golf club with particle one, the *force* on the particle is a function of time; the force of gravitational attraction is a function of *position*; etc. The analysis of these functions uses the same mathematics as the analysis of the displacement vs time curve—only the symbols are different.

The dot as a symbol for differentiation is usually reserved for differentiation with respect to time.

Questions

4-21 Carry out the indicated differentiations and integrations.

$$\frac{d(x^n)}{dx} \qquad \int x^n\,dx \qquad \int_{m_1}^{m_2} \frac{dm}{m}$$

4-22 What is df/dx if $f = ax + bx^2 + cx^3 + d$, where a, b, c, and d are constants?

4.9 VECTORS. Until now we have been dealing with motion in one dimension. All displacement has been in the (positive or negative) x-direction, and all forces, accelerations, and speeds have been along the same line. Now it is time to extend the discussion to three dimensions. In this extension it is very convenient to use *vectors*.

In order to describe completely a force acting on a particular particle in three dimensions, two pieces of information are necessary: the *magnitude* of the force and the *direction* in which the force acts. A mathematical number has magnitude. Such a number is called a *scalar*. A number alone does not indicate a direction, so a force cannot be described by a number alone. However, a *vector* is a mathematical symbol which has both *magnitude* and *direction*. Hence a vector may be used to describe a force. We say that *force is a vector quantity*.

Other important quantities in mechanics are also vector quantities. Displacement is a vector quantity because the description of the displacement of a particle must tell both *how far* the particle moved and *in what direction*. Velocity is also a vector quantity. Speed is the *magnitude* of this vector and is a scalar. But a description of velocity must include both

Fig. 4-8. A vector. **Fig. 4-9.** Equal vectors.

speed and the direction of motion. Acceleration is also a vector quantity. These four physical quantities appear to act like vector quantities: force, acceleration, velocity, and displacement. There are other physical quantities which act like vector quantities, and we shall encounter some of them later. By studying the mathematics of vectors we can better describe all these physical quantities.

Mathematically a vector is a quantity that has the properties of *magnitude* and *direction*. Figure 4-8 shows a vector. The direction in which the arrow points indicates the direction of the vector and the length of the arrow is proportional to the magnitude of the vector.

Question

4-23 How can the same kind of arrow represent both displacement and force, inasmuch as the units attached to these quantities are different?

In one very important respect, mathematical vectors differ from forces. A mathematical vector has magnitude and direction but no unique position or point of origin. Two vectors are defined to be mathematically equal if they have the same magnitude and direction. These two vectors do not have to occupy the same space in order to be equal. This means that an arrow representing a vector will represent an equal vector if it is moved around, *provided the arrow is moved in such a way that it always points in the same direction.* Figure 4-9 could be three possible positions of an arrow representing equal vectors. On the other hand, forces have not only magnitude and direction but also a place where they are applied. Clearly, a force applied to particle one will be physically distinguishable from a force of the same magnitude and direction applied to particle two. Thus, to determine a force completely, we need to specify the vector which represents its direction and magnitude and also the particle to which the force is applied.

In what follows we shall deal exclusively with the mathematical properties of vectors and shall return to their application to physical problems in Sec. 4.15.

A vector may be represented by a boldface symbol, such as **A** or **B**. The magnitude or length of the vector **A** will be represented either by the symbol |**A**| or simply by A.

4.10 VECTOR ADDITION AND SUBTRACTION. We now study the rules for adding, subtracting, and multiplying vectors. These rules may appear to be somewhat arbitrary. It might be possible, for instance, to define addition of vectors in another way than is done below. One of the advantages of mathematics is that definitions need not be limited to practical applications, and consequently the mathematician is free to define his symbols and operations in any self-consistent manner. Nevertheless, if the vector operations described below are accepted, they will provide a system which is both logically elegant and physically useful, as will appear later.

Consider two vectors **A** and **B**. Vector addition is defined as follows: Move the **B** arrow parallel to itself until the tail of the arrow coincides with the head of the **A** arrow. The vector **A** + **B** is by definition an arrow whose tail coincides with the tail of **A** and whose head coincides with the head of **B**. (See Fig. 4-10.) This sum is often called the *resultant* vector. The *magnitude* or length of the resultant vector is given the symbol |**A** + **B**|.

Questions

4-24 Demonstrate that **B** + **A** = **A** + **B**.

4-25 Show that the scalar |**A** + **B**| is not necessarily equal to the scalar $A + B$. Which one will usually be larger? Under what conditions *are* the two scalars equal?

4-26 If **A** and **B** represent consecutive directed displacements of a particle, what does **C** represent?

4-27 Demonstrate that the definition above is equivalent to defining **A** + **B** as the diagonal of the parallelogram whose sides are made up of

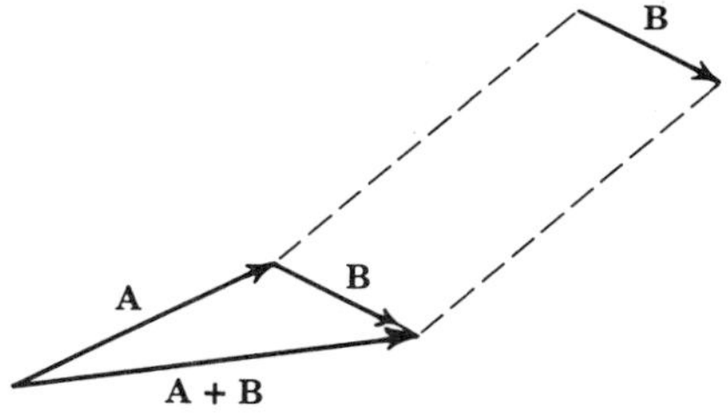

Fig. 4-10. Definition of vector addition.

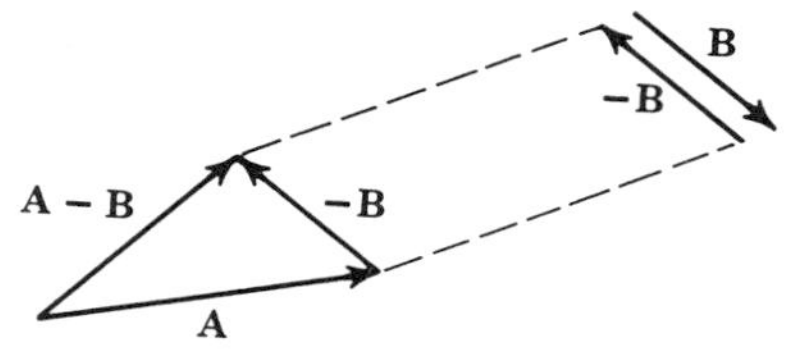

Fig. 4-11. Definition of vector subtraction.

the vectors **A** and **B**. Such a parallelogram has two diagonals; how is the correct diagonal chosen?

4-28 If the vector **C** is defined by the equation $\mathbf{C} = \mathbf{A} + \mathbf{B}$ and if **D** is another vector, show how to find the sum $\mathbf{C} + \mathbf{D} = \mathbf{A} + \mathbf{B} + \mathbf{D}$. In this way define the sum of any number of vectors. (*Answer:* Place the tail of one arrow at the head of another and continue the process until all arrows have been used once. The resultant is represented by the arrow whose tail coincides with the tail of the first arrow and whose head coincides with the head of the last arrow.) Show that the same resultant will be found if the vectors are taken in any order. Is your demonstration valid if not all the vectors lie in the same plane?

The negative of a vector **A** is written $-\mathbf{A}$ and is defined as a vector with the same magnitude as **A** but with a direction which is opposite to that of **A**.

Vector *subtraction* is defined as follows: The difference $\mathbf{A} - \mathbf{B}$ between two vectors is defined as the sum of **A** and the negative of **B**. Thus $\mathbf{A} - \mathbf{B} = \mathbf{A} + (-\mathbf{B})$. The magnitude or length of the difference $\mathbf{A} - \mathbf{B}$ is given the symbol $|\mathbf{A} - \mathbf{B}|$. (See Fig. 4-11.)

Question

4-29 Show that $\mathbf{A} - (-\mathbf{B}) = \mathbf{A} + \mathbf{B}$.

4.11 COMPONENTS OF A VECTOR. Suppose that three vectors **A**, **B**, and **C** satisfy the equation $\mathbf{C} = \mathbf{A} + \mathbf{B}$ according to the previous definition of addition of vectors. This equation says that the vector **C** may be replaced by the sum of the two vectors **A** and **B**. There are an infinite number of pairs of vectors like **A** and **B** which can be used to replace **C** by "adding up" to the vector **C**. However, if we demand that **A** and **B** lie along certain directions, then the magnitudes of **A** and **B** are uniquely determined. These directions must both lie in a common plane with **C**. The magnitudes of the vectors **A** and **B** which add up to **C** and which lie in prescribed directions are called the *components* of **C** in those directions. The method of finding such components is outlined in Fig. 4-12.

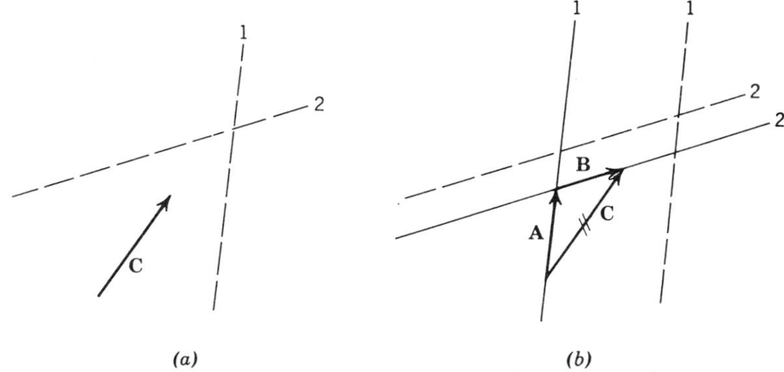

Fig. 4-12. Method for finding the components of **C** in two prescribed directions.

Figure 4-12*a*. *Problem:* Find the components of the vector **C** which lie in the directions of lines 1 and 2 as shown.

Figure 4-12*b*. *Solution:* Draw two lines parallel to the given lines, one passing through the tail of **C**, one passing through head of **C**. Construct **A** and **B** to lie along these lines in such a way that $\mathbf{A} + \mathbf{B} = \mathbf{C}$. The magnitudes A and B of the vectors **A** and **B** are then the components of **C** along the prescribed directions.

This method is called the *resolution* of a vector into components. Notice that components are scalars. In order to specify the vector **C** uniquely in terms of its components, the directions of the lines along which the components are measured must also be specified. Sometimes in diagrams where a vector has been resolved into its components, a double line is drawn across the vector, as in Fig. 4-12, to show that it has been replaced by these components.

Questions

4-30 Show that the procedure above yields unique components A and B; that is, no other two components are possible once the directions of lines 1 and 2 are chosen. Is this contradicted by the fact that line 1 above could have been redrawn through the head of **C** and line 2 through the tail of **C**?

4-31 What conditions must lines 1 and 2 satisfy? Could they be parallel?

In mathematics, special interest is attached to coordinate systems whose *axes* are perpendicular to each other. We may find components of a vector along the axes of such a coordinate system as shown in Fig. 4-13.

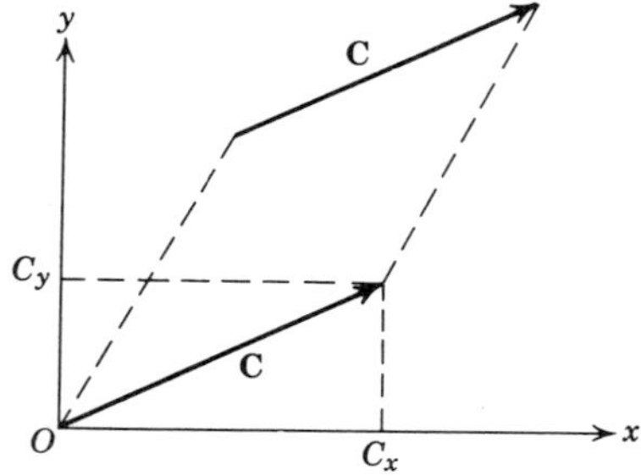

Fig. 4-13. Rectangular components of a vector **C**.

The two perpendicular lines which are called the axes of this coordinate system must both lie in the same plane as **C**. Here the arrow representing **C** has been redrawn with its tail at the origin O of the coordinate system. The component of **C** along the x-axis is called C_x, and the component of **C** along the y-axis is called C_y.

Question

4-32 Is there anything unique about the orientation of the x- and y-axes? Under what conditions would

$$C_x = |\mathbf{C}|? \qquad C_x = 0? \qquad C_x = C_y?$$

4.12 UNIT VECTORS. A vector in two dimensions is determined by its components. In three dimensions the same rule holds. If the origin of a coordinate system is placed at the tail of the vector **F** (Fig. 4-14), and

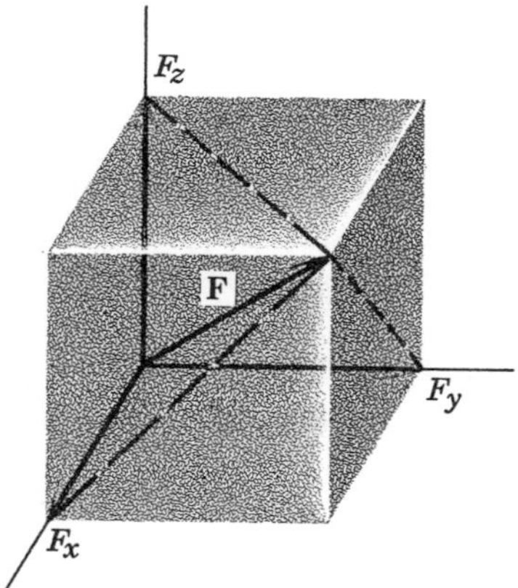

Fig. 4-14. Components of a vector.

if perpendicular lines are dropped from the head of **F** to the three perpendicular axes, then the length of the line from the origin to the foot of any one perpendicular represents the *component* of the force along this axis. The x-component, for instance, has the value $F_x = F\cos\theta$, where θ is the angle between the vector **F** and the x-axis. The vector **F** is then determined by its three components along specified axes.

Let us define three vectors of unit length which lie along the three axes (Fig. 4-15): $\hat{\imath}$ lies along the x-axis, $\hat{\jmath}$ lies along the y-axis, and $\hat{k}$ lies along the z-axis. These vectors are written $\hat{\imath}$, $\hat{\jmath}$, $\hat{k}$ (instead of **i**, **j**, **k**) to signify that they have a *unit* length. Using the unit vectors, we may write an expression for the vector **F** in terms of its components, F_x, F_y, and F_z. The symbol $\hat{\imath}F_x$ represents a vector whose magnitude is F_x and whose direction is along the x-axis.* Similarly $\hat{\jmath}F_y$ and $\hat{k}F_z$ represent vectors of magnitude F_y and F_z respectively which lie respectively in the directions of the y- and z-axes. The vector **F** may now be written as a vector sum of the vectors made of its components along the three axes.

$$\mathbf{F} = F_x\hat{\imath} + F_y\hat{\jmath} + F_z\hat{k} \tag{4-29}$$

The magnitude of **F** is given by

$$F = \sqrt{F_x^2 + F_y^2 + F_z^2} \tag{4-30}$$

The use of these unit vectors makes easy the addition and subtraction of

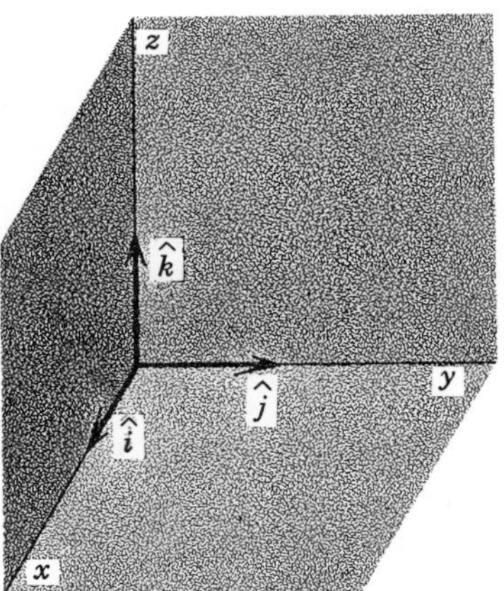

Fig. 4-15. The unit vectors.

* Carefully defined, the unit vector is an operator which, when it operates on a scalar, converts that scalar to a vector of magnitude equal to the magnitude of the scalar and with a direction specified by the unit vector.

vectors once the components are known. For instance, if

$$\mathbf{A} = A_x\hat{\imath} + A_y\hat{\jmath} + A_z\hat{k}$$
$$\mathbf{B} = B_x\hat{\imath} + B_y\hat{\jmath} + B_z\hat{k}$$

then

$$\mathbf{A} + \mathbf{B} = (A_x + B_x)\hat{\imath} + (A_y + B_y)\hat{\jmath} + (A_z + B_z)\hat{k} \tag{4-31}$$

and

$$\mathbf{A} - \mathbf{B} = (A_x - B_x)\hat{\imath} + (A_y - B_y)\hat{\jmath} + (A_z - B_z)\hat{k} \tag{4-32}$$

Class Discussion Question

4-33 How would you establish the orthogonal coordinate reference system of Fig. 4-15 in interstellar space? How would you ensure that the resulting coordinate system does not "rotate in space"?

Question

4-34 With respect to the coordinate system of the preceding question, two constant forces, $\mathbf{F}_1 = 2\hat{\imath} + 3\hat{\jmath} + 4\hat{k}$ N and $\mathbf{F}_2 = 1\hat{\imath} - 2\hat{\jmath} - 3\hat{k}$ N, act simultaneously on a particle. What is the resultant force on the particle? If the particle has a mass of 3 kg, what is the resulting acceleration?

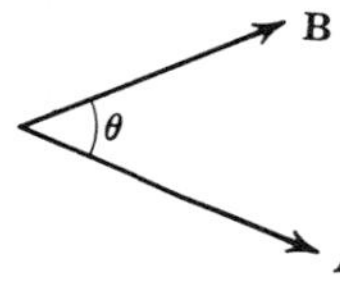

Fig. 4-16. Two vectors.

4.13 SCALAR AND VECTOR PRODUCTS. Vectors may be added and subtracted. They may also be multiplied. Two methods of multiplication have been defined for vectors. One yields a scalar as a product, the other yields a vector.

The *scalar product* or *dot product* of two vectors is defined by the expression

$$\mathbf{A} \cdot \mathbf{B} = AB\cos\theta \tag{4-33}$$

where A and B represent the magnitudes of the vectors **A** and **B** respectively. The angle θ is the angle between the two vectors. (See Fig. 4-16).

Questions

4-35 Show that the dot product of **A** and **B** can be interpreted as the scalar A times the component of **B** in the direction of **A**. Can it also be interpreted as the scalar B times the component of **A** in the direction of **B**?

4-36 Demonstrate that, if two vectors **A** and **B** lie along the same line, then either $\mathbf{A} \cdot \mathbf{B} = AB$ or $\mathbf{A} \cdot \mathbf{B} = -AB$. What distinguishes the two cases? Demonstrate that, if two vectors are perpendicular to one another, then their dot product is zero.

4-37 Demonstrate that $\mathbf{A} \cdot \mathbf{B} = \mathbf{B} \cdot \mathbf{A}$.

4-38 Show that $\mathbf{A} \cdot (k\mathbf{B}) = k\mathbf{A} \cdot \mathbf{B}$, where k is a scalar constant.

The dot products of the *unit* vectors are easily found and are equal to

$$\hat{\imath}\cdot\hat{\imath} = \hat{\jmath}\cdot\hat{\jmath} = \hat{k}\cdot\hat{k} = 1$$
$$\hat{\imath}\cdot\hat{\jmath} = \hat{\jmath}\cdot\hat{k} = \hat{k}\cdot\hat{\imath} = 0$$

Question

4-39 Show that, if each of the vectors **D**, **E**, and **F** is equal to any of the unit vectors $\hat{\imath}$, $\hat{\jmath}$, or $\hat{k}$, then

$$\mathbf{D}\cdot(\mathbf{E}+\mathbf{F}) = \mathbf{D}\cdot\mathbf{E} + \mathbf{D}\cdot\mathbf{F}$$

Using the unit vectors, the dot product of any two vectors may be expressed in terms of their components.

$$\mathbf{A}\cdot\mathbf{B} = (A_x\hat{\imath} + A_y\hat{\jmath} + A_z\hat{k})\cdot(B_x\hat{\imath} + B_y\hat{\jmath} + B_z\hat{k}) \qquad \text{(4-34}a\text{)}$$
$$= A_xB_x + A_yB_y + A_zB_z \qquad \text{(4-34}b\text{)}$$

All other terms are zero. Hence

$$\mathbf{A}\cdot\mathbf{B} = AB\cos\theta = A_xB_x + A_yB_y + A_zB_z \qquad \text{(4-35)}$$

Questions

4-40 Carry out the steps leading from Eq. (4-34*a*) to Eq. (4-34*b*).

4-41 Two vectors are given by the expressions

$$\mathbf{A} = 3\hat{\imath} + 4\hat{\jmath} + 0\hat{k} \qquad \mathbf{B} = 0\hat{\imath} + 0\hat{\jmath} + 1\hat{k}$$

What is their dot product? Could this result have been predicted by inspection?

4-42 Demonstrate that for any three vectors **A**, **B**, and **C**

$$\mathbf{A}\cdot(\mathbf{B}+\mathbf{C}) = \mathbf{A}\cdot\mathbf{B} + \mathbf{A}\cdot\mathbf{C}$$

4-43 Demonstrate that the square of the magnitude of any vector is given by its dot product with itself; that is, show that $F^2 = \mathbf{F}\cdot\mathbf{F}$.

4-44 Demonstrate that $\mathbf{F}\cdot\hat{\imath} = F_x$, etc.

The *vector product* or *cross product* of two vectors is symbolized by $\mathbf{C} = \mathbf{A}\times\mathbf{B}$. The *magnitude* of the cross product is given by

$$C = AB\sin\theta \qquad \text{(4-36)}$$

where θ is the angle between the vectors **A** and **B**. The *direction* of the vector **C** is perpendicular to the plane in which the two vectors **A** and **B** lie. Since there are two such perpendiculars (projecting from either side of the plane), we must choose between the two. The choice is made (somewhat

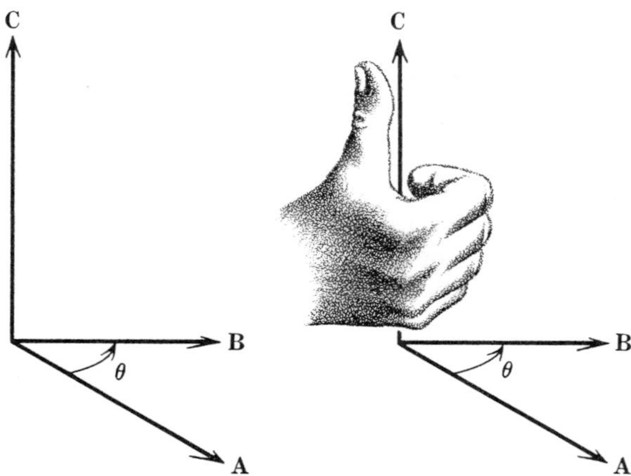

Fig. 4-17. Cross product convention.

arbitrarily) as follows: The direction of $\mathbf{C} = \mathbf{A} \times \mathbf{B}$ is the direction a right-hand screw would advance if placed perpendicular to the plane in which **A** and **B** lie and turned in the same way that vector **A** would have to be turned in order to make it coincident with **B** by rotating it through the smallest angle. Figure 4-17 shows a quick "right-hand rule" for determining the direction of $\mathbf{C} = \mathbf{A} \times \mathbf{B}$. The *right* hand is held as shown with the fingers pointing from **A** toward **B**. Then the thumb points in the direction of **C**.

Questions

4-45 Demonstrate that $\mathbf{B} \times \mathbf{A} = -\mathbf{A} \times \mathbf{B}$.

4-46 Show that $\mathbf{A} \times (k\mathbf{B}) = k\mathbf{A} \times \mathbf{B}$, where k is a scalar constant.

The cross products of the unit vectors are

$$\hat{\imath} \times \hat{\jmath} = \hat{k} \qquad \hat{\jmath} \times \hat{k} = \hat{\imath} \qquad \hat{k} \times \hat{\imath} = \hat{\jmath}$$

$$\hat{\imath} \times \hat{\imath} = \hat{\jmath} \times \hat{\jmath} = \hat{k} \times \hat{k} = 0$$

Questions

4-47 Prove these results for the unit vectors using Eq. (4-36) and the "right-hand rule."

4-48 Show that, if each of the vectors **D**, **E**, **F** is equal to any of the unit vectors $\hat{\imath}$, $\hat{\jmath}$, $\hat{k}$, then

$$\mathbf{D} \times (\mathbf{E} + \mathbf{F}) = \mathbf{D} \times \mathbf{E} + \mathbf{D} \times \mathbf{F}$$

Using the unit vectors, the cross product of any two vectors may be expressed in terms of their components.

$$\mathbf{A} \times \mathbf{B} = (A_x\hat{\imath} + A_y\hat{\jmath} + A_z\hat{k}) \times (B_x\hat{\imath} + B_y\hat{\jmath} + B_z\hat{k}) \qquad (4\text{-}37a)$$

$$\mathbf{A} \times \mathbf{B} = (A_yB_z - A_zB_y)\hat{\imath} + (A_zB_x - A_xB_z)\hat{\jmath} + (A_xB_y - A_yB_x)\hat{k} \quad (4\text{-}37b)$$

Questions

4-49 Fill in the steps that lead from Eq. (4-37*a*) to Eq. (4-37*b*).

4-50 Two vectors are given by the expressions

$$\mathbf{A} = 3\hat{\imath} + 4\hat{\jmath} + 0\hat{k} \qquad \mathbf{B} = 0\hat{\imath} + 0\hat{\jmath} + 1\hat{k}$$

What is their cross product? Could this result have been predicted by inspection?

4-51 Demonstrate that, for any three vectors **A**, **B**, and **C**,

$$\mathbf{A} \times (\mathbf{B} + \mathbf{C}) = \mathbf{A} \times \mathbf{B} + \mathbf{A} \times \mathbf{C}$$

Equation (4-37*b*) is somewhat more complicated than the corresponding expression for the dot product. For those who know how to expand a determinant in minors the following notation is more easily remembered.

$$\mathbf{A} \times \mathbf{B} = \begin{vmatrix} \hat{\imath} & \hat{\jmath} & \hat{k} \\ A_x & A_y & A_z \\ B_x & B_y & B_z \end{vmatrix} \qquad (4\text{-}38)$$

4.14 DIFFERENTIATION AND INTEGRATION OF A VECTOR. The position of a particle with respect to three perpendicular axes may be represented by a vector **r**.

$$\mathbf{r} = x\hat{\imath} + y\hat{\jmath} + z\hat{k}$$

The tail of the vector **r** is assumed to be at the origin of the coordinate system. In the earlier discussion of motion in one dimension, the velocity was defined as the derivative of a displacement with respect to time: $v = dx/dt$. Previously differentiation was carried out on scalars only. What does this differentiation mean when applied to a vector? We *define* differentiation of a vector to mean a differentiation of each component with respect to t. Since we assume that the unit vectors $\hat{\imath}$, $\hat{\jmath}$, and $\hat{k}$ are constant in time, this differentiation looks as follows:

$$\mathbf{v} = \frac{d\mathbf{r}}{dt} = \frac{dx}{dt}\hat{\imath} + \frac{dy}{dt}\hat{\jmath} + \frac{dz}{dt}\hat{k} \qquad (4\text{-}39)$$

Similarly,

$$\frac{d\mathbf{v}}{dt} = \frac{d}{dt}(v_x\hat{\imath} + v_y\hat{\jmath} + v_z\hat{k})$$

$$= \frac{dv_x}{dt}\hat{\imath} + \frac{dv_y}{dt}\hat{\jmath} + \frac{dv_z}{dt}\hat{k} \tag{4-40}$$

In the same way a vector may be integrated by integrating separately each component of the vector. For instance,

$$\int_{t_1}^{t_2} \mathbf{F}\,dt = \hat{\imath}\int_{t_1}^{t_2} F_x\,dt + \hat{\jmath}\int_{t_1}^{t_2} F_y\,dt + \hat{k}\int_{t_1}^{t_2} F_z\,dt$$

Notice we assume that the unit vectors $\hat{\imath}$, $\hat{\jmath}$, and $\hat{k}$ are constant with time, so that they are not involved in the differentiation or integration with respect to time.

Question

4-52 From the preceding rule for differentiation of a vector demonstrate that

$$\frac{d}{dt}(\mathbf{A}\cdot\mathbf{B}) = \frac{d\mathbf{A}}{dt}\cdot\mathbf{B} + \mathbf{A}\cdot\frac{d\mathbf{B}}{dt} \tag{4-41}$$

and that

$$\frac{d}{dt}(\mathbf{A}\times\mathbf{B}) = \frac{d\mathbf{A}}{dt}\times\mathbf{B} + \mathbf{A}\times\frac{d\mathbf{B}}{dt} \tag{4-42}$$

In the latter case show that the order in the cross products on the right-hand side may not be reversed.

4.15 THE VECTOR LAWS OF MOTION OF A PARTICLE. THE INERTIAL COORDINATE SYSTEM. The *position* of a particle in space may be represented by a vector **r**. The tail of this vector is assumed to be at the origin of a coordinate system. For the minute, we say nothing more about the nature of this coordinate system than that it has three mutually perpendicular axes along which the components of **r** may be found.

$$\mathbf{r} = x\hat{\imath} + y\hat{\jmath} + z\hat{k} \tag{4-43}$$

The *velocity* of the particle with respect to this coordinate system is *defined* as the rate of change of its position vector with respect to time.

$$\mathbf{v} = \frac{d\mathbf{r}}{dt} = \dot{\mathbf{r}} = \dot{x}\hat{\imath} + \dot{y}\hat{\jmath} + \dot{z}\hat{k} \tag{4-44}$$

The *speed* of the particle is defined as the *magnitude* of this velocity vector.

Question

4-53 Show that $\dot{\mathbf{r}}$ will not necessarily point in the same direction as $\mathbf{r}$.

The *acceleration* of the particle with respect to this coordinate system is *defined* as the rate of change of the velocity vector with respect to time.

$$\mathbf{a} = \frac{d\mathbf{v}}{dt} = \dot{\mathbf{v}} = \ddot{\mathbf{r}} = \ddot{x}\hat{\imath} + \ddot{y}\hat{\jmath} + \ddot{z}\hat{k} \qquad (4\text{-}45)$$

Force may be defined operationally as it was in Chapter 3, but this time its vector nature is taken into account.

Question

4-54 State such an operational definition of force as a vector quantity.

Now a series of experiments in three dimensions similar to those carried out in one dimension in Chapters 2 and 3 will result in the following *vector law of motion for a particle.*

Experimental Result. There exist coordinate systems in which the acceleration $\ddot{\mathbf{r}}$ of a particle and any force $\mathbf{F}$ which acts on it are related by the vector equation

$$\mathbf{F} = m\ddot{\mathbf{r}} = m\mathbf{a} \qquad (4\text{-}46)$$

The mass of the particle may be defined as in Chapter 3. Coordinate systems in which this law holds are called *inertial coordinate systems* or *inertial reference frames* or *Galilean reference frames.* The mass of particles may be defined as in Chapter 3, using results of experiments measured with respect to an inertial coordinate system.

Not all coordinate systems are inertial. A coordinate system which is accelerating or rotating with respect to an inertial coordinate system is not itself inertial. We shall return to these non-inertial coordinate systems in Chapter 9.

Question

4-55 Describe briefly but logically what extensions of the experiments in Chapters 2 and 3 would be required in order to establish the vector law of motion for a particle.

The inertial coordinate system is defined in such a way that the vector law of motion for a particle has a simple form in such a coordinate system. The inertial coordinate system is found to have another characteristic that at first glance may seem trivial but which in fact is astonishing. It is an experimental result that *an inertial coordinate system does not rotate with* *respect to the fixed stars.* The "fixed stars" are those stars which are very distant from any experiment. Viewed from any point in the universe, all but the very nearest stars appear to maintain their position relative to one another for long periods of time. Special equipment or observations over long time spans show some relative shift between stars, but most of our mechanics experiments will take place in times short enough that this relative motion is insignificant. Hence these stars are said to be "fixed." Now, after setting up an inertial coordinate system for our mechanics experiments, we may look out at the fixed stars. Experimentally we find that the inertial coordinate system is not rotating with respect to the fixed stars. Why is this so? Do the distant fixed stars influence a particle in such a way that the laws of motion have the form they do in a coordinate system which does not rotate with respect to these stars? This question and similar questions have been considered by Newton, Mach, and others.* One difficulty in verifying any possible answer is that we have only one set of fixed stars to work with as long as experiments are carried out near the earth; we cannot try a different arrangement of fixed stars to see how experimental results might be changed. The stars in the Milky Way, which belong to our galaxy, are nearer to us than other stars. Some very sensitive experiments designed to detect any lack of symmetry in the laws of motion with respect to the direction of the center of our galaxy have given negative results, but the interpretation of these experiments is still under discussion.†

Consider once again Eq. (4-46). In the special case that $\mathbf{F} = 0$ we have

$$\mathbf{F} = 0 = m\ddot{\mathbf{r}} = m\frac{d\dot{\mathbf{r}}}{dt} \quad \text{or} \quad \frac{d\dot{\mathbf{r}}}{dt} = 0 \quad \text{or} \quad \dot{\mathbf{r}} \text{ is a constant}$$

A particle acted on by no force will have a velocity which is a constant in *magnitude* and *direction.* In other words, it will move with constant speed in a straight line as discussed in Chapter 2. If the initial velocity is zero, it will remain zero in the absence of any force.

Questions

4-56 You are shown a coordinate system in interstellar space. How could you use the last observation about the motion of a particle subject to no forces to test experimentally whether or not the given coordinate system is inertial?

4-57 Demonstrate that a coordinate system which moves with constant velocity with respect to an inertial coordinate system is itself inertial.

* For a discussion with references see D. W. Sciama, *The Unity of the Universe*, Doubleday and Co., Inc., Garden City, 1959, Chapters 7–9.

† For references and discussion see R. H. Dicke, *Physical Review Letters*, **7**, 359 (November 1, 1961).

How will a particle move if it is acted on by two forces $\mathbf{F}_1$ and $\mathbf{F}_2$ at the same time? The first answer which comes to mind is that the particle will move as if it were being acted on by a single force equal to the vector sum of the two forces acting separately. In other words, the motion of the particle would satisfy the equation

$$\mathbf{F}_1 + \mathbf{F}_2 = m\ddot{\mathbf{r}} \tag{4-47}$$

This is a good guess, and it turns out to be the correct answer. Yet there is no reason why this *must* be the case. It might very well be, for instance, that the presence of force $\mathbf{F}_2$ changes the effect due to force $\mathbf{F}_1$. The fact that forces add like vectors is an experimental result. No experiment has been found which violates the following law.

Experimental Observation. A particle which is acted on by two or more forces will move as if it were being acted on by a single force equal to the vector sum of all the forces acting on the particle. This is called the *law of superposition of forces.*

Class Discussion Question

4-58 Show that the procedure used in Chapter 3 for calibrating a spring balance to exert two units of force *assumes* the law of superposition of forces in one dimension. Could the law of superposition of forces in three dimensions be derived from this assumption in one dimension without the use of additional experiments?

Using the vector law of motion for a particle and the tools of integration and vector analysis, it is possible to describe the motion in three dimensions of a particle which is acted on by any number of known forces, any or all of which may be varying with time in magnitude or direction. In practice this reduces to solving the one-dimensional equations of motion three times, once for each coordinate axis. An example of this method follows.

Example. A particle of mass 2 kg starts from rest at the origin of an inertial coordinate system at time $t = 0$. Thereafter a force is applied to it which is given by the expression $\mathbf{F} = 2\hat{\imath} + 4t\hat{\jmath} + 6t^2\hat{k}$ N. Find the acceleration, velocity, and position of the particle for any later time.

Question

4-59 Show that this force changes direction as well as magnitude with time. What is the magnitude of the force as a function of time? In what direction does the force vector point at $t = 0$? In what direction will the force vector point as t increases without limit?

Solution. The equation of motion (Eq. 4-46) for this case will read as follows:

$$\mathbf{F} = m\ddot{\mathbf{r}}$$

$$(2\hat{\imath} + 4t\hat{\jmath} + 6t^2\hat{k})\ \text{N} = (2\ \text{kg})\ddot{\mathbf{r}}$$

Hence the acceleration will be given by the expression

$$\ddot{\mathbf{r}} = \hat{\imath} + 2t\hat{\jmath} + 3t^2\hat{k}\ \text{m/sec}^2$$

The three components of velocity may be found by integrating the three components of acceleration separately and using the initial velocity $\mathbf{v}_1$. The x-component is found as follows.

$$v_x - v_{1x} = \int_0^t dt = t\Big|_0^t = t \quad \text{m/sec}$$

but the initial x-component of the velocity v_{1x} is equal to zero from the statement of the problem, so

$$v_x = t\ \text{m/sec}$$

Similarly, the y- and z-components of velocity are, since $v_{y1} = v_{z1} = 0$,

$$v_y = 2\int_0^t t\,dt = \frac{2t^2}{2}\Big|_0^t = t^2 \quad \text{m/sec}$$

$$v_z = 3\int_0^t t^2\,dt = \frac{3t^2}{3}\Big|_0^t = t^3 \quad \text{m/sec}$$

Hence the vector velocity is given by the expression

$$\mathbf{v} = t\hat{\imath} + t^2\hat{\jmath} + t^3\hat{k}\ \text{m/sec}$$

Similarly the three components of displacement may be found by integrating the three components of velocity separately and by using the given information that the initial displacement r_1 is equal to zero. The results are

$$x = \frac{t^2}{2}\ \text{m}$$

$$y = \frac{t^3}{3}\ \text{m}$$

$$z = \frac{t^4}{4}\ \text{m}$$

so that the displacement as a function of time is given by the expression

$$\mathbf{r} = \frac{t^2}{2}\,\hat{\imath} + \frac{t^3}{3}\,\hat{\jmath} + \frac{t^4}{4}\,\hat{k}\ \text{m}$$

EXERCISES

The first six exercises concern pairs of vectors **A** and **B**. In each case find

(*a*) $|\mathbf{A}|$ and $|\mathbf{B}|$
(*b*) $\mathbf{A} + \mathbf{B}$ and $|\mathbf{A} + \mathbf{B}|$
(*c*) $\mathbf{A} - \mathbf{B}$ and $|\mathbf{A} - \mathbf{B}|$
(*d*) $\mathbf{A} \cdot \mathbf{B}$
(*e*) $\mathbf{A} \times \mathbf{B}$ and $|\mathbf{A} \times \mathbf{B}|$
(*f*) the angle between **A** and **B**

In some cases the answers should be clear from inspection. In determining absolute values, you may leave the answers in the form of square roots if you wish.

4-1 $\mathbf{A} = \hat{\imath}$
$\mathbf{B} = \hat{\jmath}$

4-2 $\mathbf{A} = \hat{\imath} + 3\hat{k}$
$\mathbf{B} = \hat{\imath} - \hat{\jmath}$

4-3 $\mathbf{A} = \hat{\imath} + 2\hat{\jmath} - 3\hat{k}$
$\mathbf{B} = 2\hat{\imath} - 3\hat{\jmath} + \hat{k}$

4-4 **A** is a vector of magnitude two units which makes an angle of 30° with the x-axis, an angle of 60° with the y-axis, and an angle of 90° with the z-axis.

$$\mathbf{B} = 2\hat{\imath} - 3\hat{\jmath} + \hat{k}$$

4-5 **A** is three units long, **B** is five units long. The sine of the angle between them is $\frac{4}{5}$.

4-6 $\mathbf{A} = \hat{\imath} + 3t\hat{\jmath}$
$\mathbf{B} = 2\hat{\imath}$

4-7 Find a vector **B** perpendicular to vector **A**.

$$\mathbf{A} = 2\hat{\imath} + 3\hat{\jmath} + 1\hat{k}$$

Is there more than one such vector **B**? If so, find another vector **C** which is perpendicular to both **A** and **B**.

4-8 Carry out the following integrations which you will encounter in the next chapter.

$$\int_{m_1}^{m_2} dm \qquad \int_{m_1}^{m_2} m\,dm \qquad \int_{r_1}^{r} \frac{dr}{r^2} \qquad \int_{m_1}^{m_2} \frac{dm}{m}$$

$$\int_{t_1}^{t_2} \frac{d\mathbf{p}}{dt}\,dt \quad \text{where } \mathbf{p} \text{ is some vector function of time}$$

$$\int_{t_1}^{t_2} \mathbf{v} \cdot \frac{d\mathbf{v}}{dt}\,dt \quad \text{where } \mathbf{v} \text{ is some vector function of time}$$

4-9 A particle initially at rest is acted on simultaneously by the following four forces which are measured with respect to an inertial coordinate system.

$$\mathbf{F}_1 = 10\hat{\imath} + 20\hat{\jmath} + 33\hat{k} \text{ N}$$
$$\mathbf{F}_2 = -4\hat{\imath} + 13\hat{\jmath} - 61\hat{k} \text{ N}$$
$$\mathbf{F}_3 = -16\hat{\imath} - 60\hat{\jmath} + 13\hat{k} \text{ N}$$
$$\mathbf{F}_4 = 10\hat{\imath} + 7\hat{\jmath} - 5\hat{k} \text{ N}$$

In what direction and with what acceleration will the particle move?

4-10 An inertial coordinate system is set up in interstellar space. A force $\mathbf{F} = t\hat{\imath} + t^2\hat{\jmath} + t^3\hat{k}$ N measured with respect to this coordinate system is applied to a particle of mass 1 kg which is initially at rest at the origin of the coordinate system. Find the acceleration, velocity, and displacement of the particle as functions of time. Express your results as vectors, using components as above.

4-11 Two constant forces $\mathbf{F}_1 = 2\hat{\imath} + 3\hat{\jmath} + 4\hat{k}$ N and $\mathbf{F}_2 = 1\hat{\imath} - 2\hat{\jmath} - 3\hat{k}$ N act simultaneously on a particle of mass 3 kg. What is the resultant force on the particle and its acceleration? If the particle starts from rest at a point $\mathbf{r}_1 = 1\hat{\imath} + 2\hat{\jmath} + 3\hat{k}$ m, find expressions for $\dot{\mathbf{r}}$ and $\mathbf{r}$ for the particle as a function of time.

4-12 Two forces $\mathbf{F}_1 = \hat{\imath} + t\hat{\jmath}$ N and $\mathbf{F}_2 = t^2\hat{\jmath} - 3\hat{k}$ N act simultaneously on a particle of mass 1 kg. At $t = 0$ the particle has a velocity $\mathbf{v}_1 = 3\hat{\jmath}$ m/sec and is at a position $\mathbf{r}_1 = 2\hat{k}$ m. Find the acceleration, velocity, and position of the particle as functions of time.

4-13 The maximum acceleration of an automobile from rest under its own power is not constant because frictional forces and air resistance increase with increased speed. Suppose that the acceleration of a car from rest is proportional to the square root of the time. If my car reaches 60 mph (26.8 m/sec) in 16 sec, how long does it take to reach 30 mph? What distances does it cover in reaching 30 and 60 mph respectively?

4-14 You are shut in a closed railway car which runs on a straight track over level ground. In this car you have the device pictured in Fig. 4-18, consisting of a cube of mass 20 kg resting on a greased horizontal table and held by two calibrated spring balances under tension in opposite directions. Assume that the motion of the cube along the surface of the

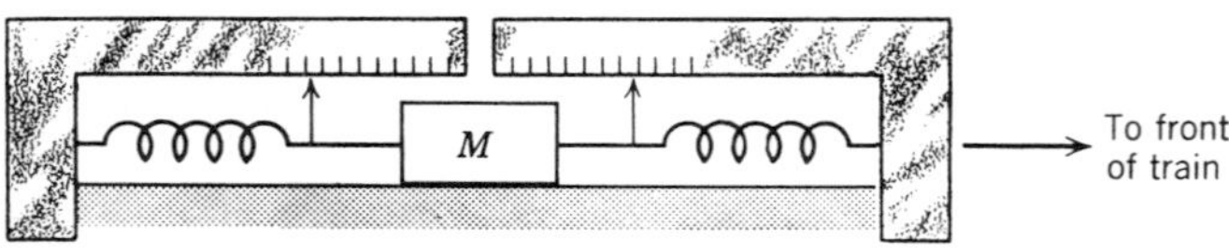

Fig. 4-18.

greased table is frictionless except that this grease keeps the cube from bouncing back and forth when the train jerks.

Before the doors are closed, you see that the railway car is at rest. After the doors are closed, you record the readings on the two spring balances as a function of time. The reading on the spring balance which pulls toward the front of the train starts at 2 N, rises linearly and uniformly to a value of 3 N at the end of 10 min, remains at 3 N for 10 min more, drops suddenly to 1 N, where it remains for 10 min, and finally increases linearly and uniformly to 2 N in 10 min, where it remains thereafter. The reading on the spring balance which pulls toward the rear of the train starts at 2 N, drops linearly and uniformly to 1 N at the end of 10 min, remains at 1 N for 10 min, rises suddenly to 3 N, where it remains for 10 min, and finally decreases linearly and uniformly to 2 N in 10 min, where it remains thereafter.

After 40 min you open the doors of the railway car. Will the car be moving? How far has the car moved in this time? This is an example of *inertial navigation*.

PROJECT I. MOTION OF A PROJECTILE

The motion of a particle in the gravitational field near the surface of the earth can be described by using the following assumptions, provided neither the velocity attained by the particle nor the horizontal or vertical distances covered by the particle are too great. Chapter 9 will delineate in more detail what distances and velocities would be "too great."

Assumptions

1. The earth is flat and fixed in space.
2. Air resistance due to the motion of the particle through the atmosphere can be neglected.
3. Any particle which is free of all forces except the force of gravity will be accelerated downward with a constant acceleration **g**. The direction of the vector **g** is vertically downward toward the earth, and its magnitude is approximately 9.80 m/sec². This magnitude may vary somewhat with location on the surface of the earth. In other words, the force of gravity exerted on any particle near the surface of the earth (the *weight* of the particle) is given by the equation

$$\mathbf{F} = m\mathbf{g}$$

It follows that the horizontal component of the force of gravity is zero.

If you complete the following problems in order, you will have worked out for yourself some of the important characteristics of the motion of a projectile near the surface of the earth.

Problems

I-1 Consider a particle of mass m resting on a table top. What gravitational force is exerted on the particle? What force does the table exert on the particle? Why does the particle not move?

I-2 A particle is dropped from rest at a height of 100 m above the ground. What equation gives the position of the particle above ground as a function of time? What is the speed of the particle as a function of time? What is the speed of the particle at the instant before it strikes the ground? the velocity at this instant? How long a time elapses between the release of the particle and its collision with the ground? When you pour water out of a pitcher, the stream becomes narrower as it descends. Why?

I-3 A particle is projected upward from the ground with an initial vertical velocity of 100 m/sec and zero initial horizontal velocity. To what height will the particle ascend? What will be its velocity at this highest point? Where will the particle strike the earth? What will be its velocity at the instant before it strikes the earth? How long will the particle be in the air?

I-4 A particle is projected upward from the edge of a cliff with an initial vertical velocity of 100 m/sec and a very small horizontal velocity such that it misses the edge of the cliff on the way down and strikes the ground 100 m below the edge of the cliff. To what height does the particle ascend? What is the velocity of the particle as it passes the edge of the cliff on the way down? With what velocity does it strike the ground? How long is it in the air?

I-5 A particle is projected at an angle of 45° to the horizontal with an initial velocity of $\sqrt{2} \times 10^2$ m/sec. What is the initial vertical component of velocity? the initial horizontal component of velocity? If the particle travels over level terrain, how long will it be in the air? How far from the point of firing will it land?

I-6 The range R of a projectile over level terrain is the horizontal distance between the point of firing and the point of impact of the projectile with the ground. Show that the range is given by

$$R = \frac{v_1^2 \sin 2\theta}{g}$$

where v_1 is the initial speed of the projectile and θ is the angle which the initial velocity makes with the horizontal direction. What is the maximum range of a projectile of given initial speed?

I-7 By eliminating the time from the equations of motion, show that the path followed by a projectile is a parabola. (Do not confuse this parabola in space with the displacement vs time curve of a particle subject to a constant linear force.)

I-8 During World War I the Germans bombarded Paris with a long range gun called Big Bertha. The muzzle velocity was 1450 m/sec, and with an angle of elevation of 55° the range was 120,000 m. Compute the

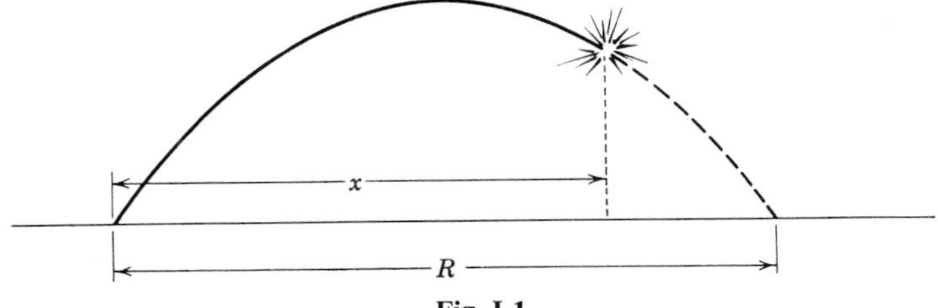

Fig. I-1.

theoretical range in the absence of air resistance and compare with the actual range. In the absence of air resistance, what is the maximum height reached by the projectile?

I-9 Find an expression for the increase in range produced for any angle of elevation if the projectile is fired from a vertical altitude h above the target.

I-10 A projectile is fired over level ground (see Fig. I-1). You stand on the ground under the trajectory a distance x from the point of launch. You wish to intercept the projectile before it reaches the target by throwing an object vertically into its path. When should you throw your object?

PROJECT II. SLIDING FRICTION

The motion of many mechanical systems is accompanied by the conversion of some mechanical energy to heat energy. When this conversion of mechanical energy to heat energy takes place as a result of two surfaces sliding over one another, the mechanical energy loss is said to be due to *sliding friction* and the force between the sliding surfaces along the line of relative motion is called a *frictional force*. There are other forces which can be called frictional, such as forces due to viscosity or turbulence in a fluid, but in what follows we shall limit ourselves to forces of sliding friction.

Consider a block of mass m in a uniform gravitational field sliding along a horizontal plane toward the right in the diagram in Fig. II-1. There are three forces acting on the block, drawn in the diagram as if they all acted at the center of the block. The first is the force of gravity, given by mg. The second is the force which the plane exerts on the block in a direction normal to the surface of the plane. This force is called the "normal force" and is given the symbol N. In the case treated here, the normal force must equal the force of gravity since the block experiences no acceleration perpendicular to the plane. In some later examples, N will not be equal in magnitude to mg. The third force acting on the block is the force of friction, which is given the symbol f. The force of friction always acts on the block in a direction opposite to the direction of motion of the block along the plane.

Experiment has shown the following laws are approximately correct.

LAWS OF SLIDING FRICTION. The force of friction f between two sliding surfaces depends on the nature of the two surfaces in contact and is directly proportional to the normal force N between them. This force is independent of the surface area of contact and is independent of the relative velocity of the two surfaces as long as this velocity is not zero.

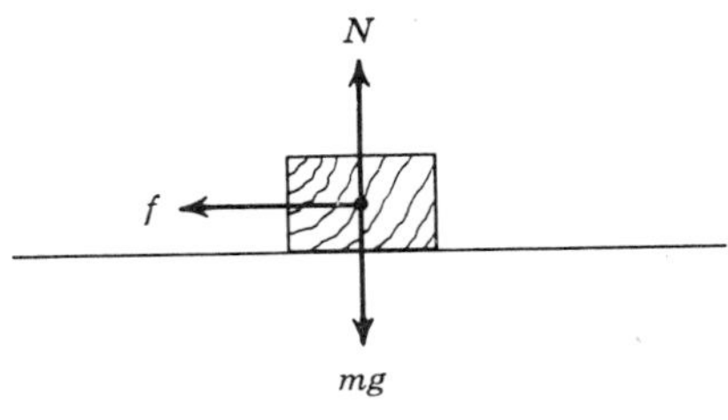

Fig. II-1.

The constant of proportionality between the frictional force and the normal force is called the *coefficient of kinetic friction* and is given the symbol μ_K. Using the law of sliding friction, the coefficient of kinetic friction is defined by the equation $f = \mu_K N$. The numerical value of μ_K depends on the nature and condition of the two surfaces. These laws are approximate ones and will yield only approximate answers.* When a particular problem requires a high degree of accuracy (better than 10 percent) or dependability (as in the legal problem below), the law must be applied with an understanding of its limitations. For this reason, your answers to the problems below should carry no more significant figures than would imply an accuracy of about 10 percent.

Problems

II-1 Demonstrate from the law above that a non-cubic block with rectangular faces experiences the same frictional force in sliding along a given surface no matter which face it slides on.

II-2 The coefficient of kinetic friction between the block and the surface in Fig. II-1 has the value $\mu_K = 0.3$. If the block has a mass of 10 kg, how much force must be applied to the block parallel to the surface to keep it in uniform motion?

II-3 The coefficient of kinetic friction between the block and the surface in Fig. II-1 has the value $\mu_K = 0.3$. If the block has an initial speed along the plane of 10 m/sec, how far will it travel before coming to rest?

A somewhat different case occurs if the block slides down a plane inclined at some angle θ to the horizontal (see Fig. II-2). Here it is necessary to resolve the gravitational force into components along the

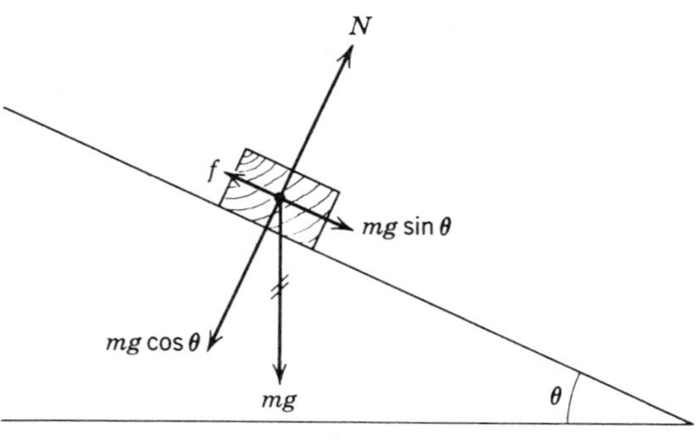

Fig. II-2.

* See F. Palmer, *American Journal of Physics*, **17,** 181, 327, 336 (1949).

plane and perpendicular to the plane as shown. The component of the force of gravity perpendicular to the plane will cause no acceleration because it is balanced by the normal force N exerted by the plane on the block. The component of the force of gravity along the plane will tend to accelerate the block down the plane. This will be opposed by the force of friction.

Example. A block of wood starts with an initial velocity down a plane inclined at an angle of 30° to the horizontal. If $\mu_K = 0.2$, will this velocity increase or decrease as time goes by?

Solution. From Fig. II-2, taking forces perpendicular to the plane,

$$N - mg \cos \theta = 0$$

From the law of friction, $f = \mu_K N = \mu_K mg \cos \theta$. Taking forces along the plane and the direction down the plane as positive,

$$mg \sin \theta - f = ma$$

or

$$\not{m}g \sin \theta - \mu_K \not{m}g \cos \theta = \not{m}a$$

$$g(\sin \theta - \mu_K \cos \theta) = a$$

but

$$\sin 30° = 0.500$$

$$\cos 30° = 0.866$$

and

$$\mu_K = 0.2$$

so that

$$a = g(0.500 - 0.2 \times 0.866)$$

$$a = 0.33g$$

Since a is positive, the velocity down the plane will *increase*.

Problems

II-4 A block of wood starts with an initial velocity of 5 m/sec *up* a plane inclined at an angle of 20° from the horizontal. If $\mu_K = 0.5$, how far will the block be displaced along the plane before it comes to rest?

II-5 An automobile strikes a pedestrian after skidding 50 m down a 5 percent grade (that is, a hill that descends 5 ft vertically for every 100 ft horizontally). The speed limit over this stretch of road is 25 mph. Later tests show the coefficient of kinetic friction between the tires and the road to be about $\mu_K = 0.5$. Was the driver exceeding the speed limit before beginning to skid?*

* *American Journal of Physics*, **28,** 498 (1960).

Experiment shows that a greater force is required to start a block of wood sliding along a horizontal surface than is required to keep it in uniform motion once it is started. The force necessary to start a block of wood from rest may be related to the normal force by the equation $f = \mu_S N$. Here μ_S is called the *coefficient of static friction*. From the argument above it should be clear that, for any two given surfaces in contact, μ_S is greater than μ_K. If a horizontal force *less* than $\mu_S N$ is applied to a block of wood at rest on a horizontal surface, the force of static friction will be equal and opposite to the force applied and will *not* equal the value $\mu_S N$ unless the block of wood is just ready to start.

Example. A horizontal force of magnitude $F = bt$, where t is the time in seconds, is applied to a block of wood of mass m at rest on a horizontal surface. The coefficient of static friction is μ_S and the coefficient of kinetic friction is μ_K. Find the acceleration of the block of wood as a function of time.

Solution. Since the force applied starts from zero magnitude at $t = 0$, the block of wood will remain at rest until this force reaches the value $\mu_S N = \mu_S mg$. This will occur at time t_1, given by

$$bt_1 = \mu_S mg \quad \text{or} \quad t_1 = \frac{\mu_S mg}{b}$$

After time t_1 the block will be in motion and the backward force of kinetic friction will be given by $\mu_K mg$. The net force will be $bt - \mu_K mg$, so that the acceleration will be given by $a = (b/m)t - \mu_K g$. In summary,

$$a = 0 \qquad t < t_1 = \frac{\mu_S mg}{b}$$

$$a = \frac{b}{m}t - \mu_K g \qquad t > t_1$$

Problems

II-6 Will the block of wood in Problem II-4 slide back down the plane after it has come to rest?

II-7 A block of wood is placed on a flat horizontal plank. The coefficients of friction between the block and the plank are $\mu_S = 0.5$ and $\mu_K = 0.3$. One end of the plank is now raised slowly. What will the angle of the plank with the horizontal be when the block of wood begins to slide down the plank? If the plank is not tilted further, what will be the acceleration of the block of wood along the plank?

II-8 Show that the tangent of the minimum angle of an inclined plane with the horizontal at which a block of wood will start sliding from rest is equal to the coefficient of static friction. Show that the tangent of the angle of an inclined plane with the horizontal at which a block of wood will move with uniform velocity down the plane is equal to the coefficient of kinetic friction. Would these results be true at the surface of the moon also?

II-9 Two blocks of equal mass are connected by a string which passes over a frictionless pulley (Fig. II-3). One block hangs free and one slides on an inclined plane as shown. If the coefficient of friction is μ_K, what angle θ must the plane make with the horizontal so that each block will move with constant velocity once it is set in motion?

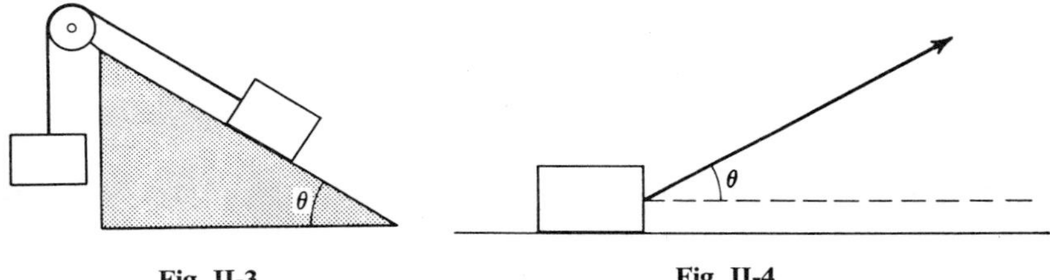

Fig. II-3. **Fig. II-4.**

II-10 A box is pulled along a horizontal floor by means of a rope which makes an angle θ with the horizontal (Fig. II-4). Derive an expression for the force necessary to keep the box in uniform motion along the floor. Find the angle at which the necessary force is a minimum.

chapter 5

Interactions between particles

5.1 THE MEASUREMENT OF FORCES NOT DUE TO SPRING BALANCES. Up to this point we have dealt only with forces which can be applied to particles by means of spring balances alone. Now it is time to take account of the experimental fact that under some circumstances particles appear to exert forces on each other without the intermediate agency of either a spring balance or any other form of physical contact. We know this is true because, when two particles are released from rest near each other, sometimes each of them will experience an acceleration toward or away from the other. Historically a large part of experimental physics has been involved in investigating and describing the conditions under which these forces exist between particles. A large part of theoretical physics has been involved in reducing the description of these forces to the simplest possible consistent terms and in predicting the physical results of these forces on the motions of more complicated systems. From the results of these activities has come a measure of agreement on how the forces that exist between particles may best be described. A description of some of these forces is presented in Sec. 5.3.

How are these forces to be measured experimentally when they are not applied directly by the use of spring balances? One way to do this is to observe the acceleration of, for example, particle one as a function of time (with respect to an inertial coordinate system) when it is near a second particle. If then the second particle is removed and a spring balance is attached to particle one, we may *define* the force which was exerted by the second particle to be equal to the force which must be applied to particle one by the spring balance in order to give it the same acceleration as a function of time which was observed in the presence of the second particle. However, we already know that accelerations which are caused by spring balance forces follow the equation $\mathbf{F} = m\ddot{\mathbf{r}}$ with respect to an inertial coordinate system. Hence what we have defined as the force exerted by the second particle on particle one can be found as a function of time simply by multiplying the acceleration of particle one by its mass. In this way the net force on any particle can be derived from its acceleration if the mass of the particle is known, no matter what the origin or origins of that net force.

We have defined force due to agencies other than spring balances. What makes this definition coherent and useful is the *experimental result* that *forces so defined obey the law of superposition of forces.* If this were not so, the laws of motion derived by using spring balances would have very little general usefulness.

Question

5-1 Particles two and three each exert an action-at-a-distance force on particle one. Devise an experiment to test the law of superposition of forces in this case.

Class Discussion Question

5-2 Review carefully the logical and experimental steps which have led from the definition of force using a spring balance to the definition of mass to the definition of the standard unit of force to the definition of the force due to agencies other than spring balances.

There is one general result of the investigation of forces between particles which is true for a large number of different kinds of forces. This is the law of action and reaction. The next section shows how this result arises from the laws of particle motion which have already been described.

5.2 THE LAW OF ACTION AND REACTION. Consider two particles numbered one and two, as in Fig. 5-1. They are connected by an inextensible thread of negligible mass. Suppose that all forces that may exist between the particles can be neglected except the force transmitted by the thread. If one of the particles, say number one, is attached to a spring balance and pulled along a straight line with constant force F, then both particles will be accelerated at the same constant rate since the thread which connects them is inextensible. Suppose that the force exerted by the thread on particle two is given the symbol F_2 and the force exerted by the thread on particle one is given the symbol F_1. Since all forces lie along the same straight line, they may be added and subtracted like scalars with due regard to sign.

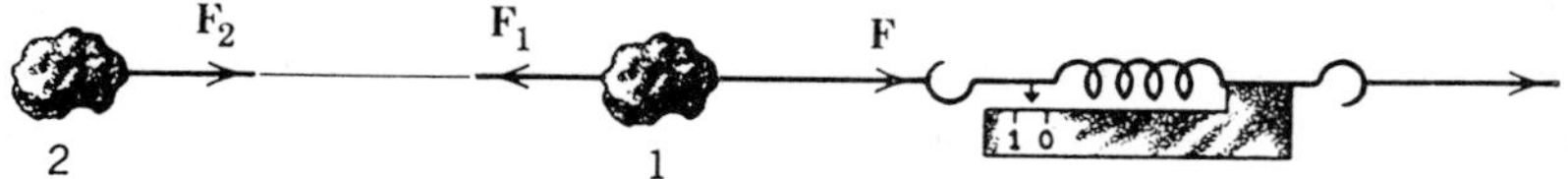

Fig. 5-1. Spring balance pulling two particles.

In Sec. 3.10 we found that if two particles are joined together they behave as if their total mass were equal to the sum of their individual masses. Since particles one and two are joined together by the string, we can expect their common acceleration to be given by the equation

$$a = \frac{F}{m_1 + m_2}$$

Since the acceleration of particle two has the same value a, the force F_2 must be given by

$$F_2 = m_2 a = \frac{m_2 F}{m_1 + m_2}$$

If this equation is solved for F it becomes

$$F = \frac{(m_1 + m_2)F_2}{m_2} \tag{5-1}$$

Now, the *net* force on particle one is given by $F + F_1$. The magnitude of this net force may be found from the equation

$$F + F_1 = m_1 a = \frac{m_1 F}{m_1 + m_2}$$

Once again this may be solved for F.

$$F = \frac{-(m_1 + m_2)F_1}{m_2} \tag{5-2}$$

Equating expressions (5-1) and (5-2) for F, we have

$$F_2 = -F_1$$

This equation says that F_2 is equal in magnitude and opposite in direction to F_1. In vector notation,

$$\mathbf{F}_2 = -\mathbf{F}_1 \tag{5-3}$$

We have shown that for this case the force with which particle one acts on particle two (via the thread) is equal in magnitude and opposite in direction to the force with which particle two acts on particle one (via the thread). This result will be generalized in what follows.

Suppose that we have again two particles numbered one and two as shown in Fig. 5-2 and that these two particles exert on each other forces of one of the types that will be described later in this chapter which does not require a material link between the particles. In order to be specific, let us suppose that this force is attractive and thus the particles tend to be pulled together (although the case of a repulsive force can be similarly treated).

The statement that the particles attract one another must mean that there is a force F_1 on particle one due to the presence of particle two and a force F_2 on particle two due to the presence of particle one.

We shall assume that the magnitude of the forces on the two particles depends on the instantaneous distance between the particles and *not* on their velocity or acceleration. From the knowledge we already have about the motion of particles we now demonstrate that, in vector notation,

$$\mathbf{F}_2 = -\mathbf{F}_1$$

As before, one of the particles, say number one, is attached to a spring balance and is pulled along a straight line with constant force F. We assume that the spring balance can be attached in such a way that the forces F_1 and F_2 are not changed. This time the magnitude of F is adjusted so that the distance between particle one and particle two remains constant. This amounts to adjusting the acceleration of the whole system to be the same as the acceleration of particle two subject to the force F_2, so that particle two never "catches up" with particle one. Since the forces F_1 and F_2 depend on the distance between the particles and not on their velocity or acceleration, these forces will not change during the acceleration and will not be different from the forces between the particles when they are at rest.

In every important detail the system we have set up is identical with the previous system using the thread. The only significant difference is that the force supplied by the thread has been replaced by the force supplied from another source. But the motion of particles is determined by the forces acting on them and not by the origin of those forces. Therefore the mathematical analysis carried out in the case using the thread is equally valid for the present case for any separation of the particles.

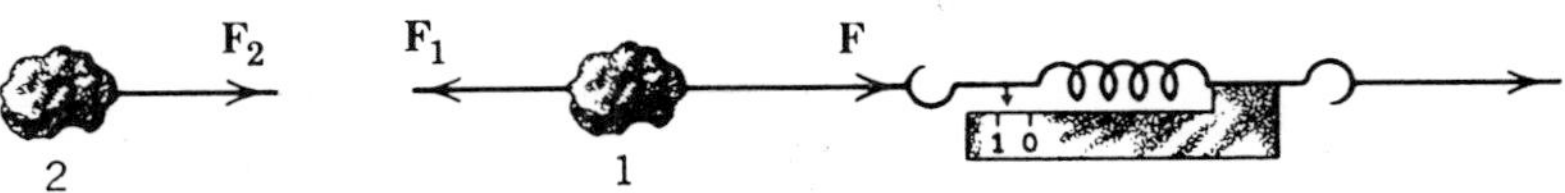

Fig. 5-2. Spring balance pulling two particles.

The result can be expressed in the following general rule: When two particles exert forces on each other that do not depend on their velocities or accelerations, then the force exerted on particle one by particle two is equal in magnitude and opposite in direction to the force exerted on particle two by particle one.

At one time the force F_2 was called the "action force" or simply the "action," and the force F_1 was called the "reaction force" or simply the "reaction." Newton expressed the foregoing result by the statement "To every action there is always opposed an equal reaction: or the mutual actions of two bodies upon each other are always equal, and directed to contrary parts." This law is sometimes called *Newton's Third Law of Motion* or *the law of action and reaction.*

We were able to predict the results of the preceding experiments without actually carrying them out. In other words, the law of action and reaction is not an independent law but follows from the definitions and experimental observations carried out previously.

Questions

5-3 How can the "action force" be distinguished from the "reaction force"?

5-4 By the same kind of argument used for attractive forces, demonstrate that the law of action and reaction is valid for *repulsive* forces between two particles.

5-5 Sometimes there will exist between two particles forces which do not lie along the straight line joining the particles. Consider the case of a "dumbbell" made of two particles connected by a rigid rod of negligible mass. A hole is drilled through one particle, and it is constrained to slide without friction along a straight rod inserted through the hole. (See Fig. 5-3.) Show that the law of action and reaction is valid if an external force is applied to one of the particles by means of a spring balance as shown. Can you generalize this case, eliminating the rod?

5-6 Consider a "dumbbell" made up of two particles connected by a rigid rod of negligible mass. Prove that, if the force on particle two due to particle one were equal in magnitude but *not* opposite in direction to

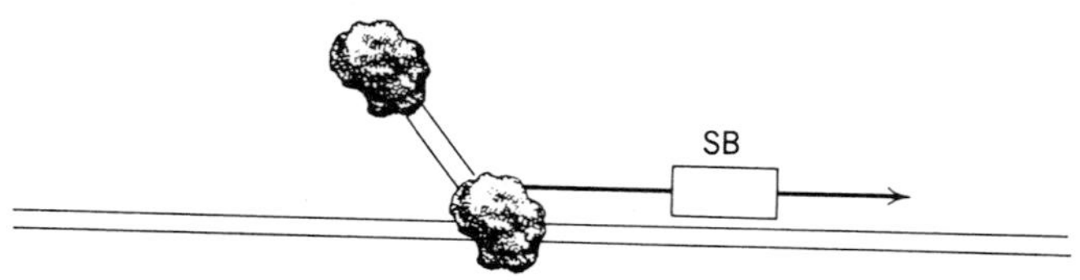

Fig. 5-3.

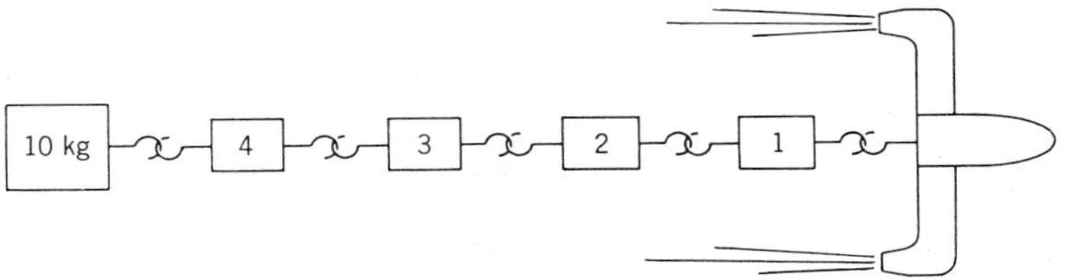

Fig. 5-4.

the force on particle one due to particle two, the dumbbell would be accelerated even though no external force was applied to it.

5-7 Consider a single particle which is acted on by a constant force exerted by a spring balance. We know that the particle is accelerating because the spring balance is exerting a force on it. Yet an equal and opposite force is exerted on the spring balance by the particle. Hence the two forces cancel out and the acceleration of the system should be zero. What is wrong with this reasoning? This is called the Horse and Carriage Paradox. (Why?)

5-8 In the example at the beginning of this section, suppose that the mass of the thread is not negligible. If the mass of the thread is m_3, find the forces which each mass exerts on the adjacent ones.

5-9 A series of spring balances are pulled by a rocket as in Fig. 5-4. Each spring balance has a mass of 1 kg. The last spring balance is attached to a block of mass 10 kg. The first spring balance has a constant reading of 13 N. What are the readings of the rest of the spring balances? What is the acceleration?

5.3 SOME TYPES OF FORCES.

We now discuss several types of forces which may exist between particles. In any particular experiment it may be difficult to determine which of these forces or which combination of them is acting on a particle under observation. In fact, whether a given force appears to be electrostatic or magnetic in origin sometimes depends on the relative motion of the coordinate system in which measurements are carried out, as you will show in what follows. Nevertheless this analytical distinction between types of forces is useful in predicting the motion of particles in the presence of known masses, charges, etc.

The force of gravity. The force of gravity is one of the most peculiar and perplexing forces which physicists have attempted to analyze. The force which holds us to the surface of the earth is the most common force we are aware of, and the man in the street acknowledges the importance of the force of gravity in keeping the planets on their courses around the sun. Very sensitive and specialized equipment is required to measure directly the gravitational attraction between two particles, because of the smallness of these forces. Unlike other forces to which particles are subject, the gravitational force cannot be "turned off" by some simple expedient such as neutralizing an electric charge or unhooking a spring balance. The reason is that the magnitude of the gravitational force exerted on (or by) a particle is related to its mass. Yet why mass and gravitational force are related is not clear. Furthermore, as will be explained in Sec. 5.5, we cannot feel the force of gravity directly. These characteristics of gravitational forces lead to serious difficulties with the operational definition of an inertial coordinate system. One reason for beginning this study of mechanics in the realm of interstellar space was to avoid the force of gravity which we experience on earth until the tools were assembled to study this force competently. Yet even with this beginning the force of gravitational attraction between particle one and the reference particle caused us some difficulty. A peculiar kind of force!

The *description* of gravitational forces is straightforward enough. Sir Isaac Newton postulated that the same kind of force which causes objects to fall to the ground on earth might account for the force which pulls the moon from a straight line path and keeps it in an orbit about the earth. The same kind of force might account for the motion of the planets around the sun. In order to obtain agreement between the calculated and observed motions of these planets it was necessary to assume that the magnitude of the attractive gravitational force F_g on each of two interacting particles is given by an equation of the form

$$F_g = \frac{Gm_1m_2}{r^2} \tag{5-4}$$

where m_1 and m_2 are the masses of the two particles, r is the distance between them, and G is a constant of proportionality called the *gravitational constant*. The force on each particle acts in the direction of the other particle. Much later this expression was verified by measuring directly the force of attraction between spheres of lead, using a sensitive torsion balance. This is called the Cavendish experiment after Henry Cavendish (1731–1810) who first performed it.* Experiments of this kind have shown that the value of G is 6.673×10^{-11} N-m²/kg².

The gravitational attraction which a body of spherical shape and radial symmetry exerts on an external particle is directed toward the center of the sphere and has the value given by Eq. (5-4), where r is the distance from the particle to the center of the sphere. This can be derived using

* See Morris H. Shamos, *Great Experiments in Physics*, Henry Holt and Company, New York, 1960, p. 75.

solid geometry or calculus and Eq. (5-4) applied to each particle which makes up the sphere. It is also true that two bodies of spherical shape and radial symmetry attract one another according to Eq. (5-4), where r is the distance between their centers. It was uncertainty on this point which caused Sir Isaac Newton to delay for twenty years the publication of his major work, *Philosophie Naturalis Principia Mathematica*,† usually referred to as the *Principia*, on which classical mechanics is based. Since the sun and all the planets are nearly perfect spheres, the foregoing conclusion simplifies considerably the calculation of planetary orbits around the sun.

Questions

5-10 Show that, if Eq. (5-4) holds true for the attraction between a uniform thin spherical shell and a particle external to the shell, where r is the distance between the particle and the center of the shell, then Eq. (5-4) will be true for the attraction between a body of spherical shape and radial symmetry and an external particle, where r is the distance between the particle and the center of the sphere. What important property of forces do you use in this proof? You may wish to ask your mathematics or physics instructor to demonstrate that Eq. (5-4) applied to the interaction of each element of mass in a thin uniform spherical shell with a particle external to the shell gives an equation of the same form for the total interaction.

5-11 Using Eq. (5-4), the value of the acceleration g near the surface of the earth, and the radius of the earth, calculate the mass of the earth.

5-12 What is the magnitude of the gravitational force on a uniform sphere of mass 1000 kg due to a similar sphere a center-to-center distance of 1 m away? Compare this to the gravitational force on the same sphere near the surface of the earth.

5-13 Consider a space probe of mass 1000 kg initially at rest with respect to the center of the earth and a distance 7000 km from it. The earth feels a gravitational force equal in magnitude and opposite in direction to the force acting on the space probe. Show that the acceleration of the earth toward the space probe is very much smaller than the acceleration of the space probe toward the earth.

5-14 Show that the acceleration of a particle toward a very massive uniform sphere is independent of the mass of the particle.

Class Discussion Question

5-15 In the light of your answer to the last question, consider the following problem. A reference particle is placed near a "particle at rest

† Sir Isaac Newton, *Mathematical Principles*, University of California Press, Berkeley, 1946.

in interstellar space," following the procedure in Chapter 1. Unknown to the observer, both particles are equidistant from a very massive sphere. Both particles are therefore accelerated toward the sphere with the same acceleration. Without looking up from his experiment, is there any way the observer can tell that his reference particle is accelerating? Can an inertial coordinate system be found in which the reference particle is at rest?

Electrostatic forces. Sometimes there exist between particles forces which have come to be called *electrical* forces. These forces may be either attractive—tending to pull the particles together—or repulsive—tending to push them apart. The magnitude of an electrical force involves the "quantity of charge" which resides on a particle. The term "quantity of charge" or simply "charge" can be defined operationally, just as force and length have been defined operationally, but we shall not define them here.* The smallest quantity of charge which has been detected is that of an electron.* We shall use the symbol q for quantity of charge. Mathematically q is a scalar and may be positive or negative.

Experiments show that the magnitude of the electrical force on each of two interacting particles in a vacuum is inversely proportional to the square of the distance between the particles and directly proportional to the product of the quantities of charge on each particle. This force acts along the straight line connecting the two particles. If the charges have the same algebraic sign, the force between the two particles is a repulsive one; if the charges have opposite signs, the force is attractive. The magnitude of the force on each particle can be expressed mathematically by the equation

$$F = \frac{kq_1q_2}{r^2}$$

where q_1 and q_2 are the charges on the two particles, r is the distance between them, and k is a constant of proportionality. This equation is called Coulomb's Law after its discoverer, Charles Coulomb (1736–1806). If q is expressed in coulombs and r in meters, then experiment shows that k has the value 8.988×10^9 N-m²/coulombs². Because of the usefulness of the symbol ϵ_0 in more advanced theory of electricity, k is often expressed as

$$k = \frac{1}{4\pi\epsilon_0} = 8.988 \times 10^9 \text{ N-m}^2/\text{coulombs}^2$$

* D. Halliday and R. Resnick, *Physics for Students of Science and Engineering*, John Wiley and Sons, Inc., New York, 1962, Chapters 26 and 27.

Then the preceding equation becomes

$$F = \frac{1}{4\pi\epsilon_0}\frac{q_1 q_2}{r^2} \tag{5-5}$$

The symbol ϵ_0 is called the *permittivity of free space.*

The electrical force which a radially symmetric distribution of charge exerts on a charged particle external to it is directed toward the center of the spherical distribution and has the value given by Eq. (5-5), where q_1 is the total charge on the spherical distribution, q_2 is the charge on the charged particle, and r is the distance from the particle to the center of the distribution. This can be derived by using solid geometry or calculus and Eq. (5-5) applied to each element of charge which makes up the sphere. The analysis is mathematically equivalent to that of the similar gravitational case. It is also true that two radially symmetric charge distributions which are external to one another exert a force on each other given by Eq. (5-5), where q_1 and q_2 are the total charges on the two distributions and r is the distance between their centers.

This analysis of electrical forces is strictly true only for charges all of which are at rest with respect to the inertial coordinate system in which they are observed. For this reason these are called *electrostatic* forces. The laws of electrostatics will hold approximately for particles which are near one another if their velocities are small compared to that of light. For particles which move with respect to one another, magnetic forces also have to be taken into account.

Questions

5-16 What is the ratio of the electrical to the gravitational forces which two electrons exert on each other?

5-17 Two particles of mass m_1 and m_2 are a distance r apart. Find the charges q_1 and q_2 which must be placed on the two particles so that the electrical repulsion will exactly cancel the gravitational attraction. Are these charges uniquely determined by the condition given? If r is changed, will the net force on each particle still be zero? What equal charges placed on the earth and moon would cancel their gravitational attraction for one another if these charges were distributed uniformly on each body?

Magnetic forces. In addition to the electrical forces which exist between charged particles at rest, there are forces which exist, under certain circumstances, between charged particles when *both* of them are in motion. These forces are called *magnetic* forces. Magnetic forces depend on the velocities of the particles involved, do not always satisfy the law of action and reaction, and do not necessarily lie on the line joining the two particles.

Magnetic fields associated with electromagnets and bar magnets result respectively from the ordered motion of electrons in wires and in the atoms of the material of which the magnet is made. An analysis of magnetic forces is beyond the scope of a book on mechanics. However, magnetic forces play a very large part in theories which describe the movement of charged nuclear particles in space, the movement of gases in the interior of stars, and the commercial generation of electricity.

Questions

5-18 Show that the proof of the law of action and reaction in Sec. 5.2 is not valid for magnetic forces.

5-19 Prove that electrical effects cannot be strictly separated from magnetic effects by considering the following thought experiment. Two particles charged with the same positive charge are held together by a spring balance (Fig. 5-5). No external forces are applied to the system. The spring balance measures the force of repulsion between the particles. When viewed from a reference frame in which the particles are at rest, there is no magnetic force between the particles because neither has any velocity. However, when viewed from a reference frame in which the particles move with constant velocity to the right in the diagram, the laws of magnetic forces predict that there will be a small attractive magnetic force between the particles. Now the reading of the spring balance cannot depend on the reference frame from which it is viewed. From these considerations show that the electrical force between the particles must appear different in the frame in which the particles are moving and in the frame in which the particles are at rest. In practice this effect will be significant only for a reference frame in which the velocity of the particles is comparable to that of light.

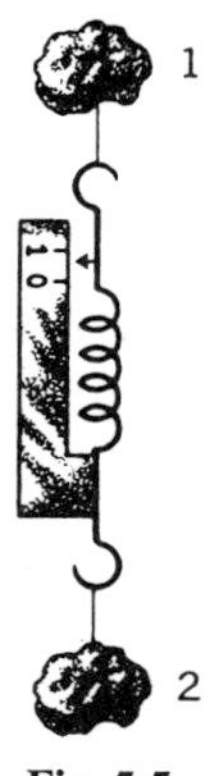

Fig. 5-5.

Other forces. There are other forces which may be exerted on particles. Light falling on a particle exerts a small force on it. This force is negligible for most of the experiments we have been discussing, but it cannot always be neglected. For instance, owing to the pressure of light from the sun, the luminous gas in the tail of a comet is observed to point radially outward from the sun when the comet is close to the sun. There is also a set of forces which exist between atoms and nuclear particles which have not been discussed. Such force or forces, for instance, are responsible for holding the nucleus together despite the electrical repulsion of the nuclear fragments of which it is made. Since we have not defined length in such a way that it can be applied to objects as small as the nucleus, and since at least one of the experimental observations of Sec. 3.12 concerning particles is not valid in this case, we leave a discussion of these forces to other books.

Question

5-20 Consider the problem of setting up a reference particle in interstellar space treated in Chapter 1. What complications will be introduced by the presence of electrical forces? How would you go about solving these complications?

5.4 NEWTON'S LAWS AND MACH'S LAWS. We are now in a position to appreciate the power and elegance of the laws of classical mechanics as presented by Sir Isaac Newton and later refined by Professor Ernst Mach.

Newton's Laws of Motion. There is little doubt that the work of Sir Isaac Newton (1642–1727) has had greater impact on the course of science than that of any other single scientist who ever lived. He is known for pioneering research in several fields of physics. One mark of his genius was his ability to see the connection between scientific results in apparently widely different areas of inquiry. For instance, he showed the connection between the laws of terrestrial motion described by Galileo and the laws of planetary motion described by Kepler. Although Newton's laws of motion are not without inconsistencies, they represent a remarkable synthesis of observations and they provided a firm foundation for further development and correction. The laws below are taken from *The Mathematical Principles of Natural Philosophy** (published in 1686) and are rephrased in terms of the concepts we have defined.

1. *Definition.* The mass of a body is equal to the product of its density and its volume.
2. *Definition.* An impressed force is an action exerted upon a body, in order to change its state, either of rest or of uniform motion in a straight line.
3. *Explanation.* Absolute, true, and mathematical time, of itself, and from its own nature flows equably without regard to anything external, and by another name is called duration: relative, apparent, and common time is some sensible and external (whether accurate or unequable) measure of duration by the means of motion, which is commonly used instead of true time; such as an hour, a day, a month, a year.
4. *Explanation.* Absolute space, in its own nature, without regard to anything external, remains always similar and immovable. Relative

* Sir Isaac Newton, *op. cit.*

space is some movable dimension or measure of the absolute spaces; which our senses determine by its position relative to bodies. . . .

The Three Laws of Motion

I. Every body perseveres in its state of rest, or of uniform motion in a straight line, unless it is compelled to change that state by forces impressed thereon.

II. The alteration of motion is always proportional to the motive force impressed and is made in the direction of the straight line in which the force is impressed.

III. To every action there is always opposed an equal reaction: or, the mutual actions of two bodies on each other are always equal, and directed in opposite directions.

Consider first the three laws of motion themselves. The second law is clearly the central one because it relates force to "the alteration of motion." If this law is understood to be a vector law, then, as we saw in Sec. 4.15, the first law follows from the second law. Hence it might be more logical to present the first law as a corollary to the second.

However, if you look more carefully at the first law, you will see that it provides a method by which to test whether or not a particular reference frame is inertial. The first law could be rephrased to read, "Inertial reference frames are by definition those with respect to which a particle subject to no forces remains at rest or moves with constant velocity." The first law expressed in this way is an *operational definition* of an inertial reference frame in that it tells what experiment or operation an observer must carry out to determine whether or not a given reference frame is inertial. This operational procedure for defining a reference frame was used in the first two chapters of this book. The question of how to tell that no forces are acting on a particle was side-stepped by assuming that all bodies capable of exerting forces were at a great distance.

If the first law is rephrased in the way suggested above, then the second law should begin, "With respect to an inertial reference frame, the alteration of motion. . . ."

Is the third law independent of the second law? In Sec. 5.2 we derived the third law using the second law and the law of superposition of forces and the additive property of mass. Definition one might be made to imply the additive property of mass, and the law of superposition of forces is tacked onto the second law by Newton in his original formulation even though it is really a separate experimental result. With this addition the third law follows from the second law.

Now let us turn to the definitions and explanations. Definition one will be left to a question below. Definition two has been seriously criticized because it defines force in such a way that the second law almost follows from it *as a definition.** Indeed, we have used the second law to define forces which are not exerted by spring balances, and many physicists look upon the second law itself as simply a definition of force. There is nothing logically wrong with such a definition, but apparently Newton did not realize that his definition of force included part of the second law.

Explanations 3 and 4 concerning absolute time and space have long since fallen to the demand, "Show me experiments by which absolute time and space may be distinguished from other possible measures of these quantities." Our reformulation of the first law has provided the definition of an inertial reference frame, so that absolute space is no longer a useful concept in the analysis of mechanics experiments. Even though for many years physicists were doubtful about the significance of absolute time and space, they nevertheless accepted them as a kind of practical hypothesis because of the power of Newton's laws in solving mechanics problems.

It is interesting and quite astonishing how useful Newton's laws were to physicists for over two centuries, even though these laws contain confusions and logical inconsistencies. In fact, many modern texts accept these laws more or less in their original form as the foundation of mechanics. One of the secrets of science carefully kept from the layman is that scientists can proceed fruitfully for many years in a given field without really knowing what they are doing. Indeed, one of the principal goals of scientists is simply to *find out* what they are doing.

Perhaps Ernst Mach best described the contribution which Newton made to the science of mechanics. "Newton," Mach says, "discerned in an admirable manner the concepts and principles that were *sufficiently assured* to allow of being further built upon. . . . To some extent, however, he was, as is possible to prove, not perfectly clear himself concerning the import and especially concerning the source of his principles. This cannot, however, obscure in the slightest his intellectual greatness. He that has to acquire a new point of view naturally cannot possess it so securely from the beginning as they that receive it unlaboriously from him. He has done enough if he has discovered truths on which future generations can build."†

* Bertrand Russell, *Principles of Mathematics*, Cambridge University Press, London, 1903, p. 483.

† Ernst Mach, *The Science of Mechanics*, The Open Court Publishing Company, La Salle, Ill., 1960, p. 304.

Questions

5-21 Demonstrate that, if density is defined as the number of kilograms per cubic meter, then definition one is circular. Demonstrate that definition one is not circular if density means *relative* density with respect to some standard substance such as water, in which case density becomes the primary definition, and mass a definition derived from density. It is not clear which of these definitions Newton intended.

5-22 In what ways does the second law follow directly from definition two? In what ways is the second law independent of definition two?

Mach's Laws of Motion. Ernst Mach (1838–1916) was a German professor whose careful study of the physical basis of scientific assertions helped lay the foundation for the point of view of modern physics. Mach's work is typified by accuracy and simplicity and a careful distinction between theory and experimental observation. Mach built on the work of Newton by rephrasing the laws of motion to eliminate inconsistencies and repetitions and to provide a physically meaningful definition of mass. The reader should walk several times around this monument of careful scientific thought.*

(a) *Experimental proposition.* Bodies set opposite each other induce in each other, under certain circumstances to be specified by experimental physics, contrary accelerations in the direction of their line of junction.

(b) *Definition.* The mass ratio of any two bodies is the negative inverse ratio of the mutually induced accelerations of those bodies.

(c) *Experimental proposition.* The mass ratios of bodies are independent of the character of the physical states of the bodies that condition the mutual accelerations produced, be those states electrical, magnetic, or what not; and they remain, moreover, the same whether they are obtained directly or indirectly.

(d) *Experimental proposition.* The accelerations which any number of bodies, A, B, C, . . . , induce in a body K are independent of each other. . . . .

(*e*) *Definition.* Moving force is the product of the mass value of a body and the acceleration induced in that body.

In proposition (*a*) the circumstances under which bodies accelerate in contrary directions are to be explained by experimental physics. This refers, of course, to forces which we have come to distinguish as electrical, magnetic, gravitational, and so forth; but Mach has not yet defined force, so he confines himself to the observation of accelerations. Notice that no word is said about the coordinate system with respect to which these

* Taken from Ernst Mach, *op. cit.*, p. 303; a few words have been altered for clarity.

accelerations are to be measured and no instructions are given about the measurement of time.

Proposition (*b*) is a very neat definition of mass before force has been defined. Proposition (*c*) states, first of all, that this definition of mass ratio yields the same result for different sources of the contrary accelerations of particles and, second, that the intercomparison of masses using this method yields consistent results. For instance, if the ratios m_1/m_2 and m_2/m_3 are measured separately, then the measured ratio m_1/m_3 will be the same as the product $(m_1/m_2)(m_2/m_3)$ of the first two measured ratios.

Proposition (*d*) is equivalent to the law of superposition of forces, but, since force has not yet been defined, the proposition is framed in terms of accelerations. Finally, the definition of force is given in proposition (*e*).

Mach was fully aware that, although this formulation of the laws of motion removed some of the inconsistencies in Newton's laws, it failed to remove the complications and indefinite features of Newton's definitions of time and space. Mach himself worked to clarify these definitions with some success. He rejected the idea of "absolute" time and space, thus helping to lay the groundwork for the theory of relativity, part of which we shall study in Chapters 10 through 13. Although the theory of relativity has cleared up some of the ambiguities concerning time and space, there are many questions about them still under study.

Questions

5-23 In proposition (*b*), why is the mass ratio defined as the *negative* inverse ratio of the mutually induced accelerations?

5-24 Suppose that you are given a coordinate system in which the experiments implied by propositions (*a*), (*c*), and (*d*) can be carried out with consistent results. Is this an inertial coordinate system? Explain how you would set up a coordinate system in which the accelerations of particles set opposite each other were in the *same* direction rather than in contrary directions.

5.5 FIELDS. In Sec. 5.3 it was shown that the gravitational force between particle one and particle two of mass m_1 and m_2 respectively separated by a distance r is given by the equation $F_g = Gm_1m_2/r^2$. Similarly, the electrostatic force between particle one and particle two of charge q_1 and q_2 respectively separated by a distance r is given by the equation $F_e = (1/4\pi\epsilon_0)(q_1q_2/r^2)$. Sometimes it is convenient to consider these forces in a different way. We suppose that particle one sets up a (gravitational or electrostatic) *force field*, which then acts on particle two. For instance, the magnitude of the gravitational force field γ_1 due to particle one can be defined in such a way that the magnitude of the gravitational force on particle two is simply the value of this force field at the position of particle two times the mass of particle two.

$$F_{g2} = \frac{Gm_1}{r^2} m_2 = \gamma_1 m_2$$

so that

$$\gamma_1 = \frac{F_{g2}}{m_2} = \frac{Gm_1}{r^2}$$

where F_{g2} means "the gravitational force on particle two." Similarly, the magnitude of the electric field E_1 due to charge q_1 is defined in such a way that the magnitude of the electrostatic force on particle two is the value of this force field times the electric charge q_2 on particle two.

$$F_{e2} = \frac{1}{4\pi\epsilon_0} \frac{q_1}{r^2} q_2 = E_1 q_2$$

so that

$$E_1 = \frac{F_{e2}}{q_2} = \frac{1}{4\pi\epsilon_0} \frac{q_1}{r^2}$$

where F_{e2} means "the electrostatic force on particle two."

Question

5-25 Find expressions for the force fields γ_2 and E_2 due to particle two in the two cases. Will $\gamma_1 = \gamma_2$? Will $E_1 = E_2$?

Both forces and force fields are most easily described by using vectors. A vector force field at a given point is *defined* in terms of the vector force exerted on a particle of mass m or charge q placed at that point. These definitions are given by the following equations.

$$\boldsymbol{\Upsilon} = \frac{\mathbf{F}_g}{m} \tag{5-6}$$

$$\mathbf{E} = \frac{\mathbf{F}_e}{q} \tag{5-7}$$

Equations (5-6) and (5-7) may be taken to be the operational *definitions* of the gravitational and electrostatic fields. They are true no matter how many particles are involved in setting up the fields. In the *special case* in which the gravitational and electrical fields are set up by the mass and charge of a single particle, these definitions are equivalent to

$$\boldsymbol{\gamma}_1 = -\frac{Gm_1}{r^2}\hat{r} \tag{5-8}$$

$$\mathbf{E}_1 = \frac{1}{4\pi\epsilon_0}\frac{q_1\hat{r}}{r^2} \tag{5-9}$$

where $\hat{r}$ is a unit vector pointing in the direction of increasing r from a center at particle one.

In a somewhat different manner a magnetic force field can be defined.

Questions

5-26 Show that near the surface of the earth $\boldsymbol{\gamma} = \mathbf{g}$, where g is the acceleration due to gravity and $\mathbf{g}$ points vertically downward.

5-27 If particle two suffers a force $\mathbf{F}_2$, what experiment can you use to determine whether this force is gravitational or electrostatic in origin?

It is somewhat pointless to ask at this stage whether these force fields "actually exist" by themselves. For the present the only assertions we make about their existence is that a particle of mass m in a gravitation field $\boldsymbol{\gamma}$ experiences a force given by $m\boldsymbol{\gamma}$ and that a particle with a net charge q in an electric field $\mathbf{E}$ experiences a force given by $q\mathbf{E}$.

The usefulness of the concept of force field is that it allows us to analyze more complicated gravitational or electrical interactions with some economy of thought. For instance, if a particle is acted on by the gravitational force due to several nearby bodies, it is possible to treat the motion of this particle as if it were acted on by a single force field. This single field at any point will equal the *vector* sum of the separate force fields due to the nearby bodies.

Questions

5-28 From the law of superposition of forces verify that the resultant force field at any point must be the *vector sum* of the fields due to the separate surrounding bodies.

5-29 Two particles of equal mass m are situated at the points $\mathbf{r} = 1\hat{\imath}$ and $\mathbf{r} = -1\hat{\imath}$. What is the direction and magnitude of the resultant gravitational force field at $\mathbf{r} = 1\hat{\jmath}$?

5-30 Consider two particles in a uniform gravitational field (i.e., one in which $\boldsymbol{\gamma}$ is the same everywhere in the region being considered). Show that, if both particles are subject to the gravitational field alone and if they are initially at rest with respect to each other, they will remain at rest with respect to each other; hence, if there is any bond between these two particles, the forces due to the uniform gravitational field will not cause any force to be applied to this bond. Consider the human body to be made up of particles held together by chemical bonds. Demonstrate why the human body in free fall feels "weightless"; that is, demonstrate that we cannot feel the force due to a gravitational field alone. If this is so, explain the source of the feeling of weight we have when standing on the earth.

5.6 WORK. There are certain combinations of physical quantities which are so useful in mechanics that they are given their own names. Two of these are *energy* and *momentum*. These combinations are useful because in some experiments one or both of them remain constant; that is, they are *conserved* in these experiments. The fact that they are conserved can make such experiments very much easier to analyze. We shall distinguish between two kinds of energy, *potential energy* and *kinetic energy*, and shall define two auxiliary terms, *power* and *work*. We shall begin with work.

We begin to sweat when we have to get out and push a car in hot weather. We say, "This is hard work!" The harder we have to push, the harder work it is. Our idea of work involves force in some way. It also involves the distance the car must be pushed or the time spent pushing. After several false starts, physicists have found that the most convenient way to define work is the dot product of force and the displacement of the particle which is acted on by the force. If the symbol for work is W, then

$$W = \mathbf{F} \cdot \mathbf{s} \tag{5-10}$$

where $\mathbf{s}$ is the displacement of the particle. Work is a scalar and can be interpreted as the product of the magnitude of the displacement and the component of force in the direction of the displacement.

Question

5-31 Show that work can just as well be interpreted as the product of the magnitude of the force and the component of displacement in the direction of the force.

The units of work are those of force times distance. If the unit of force is the newton and the unit of distance is the meter, the unit of work is the newton-meter or (kilogram-meter/second^2) meter or kilogram-meter^2/second^2. This is such an important quantity in mechanics that this set of units is given the name *joule*.

$$\begin{aligned} 1 \text{ joule} &= 1 \text{ newton-meter (N-m)} \\ &= 1 \text{ kilogram-meter}^2/\text{second}^2 \text{ (kg-m}^2/\text{sec}^2) \end{aligned}$$

If the unit of force is the dyne and the unit of distance is the centimeter, the unit of work is the dyne-centimeter or the (gram-centimeter/second^2) centimeter or gram-centimeter^2/second^2. This quantity is given the name *erg*.

$$1 \text{ erg} = 1 \text{ dyne-centimeter (dyn-cm)}$$
$$= 1 \text{ gram-centimeter}^2/\text{second}^2 \text{ (g-cm}^2/\text{sec}^2)$$

Another commonly used unit of work is the electron-volt. Its value is as follows.

$$1 \text{ electron-volt} = \text{approximately } 1.6021 \times 10^{-19} \text{ joule}$$
$$= \text{approximately } 1.6021 \times 10^{-12} \text{ erg}$$

The abbreviation eV is sometimes used for the electron-volt. Since the electron-volt is such a small unit of work, multiples are often used.

$$1 \text{ kilo-electron-volt (keV)} = 10^3 \text{ electron-volts (eV)}$$
$$1 \text{ million electron-volts (MeV)} = 10^6 \text{ electron-volts (eV)}$$
$$1 \text{ giga-electron-volt (GeV)} = 10^9 \text{ electron-volts (eV)}$$

An older term for the giga-electron-volt is a billion electron-volts (BeV).

Questions

5-32 How many ergs are equal to 1 joule? *Answer*: 1 joule equals 10^7 ergs.

5-33 A constant force of 6 N accelerates a particle of 4 kg mass through a linear distance of 10 m. How much work does the force do on the particle?

5-34 A particle of 1-kg mass initially moving with speed v_1 is brought to rest by a constant force of 1 N which acts in a direction opposite to the direction of motion of the particle. If the mass is brought to rest in 1 m, how much work is done on the particle by the force? The answer is a negative quantity. Why?

5-35 A particle initially moving in a straight line is acted on by a force whose direction is kept always perpendicular to the direction of the particle's velocity. Show that this force does no work on the particle.

5.7 POTENTIAL ENERGY. Consider a stone of mass m resting on the surface of the earth. We shall assume in what follows that the stone will stay near enough to its initial point that the earth's surface is accurately enough described as a plane and the gravitational field of the earth can be assumed to act vertically downward toward this plane and not to vary with altitude. Whenever the stone is in this region, then, it is acted on by a constant vertical force given by the expression

$$\mathbf{F} = m\boldsymbol{\gamma} = -\hat{k}mg \approx -\hat{k}\,\frac{GMm}{r_e^{\,2}}$$

where M is the mass of the earth and r_e is the radius of the earth. The magnitude g of the local acceleration of gravity is approximately equal to the quantity GM/r_e^2.

Question

5-36 Demonstrate that the last sentence is true. What conditions might cause g to deviate from the value GM/r_e^2?

To begin with, the stone is resting against the ground. It does not move because the gravitational attraction of the earth for the stone is exactly balanced by the upward force exerted on the stone by the ground underneath it.

Now suppose that the stone is picked up from the ground and placed on a shelf a height h above the ground. How much work is done in moving the stone from the ground to the shelf? In order to raise the stone from the ground, a force $\mathbf{F}_1$ is applied to the stone in an upward direction. In order to get the stone moving in an upward direction, the force needs to be only a little greater than $+mg\hat{k}$, and if we are willing to wait long enough the incremental force above the value $+mg\hat{k}$ can be as small as desired. Once the stone is moving upward, a force exactly equal to $+mg\hat{k}$ is all that is required to keep it moving. As the stone approaches the

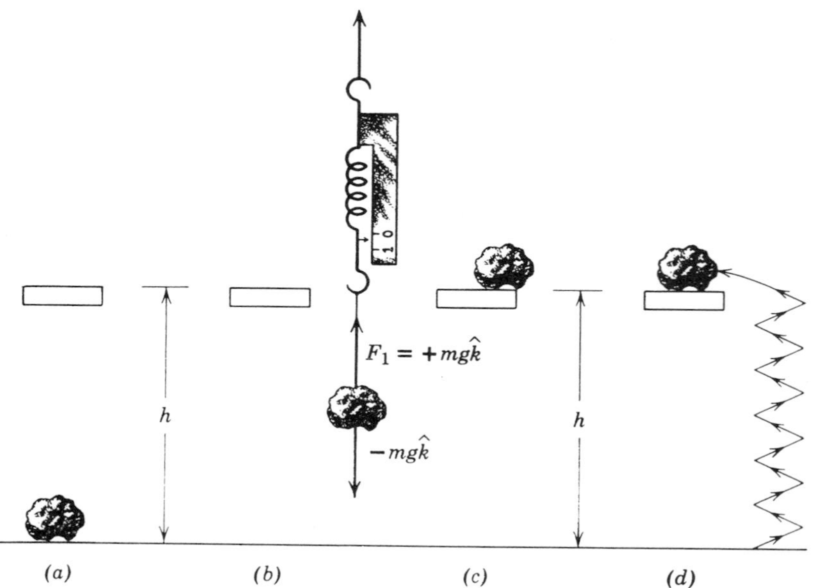

Fig. 5-6. Raising a stone from the ground to a shelf.

height of the shelf, a force slightly *less* than $+mg\hat{k}$ will be sufficient to allow it to come to rest at the height of the shelf. (See Fig. 5-6.)

Question

5-37 Show that sliding the stone onto the shelf from a height equal to the height of the shelf requires no work.

In summary, a force arbitrarily close to $+mg\hat{k}$ has raised the stone from the ground to the shelf at a height h above the ground.

Since the force has been parallel to the displacement, the work done by the force on the stone is given by the equation

$$W = \mathbf{F}_1 \cdot \mathbf{s} = mgh \tag{5-11}$$

Question

5-38 Show that, if the stone had been raised to height h by a zigzag path such as shown in Fig. 5-6*d*, the work done by the force on the stone would still be given by mgh.

Now the stone sits on its shelf. It is possible to "get back" the work we did to lift the stone to the shelf. We can get this work back by lowering the stone in the same way we raised it. This time the displacement of the stone is in a direction *opposite* to the force $\mathbf{F}_1$. Therefore the work done *on* the stone *by* the force is $-mgh$, or we might say that "the stone does work" against the force which restrains it as it is lowered. By this we mean that we could use the falling stone to do useful work for us, such as running a clock or raising water from a well.

In short, the work done in raising the stone to the shelf is "available energy" or "potential energy" in that it may be reclaimed later if desired. The *potential energy* of the stone with respect to the ground is given the symbol V, and in this case it has the value $V = mgh$. Potential energy is a scalar.

Notice that it is only the *difference* in potential energy of the stone between the ground and the shelf which we can measure. If we should raise the stone to the shelf and then dig a hole in the ground under the shelf, we could "get back" more energy than we had expended to raise the stone to the shelf in the first place by lowering the stone from the shelf all the way to the bottom of the hole. By definition, the absolute value of the potential energy cannot be known; only its relative value at different points can be known. A *reference point* is a point to which the potential energy can be referred. In this case, ground level was chosen as the reference point. Stones above the level of the ground have positive potential energy, and stones below the level of the ground have negative potential energy, with respect to this reference point.

Consider another case in which potential energy can be defined. A particle of mass m is at rest a distance r_1 from the center of the earth. We suppose that r_1 is greater than the radius of the earth. The magnitude of the earth's gravitational force on the particle is then GMm/r_1^2, where M is the mass of the earth. Now suppose that a radial force $\mathbf{F}_1$, whose magnitude can be made to be arbitrarily close to the magnitude of the gravitational force at every point, is used to change the radial position of the particle. The magnitude of this force will depend on the changing radial distance r of the particle from the center of the earth. However, for a short path length Δr the force can be considered approximately constant, and for an infinitesimally short path length dr this approximation becomes very good. The work dW done by the force $\mathbf{F}_1$ in this infinitesimal displacement is

$$dW = \mathbf{F}_1 \cdot d\mathbf{r}$$

But, since $\mathbf{F}_1$ is parallel to $d\mathbf{r}$ the dot product becomes $dW = F_1\, dr$. The total work done by the force on the particle is the sum of all these small contributions along the path length.

$$W = \int_{r_1}^{r_2} dW = \int_{r_1}^{r} \mathbf{F}_1 \cdot d\mathbf{s} = GMm \int_{r_1}^{r} \frac{dr}{r^2} = GMm\left(-\frac{1}{r}\right)\Big|_{r_1}^{r} = V - V_1$$

or

$$V - V_1 = -\frac{GMm}{r} - \left(-\frac{GMm}{r_1}\right)$$

Question

5-39 For a very small change h in r, show that $V - V_1 = mgh$, where g is the magnitude of the local acceleration of gravity (not necessarily equal to g at the surface of the earth).

Once again the potential energy V at r can be related to the potential energy V_1 at some reference point r_1. We could choose the reference point r_1 to be at the surface of the earth. More often the reference point r_1 is chosen to be "a very great distance from the earth," so that the magnitude of the term GMm/r_1 is negligibly small compared with the other potentials in the problem. In this case we say that "with respect to a point at infinity" the potential energy of a particle of mass m in the gravitational field of the earth is given by the expression

$$V = -\frac{GMm}{r} \tag{5-12}$$

Since gravitational force is attractive, this potential energy is everywhere negative.

Questions

5-40 In both of the previous examples show that the potential energy V has the units of work. Show that potential energy always has the units of work by definition.

5-41 Why could not the reference point of potential energy be chosen at the *center* of the earth?

5-42 Suppose that the path from r_1 to r consists of radial segments and circular segments at constant radius. Show that the difference in potential energy between r_1 and r would be the same in this case as in the previous case.

In both of these examples of potential energy the potential energy difference along a path depends only on the endpoints of the path and not on the length or shape of that path or on the time. Force fields which satisfy this condition are called *conservative fields* and are very important in the study of mechanics. In carrying out analyses similar to the two above for any conservative force field, the applied force $\mathbf{F}_1$ is opposite in direction to and arbitrarily near the magnitude of the force $\mathbf{F}$ exerted on the particle by the field. In vector notation $\mathbf{F} = -\mathbf{F}_1$. Hence the change in potential energy of a particle in a conservative force field can be given by the expression

$$V_2 - V_1 = \int_1^2 \mathbf{F}_1 \cdot d\mathbf{s} = -\int_1^2 \mathbf{F} \cdot d\mathbf{s} \tag{5-13}$$

where $\mathbf{F}$ is the force exerted on the particle by the field. Notice that the quantity under the integral sign is a scalar.

Question

5-43 Show that the electrostatic potential energy of a particle of net charge q_2 in the field set up by another particle of net charge q_1 is given by the expression

$$V = \frac{1}{4\pi\epsilon_0}\frac{q_1 q_2}{r}$$

where r is the distance between the two particles and the reference potential energy is taken at "infinite" separation. Is the electrostatic force field a conservative field?

5.8. KINETIC ENERGY. In the last section we were careful to calculate the potential energy of a particle only when it was at rest. Potential energy is an energy of *position*. There is another form of energy, an energy of *motion*. We call this *kinetic energy*.

Suppose that a net force $\mathbf{F}$ acts on a particle. This force can be due to a force field or a spring balance, or it can be the resultant of any combination of forces. This net force $\mathbf{F}$ may change in magnitude or direction or both as the particle moves. Nevertheless, for a short enough displacement $\Delta\mathbf{s}$ the force can be considered approximately constant, and for an infinitesimally short displacement $d\mathbf{s}$ this approximation becomes very good. The work dW done by the force in this infinitesimal displacement is

$$dW = \mathbf{F} \cdot d\mathbf{s} \tag{5-14}$$

The total work done by the force on the particle is the sum of all of these small contributions along the path length:

$$\int_1^2 dW = \int_1^2 \mathbf{F} \cdot d\mathbf{s}$$

Notice that the quantity under the integral sign is a scalar.

Question

5-44 Set $\mathbf{F} \cdot d\mathbf{s} = (F \cos \theta)\, ds$, where θ is the instantaneous angle between the vectors $\mathbf{F}$ and $d\mathbf{s}$. Draw a possible curve $F \cos \theta$ vs s and show that the area under this curve between any two values of s is numerically equal to the work done by the force on the particle between these two displacements. What if $F \cos \theta$ is negative for part of the curve?

Just as the force is considered constant during an infinitesimal displacement $d\mathbf{s}$, so can the velocity be considered constant during an infinitesimal displacement even though it may be different at different points on the path of the particle. Hence

$$d\mathbf{s} = \mathbf{v}\, dt$$

Substituting this into the integral,

$$W = \int_{t_1}^{t_2} \mathbf{F} \cdot \mathbf{v}\, dt$$

But the law of motion for a particle says

$$\mathbf{F} = m\mathbf{a} = m \frac{d\mathbf{v}}{dt}$$

so

$$W = m \int_{t_1}^{t_2} \frac{d\mathbf{v}}{dt} \cdot \mathbf{v}\, dt$$

Now Eq. (4-41) in the last chapter tells us that

$$\frac{d(\mathbf{v}\cdot\mathbf{v})}{dt} = \frac{d\mathbf{v}}{dt}\cdot\mathbf{v} + \mathbf{v}\cdot\frac{d\mathbf{v}}{dt} = 2\frac{d\mathbf{v}}{dt}\cdot\mathbf{v}$$

from which, using the results of Question 4-43,

$$\frac{d\mathbf{v}}{dt}\cdot\mathbf{v} = \frac{1}{2}\frac{d}{dt}(\mathbf{v}\cdot\mathbf{v}) = \frac{1}{2}\frac{d}{dt}(v^2)$$

so that the integral above can be solved using Eq. (4-21) with the function f replaced by v^2.

$$W = m\int_{t_1}^{t_2}\frac{d\mathbf{v}}{dt}\cdot\mathbf{v}\,dt = \frac{m}{2}\int_{t_1}^{t_2}\frac{d}{dt}(v^2)\,dt = \tfrac{1}{2}mv_2^{\,2} - \tfrac{1}{2}mv_1^{\,2} \qquad (5\text{-}15)$$

where v_1 and v_2 are the speeds of the particle at times t_1 and t_2 respectively.

Thus the work done by any force on a free particle is given by the change in the quantity $\frac{1}{2}mv^2$. This quantity is called the *kinetic energy* of the particle. Work done by any force on a particle appears as an increase or decrease in the kinetic of that particle. This is true for any force, including frictional forces.

Kinetic energy is given the symbol T.

$$T = \tfrac{1}{2}mv^2 \qquad \text{definition} \qquad (5\text{-}16)$$

so that Eq. (5-15) becomes

$$T_2 - T_1 = \tfrac{1}{2}mv_2^{\,2} - \tfrac{1}{2}mv_1^{\,2} = \int_1^2 \mathbf{F}\cdot d\mathbf{s} \qquad (5\text{-}17)$$

Questions

5-45 Show that kinetic energy has the same units as work.

5-46 Show that the kinetic energy of a given particle can have a different value when measured with respect to different inertial coordinate systems.

5-47 A particle is whirled in a circular path on the end of a string. If the string runs from the particle to the center of the circle at all times, show that the force exerted by the string on the particle will not change the speed of the particle. Will this force change the velocity of the particle? Will it change the kinetic energy of the particle?

5.9 CONSERVATION OF MECHANICAL ENERGY. Suppose that the only force on a particle is due to a conservative force field. Since the potential energy of a particle in a conservative force field depends only on position, it will not depend on the velocity of the particle. Equation (5-13) says that under these circumstances

$$V_2 - V_1 = -\int_1^2 \mathbf{F}\cdot d\mathbf{s}$$

But, from Eq. (5-17) for a particle subject to any net force **F**,

$$\int_1^2 \mathbf{F} \cdot d\mathbf{s} = \tfrac{1}{2}mv_2^2 - \tfrac{1}{2}mv_1^2 = T_2 - T_1$$

Equating equal integrals from these two equations, we have

$$V_2 - V_1 = -(T_2 - T_1)$$

or

$$T_2 + V_2 = T_1 + V_1 \tag{5-18}$$

If we let $E = T + V$ and call E the *total mechanical energy* of the particle, then Eq. (5-18) says that, *if all forces on a particle are due to conservative force fields, the total mechanical energy remains constant.* This is called the *law of conservation of mechanical energy.*

The law of conservation of mechanical energy in conservative fields is one special case of a more general law of conservation of energy. It has been found that, even if mechanical energy is lost, for instance to friction, the same amount of energy will appear in some other form, such as heat energy. Einstein has shown that mass itself is a form of energy, so that under certain circumstances mass may be created or destroyed with a corresponding decrease or release of other forms of energy.

Physicists have become very attached to the law of conservation of energy. They will go to great lengths to preserve its validity. Some years ago it was found that in a certain nuclear reaction energy did not appear to be conserved. In order to preserve the law of conservation of energy a new particle called the neutrino, with peculiar and elusive properties, was invented to carry away the missing energy. It was much later that the neutrino itself was detected and thus its existence proved directly.*

Questions

5-48 A stone is released from a height of 100 m above the surface of the earth. Use the law of conservation of mechanical energy to calculate the velocity with which the stone will strike the ground. Neglect air resistance.

5-49 If air resistance can be neglected, with what vertical velocity must a particle be projected from the surface of the earth in order to escape entirely from the gravitational field of the earth? Show that this velocity could just as well be in the horizontal direction.

5.10 POWER. Consider the work dW done by a force **F** acting on a particle during an infinitesimal displacement $d\mathbf{s}$.

$$dW = \mathbf{F} \cdot d\mathbf{s}$$

* See Philip Morrison, "The Neutrino," *Scientific American*, January 1956.

If we divide both sides of this equation by dt, we have

$$\frac{dW}{dt} = \mathbf{F} \cdot \frac{d\mathbf{s}}{dt}$$

But $d\mathbf{s}/dt$ is the velocity $\mathbf{v}$ of the particle. The expression dW/dt is the rate at which the force does work. This rate is called *power* and is given the symbol P. The power P is equal to the rate at which a force $\mathbf{F}$ does work.

$$P = \mathbf{F} \cdot \mathbf{v} \tag{5-19}$$

Like work, power is a scalar. It has the units joules per second. One joule per second is given the name one *watt*. Other units of power are derived from the *watt*. The abbreviation for watt is W.

1 kilowatt (kW) = 10^3 watts (W)
1 megawatt (MW) = 10^6 watts (W)
1 horsepower (hp) = approximately 746 watts (W)

One horsepower was originally equal to the rate at which an average horse could work steadily for an average working day. Improvements in breeding have increased the "horsepower" of the average horse, but the original value of the horsepower is still used.

Questions

5-50 A horizontal force of 100 N is used to drag a block of wood along the floor at a constant velocity of 1 m/sec. How much power is developed by this force?

5-51 Express the power of a 300-hp car in kilowatts.

5-52 The kilowatt-hour (kWh) is a unit of work equal to the total work done by a force working at the rate of 1 kW for 1 h. How many joules equal 1 kWh?

5-53 My Voomflauten X-100 sports car has a mass of 1400 kg (including me) and can accelerate from 0 to 60 mph (26.8 m/sec) in 7 sec. What is the average horsepower developed by the engine during this interval? What happened to the 350 hp I read about in the advertisement for the car?

5.11 MOMENTUM. The product of mass and velocity is called *momentum* and is given the symbol $\mathbf{p}$.

$$\mathbf{p} = m\mathbf{v} \qquad \text{definition}$$

Momentum is a vector with units of kilogram-meters per second. The plural of momentum is momenta.

Since

$$m\mathbf{a} = m\frac{d\mathbf{v}}{dt} = \frac{d(m\mathbf{v})}{dt} = \frac{d\mathbf{p}}{dt}$$

the law of motion may be rewritten

$$\mathbf{F} = \frac{d\mathbf{p}}{dt} \tag{5-20}$$

Newton defined the "quantity of motion" in the same way we define momentum. In Newton's second law the phrase "alteration of motion" means "change of momentum," so that Eq. (5-20) more nearly represents Newton's second law than does the equation $\mathbf{F} = m\mathbf{a}$. If the mass of a particle is constant, the two expressions are equivalent.

5.12 CONSERVATION OF MOMENTUM. Suppose that two particles collide. Suppose also that no forces are exerted on the particles except those due to physical contact between them during the collision. We shall now show that the vector sum of the momenta of particle one and particle two before the collision is equal to the vector sum of the momenta of the two particles after the collision.

Let $\mathbf{p}_1$ and $\mathbf{p}_2$ be the momenta of particle one and particle two respectively before the collision, and $\bar{\mathbf{p}}_1$ and $\bar{\mathbf{p}}_2$ (with bars) be the respective momenta of the two particles after the collision. There are no forces on either particle before and after the collision. Hence, except for the instant of collision, $\mathbf{p}_1$, $\mathbf{p}_2$, $\bar{\mathbf{p}}_1$, and $\bar{\mathbf{p}}_2$ are all constants. We shall now show that

$$\mathbf{p}_1 + \mathbf{p}_2 = \bar{\mathbf{p}}_2 + \bar{\mathbf{p}}_1$$

Note that this is a vector equation.

During the collision the force between the particles may vary violently with time. Consider first the force on particle one. Call this force $\mathbf{F}_1$. A possible graph of F_1 vs t is shown in Fig. 5-7. Choose a time t_1 before the collision and a time t_2 after the collision. Consider the integral

$$\int_{t_1}^{t_2} \mathbf{F}_1\, dt$$

Since $\mathbf{F}_1 = d\mathbf{p}_1/dt$ at every instant according to Eq. (5-20)

$$\int_{t_1}^{t_2} \mathbf{F}_1\, dt = \int_{t_1}^{t_2} \frac{d\mathbf{p}_1}{dt}\, dt = \bar{\mathbf{p}}_1 - \mathbf{p}_1 \tag{5-21}$$

where we have used Eq. (4-21). From Newton's third law, the force on particle two at any instant is equal in magnitude and opposite in direction

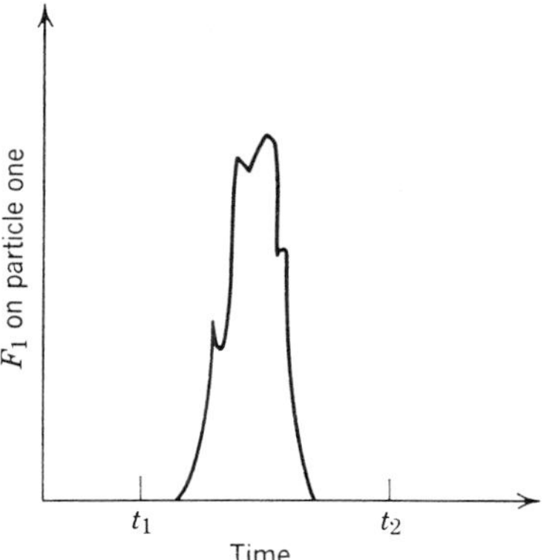

Fig. 5-7. Force on particle one during a collision.

to the force on particle one. Call the force on particle two $\mathbf{F}_2$. Then $\mathbf{F}_2 = -\mathbf{F}_1$. As before,

$$\int_{t_1}^{t_2} \mathbf{F}_2\, dt = \int_{t_1}^{t_2} \frac{d\mathbf{p}_2}{dt}\, dt = \bar{\mathbf{p}}_2 - \mathbf{p}_2$$

but

$$\int_{t_1}^{t_2} \mathbf{F}_2\, dt = -\int_{t_1}^{t_2} \mathbf{F}_1\, dt = \bar{\mathbf{p}}_2 - \mathbf{p}_2$$

Substitute for $+\int F_1\, dt$ from Eq. (5-21).

$$-(\bar{\mathbf{p}}_1 - \mathbf{p}_1) = \bar{\mathbf{p}}_2 - \mathbf{p}_2$$

or

$$\mathbf{p}_1 + \mathbf{p}_2 = \bar{\mathbf{p}}_1 + \bar{\mathbf{p}}_2 \tag{5-22}$$

Thus the vector sum of the momenta of the two particles before the collision is equal to the vector sum of the momenta of the two particles after the collision. This statement is called the *law of conservation of momentum*.

Questions

5-54 Particle one is initially at rest. Its mass is 1 kg. Particle two has a mass of 2 kg and an initial velocity of 10 m/sec toward particle one. After the collision, particle two moves with a velocity of 5 m/sec in a direction which makes an angle of 30° with its initial velocity vector. What are the direction and magnitude of the velocity of particle one after the collision?

5-55 Is kinetic energy conserved in the collision of the preceding question?

5-56 Particles one and two each have a mass of 1 kg. Particle one moves in the positive x-direction with a velocity of 10 m/sec. Particle two moves in the negative y-direction with a velocity of 5 m/sec. The two particles collide. What is the velocity of each particle after the collision?

5-57 In the last question what would the final velocity of particle two be if the final velocity of particle one is 5 m/sec at an angle of 45° with the positive x-axis? Is kinetic energy conserved in this collision?

5-58 Two particles at rest are tied tightly together by string with a compressed spring of negligible mass between them. The string holding them together is cut and the spring pushes the two particles apart. Particle one moves along the positive x-axis with a velocity of 2 m/sec. Particle two moves along the negative x-axis with a velocity of 1 m/sec. The mass of particle one is 1 kg. What is the mass of particle two? This is called the *reaction car experiment* and is sometimes used to define mass before force has been defined.

5-59 Prove that Eq. (5-22) is valid at any instant during the collision if $\bar{\mathbf{p}}_1$ and $\bar{\mathbf{p}}_2$ are the momenta of particles one and two at that instant. Show that this equation is valid for particles which interact with forces other than contact forces as long as the law of action and reaction applies to these forces.

5.13 IMPULSE. Let us return to Eq. (5-21). For a given particle,

$$\int_{t_1}^{t_2} \mathbf{F}\,dt = \bar{\mathbf{p}} - \mathbf{p} \tag{5-23}$$

The integral on the left side of this equation is called the impulse and is given the symbol **J**.

$$\mathbf{J} = \int_{t_1}^{t_2} \mathbf{F}\,dt \qquad \text{definition} \tag{5-24}$$

Impulse is a vector and has the units kilogram-meter per second. Equation (5-23) says that the impulse applied to a particle is equal to its change of momentum

$$\mathbf{J} = \bar{\mathbf{p}} - \mathbf{p} \tag{5-25}$$

Impulse is used to describe the action of forces which are large in magnitude but short in duration (impulsive forces) such as those involved in collisions.

Questions

5-60 A golf club acts on a golf ball with an average force of 250 N for 10 msec. What is the total impulse applied to the golf ball? If the ball has a mass of 45 g and starts from rest, how fast will it be moving after receiving the impulse?

5-61 Suppose that the net linear force in newtons on a bullet fired from a gun at $t = 0$ is given by the expression

$$\begin{aligned} F &= 10^7(25 \times 10^{-6} - t^2) \qquad & 0 < t < 5 \text{ msec} \\ &= 0 & t > 5 \text{ msec} \end{aligned}$$

What is the total impulse which acts on the bullet? If the bullet has a mass of 2 g, how fast will it move after leaving the gun?

5.14 THE ROCKET IN SPACE. A particle will move with constant (or zero) speed along a straight line unless acted on by a force. Forces may be gravitational or electrical or magnetic, may be due to the pressure of light, or maybe be the result of a collision of one particle with another. Such forces are difficult to come by in interstellar space in sufficient strength and in direction adequately controllable to operate a space vehicle. To propel and guide our space ships we depend on the rocket. The rocket is simply one application of the law of conservation of momentum.

Consider the following experiment (see Fig. 5-8). A space ship of mass m moves with velocity $\mathbf{v}$ in the positive x-direction of an inertial reference frame. The rockets are turned off and there are no other forces on the space ship, so that its velocity $\mathbf{v}$ is constant in direction and magnitude. Since all velocities in the subsequent problem are along the (positive or negative) x-axis we can add and subtract them like scalars; therefore the vector notation will be dropped.

Now suppose that a mass dm is fired out of the rear of the space ship with an *exhaust velocity* $(-v_0)$ *with respect to the space ship.* The mass dm has a velocity $v - v_0$ with respect to the reference frame. After the small mass has been fired out of the rear of the space ship, the mass of the space ship is less by an amount dm and its velocity is greater than v.

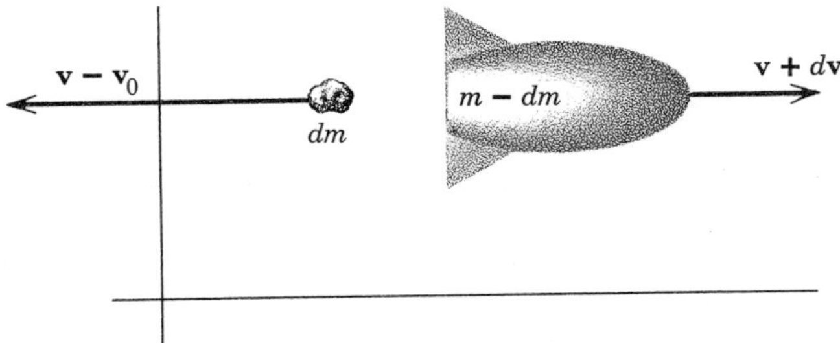

Fig. 5-8. Derivation of the law of motion for a rocket ship.

Denote the new velocity of the space ship by $v + dv$. Then, from the law of conservation of momentum,

$$\begin{bmatrix}\text{initial momentum}\\ \text{of space ship}\end{bmatrix} = \begin{bmatrix}\text{final momentum}\\ \text{of space ship}\\ \text{less mass } dm\end{bmatrix} + \begin{bmatrix}\text{final momentum}\\ \text{of mass } dm\end{bmatrix}$$

$$mv = (m - dm)(v + dv) + dm(v - v_0) \tag{5-26}$$

whence

$$m\,dv = v_0\,dm + dv\,dm$$

Divide through by mv_0:

$$\frac{dv}{v_0} = \frac{dm}{m} + \frac{dv}{v_0}\frac{dm}{m} \tag{5-27}$$

Now, dm/m is the fractional change in mass of the space ship due to the release of the mass dm. Also, dv/v_0 is the ratio of the change in velocity of the space ship to the exhaust velocity of the mass dm. Both of these fractions are very small because dm is really an infinitesimal. Hence the product of the two fractions is so small as to be negligible compared to either of them alone.

Question

5-62 Suppose $dm/m = dv/v_0 = 10^{-6}$. What is the relative magnitude of the product $(dm/m)(dv/v_0)$ compared to (dm/m) or (dv/v_0)?

The equation may be written

$$dv = v_0\frac{dm}{m}$$

The mass dm is the mass shot out of the rear of the space ship. This is equal to the *negative* of the change in mass of the space ship. (The amount shot from the rocket results in a decrease in rocket mass.) Hence the last equation may be rewritten

$$dv = -v_0\frac{dm}{m} \tag{5-28}$$

where *dm now represents the change in mass of the space ship.* Suppose now that a whole series of particles are shot out the rear of the space ship in a steady stream with the constant exhaust velocity $(-v_0)$ with respect to the ship. For each such particle ejected, the velocity of the space ship will change according to Eq. (5-28), where m is the mass of the space ship before that particle is ejected. The resultant change in the velocity of the space ship is given by summing all the incremental velocity changes described by Eq. (5-28). Such a sum will be an integral. Remember that v_0 is a constant but m is not.

$$\int_{v_1}^{v_2} dv = v_2 - v_1 = -v_0 \int_{m_1}^{m_2} \frac{dm}{m}$$

$$\begin{aligned} v_2 - v_1 &= -v_0[\ln m_2 - \ln m_1] \\ &= +v_0[\ln m_1 - \ln m_2] \end{aligned}$$

$$v_2 - v_1 = v_0 \ln \frac{m_1}{m_2}$$

where use has been made of Eq. (4-20) at the end of Section 4.6. But m_2 is the mass of the rocket at any instant, v_2 is its velocity at the same instant. If we let $m_2 = m$ and $v_2 = v$, the equation becomes

$$v - v_1 = v_0 \ln \frac{m_1}{m} \tag{5-29}$$

where m_1 and v_1 are the initial mass and velocity of the space ship respectively and $(-v_0)$ is the "constant velocity" of the rocket exhaust with respect to the space ship.

Equation (5-29) shows that v increases as m decreases. The largest v will occur when the rocket fuel is used up. This exhaustion of rocket fuel is referred to as *burnout*.

Questions

5-63 A fully loaded and fueled rocket has a mass of 1000 kg. Its rocket motors accelerate it from rest along a straight line with constant exhaust velocity of 1000 m/sec. After burnout the shell and payload of the rocket have a total mass of 200 kg. What is the terminal velocity of the rocket?

5-64 Is the acceleration of the rocket constant while the engine is on if dm/dt is constant?

5-65 Show that Eq. (5-29) is correct even if the burning rate dm/dt is not constant.

One practical difficulty encountered in designing a rocket for high terminal velocities starting from rest is that the minimum terminal mass is increased by casings, empty fuel tanks, and deadweight gear necessary for the operation of the rocket engines. One way to circumvent this problem is to use *multistage rockets*. In the multistage rocket the payload of one rocket is a second rocket. After the first rocket has achieved terminal velocity, the second one is fired. In this way all the deadweight of the first rocket gear is left behind and does not require further acceleration.

Suppose that a two-stage rocket starts from rest. The terminal velocity of the first stage is

$$v_2 = v_0 \ln \frac{m_1}{m_2}$$

where m_1 is initial "takeoff" mass, m_2 is terminal mass of first rocket and its payload. Suppose that $m_2 = m_A + m_B$, where m_A is a "payload" made up of a second-stage rocket and m_B is the remainder of the terminal mass of the first rocket, made up of fuel tanks, casings, and running gear. Now the second stage blasts off from the first. If the exhaust velocity of the second stage is also $(-v_0)$, then the additional velocity achieved by the second stage is

$$v_3 - v_2 = v_0 \ln \frac{m_A}{m_C}$$

where m_C is the terminal mass of the second stage. The total terminal velocity of the second stage is

$$v_3 = v_2 + v_0 \ln \frac{m_A}{m_C} = v_0 \ln \frac{m_1}{m_2} + v_0 \ln \frac{m_A}{m_C}$$

$$v_3 = v_0 \ln \left(\frac{m_1}{m_2} \cdot \frac{m_A}{m_C}\right) \tag{5-30}$$

Question

5-66 Extend the preceding results to a three-stage rocket each of whose stages has a different exhaust velocity.

The acceleration of a rocket-propelled space ship is not due to any external force but rather follows from the conservation of momentum, as we have seen. In operating an actual space ship, however, we are not interested in the fate of the exhaust material shot from the rear of the rocket. Usually all that concerns us is the motion of the space ship itself. Since the space ship itself does in fact accelerate when the rockets are turned on, *it moves as if it were acted on by an external force.* What external force would cause the same acceleration of the space ship as its rocket engines do? The answer to this question can be found by using Eq. (5-28).

$$dv = -v_0 \frac{dm}{m}$$

Multiply both sides of this equation by m and divide both sides by dt.

$$m \frac{dv}{dt} = -v_0 \frac{dm}{dt} \tag{5-31}$$

The left side of this equation is equal to the right side of the equation of motion $F = ma$. If we define the *thrust* of a rocket as equal to the mass of the rocket times its instantaneous acceleration, then Eq. (5-31) becomes

$$\text{Thrust} = -v_0 \frac{dm}{dt} \tag{5-32}$$

Since the rocket is decreasing in mass, dm/dt is a negative quantity and thrust is a positive quantity.

The effect of rockets on the motion of a space ship can be found by assuming that the space ship is acted on by an external force given by the last equation. This external force, of course, does not exist. It must also be borne in mind that the mass of the space ship is constantly changing, so that with a constant thrust the acceleration increases with time.

Question

5-67 Using the myth of thrust, derive Eq. (5-29) for the motion of a single-stage rocket.

EXERCISES

5-1 A moving particle collides with a particle of different mass which is initially at rest. After the collision the two particles stick together. What fraction of the initial kinetic energy is lost in the collision?

5-2 A moving particle collides with a second particle of equal mass which is initially at rest. No energy is lost in the collision. Show that after the collision the angle between the velocity vectors of the two particles is 90° unless one of the particles is at rest.

5-3 By accident George Jones stumbles out of his space ship into interstellar space. By the time his automatic space suit has inflated and he has collected his wits, George realizes that the space ship is moving away from him with a velocity of 3.40 m/sec. Luckily the rocket motors of the ship are turned off and luckily George has an extra pressurized tank of oxygen with him. George and his clothes have a mass of 70 kg, the oxygen in the tank has a mass of 5 kg, and the tank itself has a mass of 2 kg. If the tank is turned on, the oxygen will escape with a constant velocity of 50 m/sec until the tank is empty. Can George Jones make it back to his space ship unaided?

5-4 Find an expression for the effective power of my car in terms of the maximum constant velocity with which it can drive up a hill with constant slope. Neglect friction and air resistance.

5-5 A block of wood slides along a horizontal plane with initial velocity v_1. Calculate how far it will slide before coming to rest by using the law of conservation of energy.

Fig. 5-9.

5-6 The booster for a certain rocket develops a thrust of 360,000 lb of force (1.6×10^6 N). What power does this engine develop when the rocket is traveling at a speed of 1000 mph (about 450 m/sec)? Express your answer in horsepower.

5-7 A rocket has an initial mass of 2×10^4 kg, a mass ratio of 3, a burning rate of 100 kg/sec, and an exhaust velocity of 980 m/sec. The rocket is fired vertically from the surface of the earth. How long after ignition of the engines will the rocket leave the ground?

5-8 A double drawbridge is partially opened and stationary. (See Fig. 5-9.) An automobile coasts up one side, starting at the bottom with an initial speed v_1, and attempts to jump the gap to the other half-span. What is the maximum angle of the drawbridge with the horizontal for which this attempt will be successful? Treat the car as a particle, and assume that mechanical energy is conserved. If you are not able to obtain an explicit expression for this angle, explain how you would use your final equation or equations to obtain a numerical answer if appropriate numerical values were given.

5-9 Consider a uniform non-rotating spherical asteroid alone in interstellar space. The mass of the asteroid is very much greater than the mass of a man. How high must the world's champion high-jumper be able to jump on earth if he is to be able to jump high enough from the surface of this asteroid to escape from its gravitational field? How fast must a runner be able to sprint tangential to the surface of the asteroid in order to escape from its gravitational field?

5-10 Consider the U-shaped frame shown in Fig. 5-10 which moves with constant velocity to the right with respect to an inertial reference frame. A block of mass M is held between two spring balances so that it

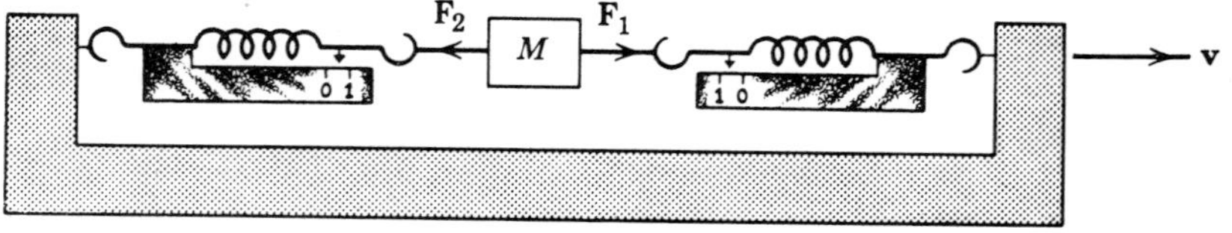

Fig. 5-10.

is at rest with respect to the U-shaped frame. What is the power supplied to the block by the spring balance in front? What happens to this energy?

5-11 The *specific impulse* of a rocket is defined as the ratio of thrust to weight flow rate of propellant exhausted. The weight of propellant is measured at the surface of the earth. Show that the specific impulse of a simple rocket is given by the expression

$$\text{Specific impulse} = \frac{v_0}{g}$$

Show that the unit of specific impulse is the second.

PROJECT III. VERTICAL ASCENT OF A ROCKET

The takeoff of a rocket from the surface of the earth is rather difficult to analyze. The rocket thrust may be used not only to carry the rocket aloft but also to give it a horizontal component of velocity in addition to the tangential velocity of the surface of the rotating earth. The burning rate of the fuel may be controlled to vary the thrust with time. The main engine or auxiliary engines may supply additional thrusts to give the rocket guidance or stability of attitude. Several stages may be employed, with the burning rate or exhaust velocity or both different for each stage. Some of the later stages may coast upward for considerable times before firing. Air resistance and the effects of the presence of air on thrust must be taken into account. The force of gravity, of course, will enter all calculations and will decrease with height. In general, the number of stages in the rocket, the burning rate of each stage, the timing of separation of stages, and the trajectory of the rocket will be so chosen as to take the greatest advantage of the hardware available at the time.

In order to simplify the calculations we shall study the vertical ascent of a rocket under the following assumptions:

1. Forces due to the presence of the atmosphere can be neglected.
2. The rocket thrust is vertical, and horizontal forces will not be taken into account.
3. The acceleration of gravity does not vary with height.
4. The rocket has only a single stage.
5. The rate of change of mass of the rocket is constant until burnout.

Using these assumptions and the following outline, work out the equations for the vertical ascent of a rocket. The problems will help you to apply these equations.

Using Assumption 5, set

$$\frac{dm}{dt} = -k \tag{III-1}$$

so that k is a positive constant. Taking the positive direction upward, show that the equation of motion of the rocket is

$$ma = v_0k - mg$$

or

$$\frac{dv}{dt} = \frac{v_0k}{m} - g \tag{III-2}$$

where v_0 is the exhaust velocity of the rocket. Multiply both sides of Eq. (III-2) by dt, and substitute for dt from Eq. (III-1) to obtain

$$dv = -v_0 \frac{dm}{m} + \frac{g}{k}\, dm$$

If the initial velocity is zero, the velocity at a later time will be found by summing or integrating these velocity increments. Integrate this equation from an initial mass m_1 to a mass m at a later time. Show that the velocity at this later time is

$$v = -(v_0 \ln m) + (v_0 \ln m_1) + \frac{g}{k} m - \frac{g}{k} m_1 \qquad \text{(III-3)}$$

If the final mass of the rocket at burnout is m_2, show that the vertical velocity v_b at burnout is given by

$$v_b = \left(v_0 \ln \frac{m_1}{m_2}\right) - g \frac{(m_1 - m_2)}{k}$$

If t_b is the time to burnout and $R = m_1/m_2$ is the mass ratio of the rocket, show that this equation may be written

$$v_b = (v_0 \ln R) - g t_b \qquad \text{(III-4)}$$

This is the vertical velocity of the rocket at burnout.

Problems

III-1 A single-stage sounding rocket has an initial mass 1000 kg, a final mass 200 kg, a burning rate of 80 kg/sec, and an exhaust velocity of 3000 m/sec. If it is fired vertically, what will be the vertical velocity of the sounding rocket at burnout?

III-2 For a given initial mass and burning rate, what is the minimum exhaust velocity which will cause a rocket to leave the ground immediately after ignition?

III-3 What is the maximum acceleration of a rocket which takes off vertically? During launch, the instruments in the rocket of Problem III-1 must sustain how many times their own weight on earth?

New let us find the height of the rocket above the ground at burnout. Let z be the vertical coordinate. Set $v = dz/dt$ in Eq. (III-3), multiply through by dt, and substitute for dt from Eq. (III-1) once more to obtain the equation

$$dz = +\left(\frac{v_0}{k} \ln m\right) dm - \frac{g}{k^2} m\, dm + \left(\frac{g}{k^2} m_1 - \frac{v_0}{k} \ln m_1\right) dm$$

If the initial height is zero, the height z_b at burnout will be found by summing or integrating these increments of height. Integrate this equation from an initial mass m_1 to a final mass m_2 at burnout. You will need to use the indefinite integral

$$\int (\ln m)\, dm = (m \ln m) - m$$

for the first integral on the right side.* Check this indefinite integral by differentiation. Show that the height z_b at burnout is given by the equation

$$z_b = \left(\frac{v_0 m_2}{k} \ln m_2\right) - \frac{v_0}{k} m_2 - \left(\frac{v_0 m_1}{k} \ln m_1\right) + \frac{v_0}{k} m_1$$
$$- \frac{1}{2}\frac{g}{k^2}(m_2^2 - m_1^2) + \left(\frac{g}{k^2} m_1 - \frac{v_0}{k} \ln m_1\right)(m_2 - m_1)$$

If once again t_b is the time to burnout and $R = m_1/m_2$ is the mass ratio, show that this equation may be written

$$z_b = v_0 t_b - \tfrac{1}{2} g t_b^2 - \frac{m_2 v_0}{k} \ln R \qquad \text{(III-5)}$$

This is the altitude of the rocket at burnout.

Problem

III-4 What is the altitude of the sounding rocket of Problem III-1 at burnout?

The rocket will usually be designed to have vertical velocity at burnout, so that after burnout it will continue to climb, but now without power. From the law of conservation of energy show that the *additional* height h which the rocket will climb after burnout is given by the equation

$$h = \frac{v_b^2}{2g} \qquad \text{(III-6)}$$

Using Eqs. (III-4), (III-5), and (III-6) and some manipulation, show that the total height, $z_{\max} = z_b + h$, achieved by a sounding rocket can be written

$$z_{\max} = \frac{v_0^2 \ln^2 R}{2g} - v_0 t_b \left[\frac{\ln R}{1 - (1/R)} - 1\right] \qquad \text{(uniform gravitational field)}$$

(III-7)

* H. B. Dwight, *Tables of Integrals and Other Mathematical Data*, The Macmillan Company, New York, 1957, Formula 610.

This is the maximum altitude reached by a single-stage sounding rocket in a uniform gravitational field.

Problems

III-5 What will be the maximum altitude reached by the sounding rocket of Problem III-1?

III-6 What maximum altitude will be reached by a sounding rocket if the burning time is negligibly small? Show that all maximum heights actually obtained are less than this.

III-7 A rocket drops from rest at a height z_{max} in a uniform gravitational field. The rocket engines are fired in such a way as to break the fall, ignition being timed so that burnout is reached just as the rocket reaches the ground. The vertical velocity is zero as the rocket reaches the ground. This is called a *soft landing*. By physical arguments show that Eqs. (III-4), (III-5), and (III-7) can be made to describe a soft landing also.

Equation (III-7) is derived on the assumption that the rocket moves in a uniform gravitational field even after burnout. In many cases of practical interest this assumption can be relaxed for the following reason. In designing rockets for takeoff from the earth, rocket designers work for the maximum exhaust velocity and maximum burning rate. This is because of the term $(-gt_b)$ in Eq. (III-4). The longer it takes for a rocket to burn out, the more of its burnout velocity has been robbed by the negative acceleration due to gravity. As rocket engines improve, limitations of burning rate will be set more and more by the maximum accelerations which instruments and passengers can sustain. As a result of this design goal, most rockets will achieve burnout at fairly low altitudes. At these low altitudes the gravitational acceleration is near that at the surface of the earth, so that our assumption that the acceleration of gravity does not vary with height is approximately fulfilled. The height and velocity at burnout being known, the maximum height can be calculated by using conservation of energy *without* assuming that the gravitational acceleration is constant with further increase in height. If v_b is the velocity of the rocket at burnout, calculated using Eq. (III-4), r_b is the radius of the rocket at burnout with respect to the center of the earth, and r_{max} is the maximum radius achieved by the rocket measured with respect to the center of the earth, then Eqs. (5-12) and (5-18) can be used to obtain

$$\tfrac{1}{2}\cancel{m}v_b^2 - \frac{GM\cancel{m}}{r_b} = 0 - \frac{GM\cancel{m}}{r_{\max}} \quad \text{(central gravitational field)} \qquad \text{(III-8)}$$

where M is the mass of the earth and G is the gravitational constant.

The maximum altitude with respect to the surface of the earth achieved by the rocket can be found from Eq. (III-8) by subtracting the radius of the earth from r_{max}. Equation (III-8) neglects the component of velocity tangential to the surface of the earth which is given to the rocket by the rotation of the earth. The importance of this additional component of velocity will be seen after the study of satellite orbits in Chapter 6.

Problems

III-8 Calculate the maximum height achieved by the sounding rocket of Problem III-1, using Eqs. (III-4) and (III-8), and compare the maximum height calculated from Eq. (III-7).

III-9 A three-stage rocket has the following specifications.

	Stage 1	Stage 2	Stage 3
Total initial mass, in kilograms (including later stages)	100,000	10,000	1,000
Total mass at burnout, in kilograms (including later stages)	20,000	2,000	200
Exhaust velocity, in meters per second	2,500	2,500	2,500
Burning rate, in kilograms per second	2,000	200	20

The rocket is fired vertically. The second and third stages are each fired immediately after the burnout of the previous stage. This rocket is designed to escape the earth's gravitational field. Will it?

SUMMARY OF SYMBOLS

$k = -dm/dt$, burning rate of fuel—assumed constant in this analysis

$m =$ mass of the rocket at any instant

$m_1 =$ initial mass of the rocket at takeoff

$m_2 =$ final mass of rocket at burnout (when all the fuel is burned up)

$R = m_1/m_2$, the mass ratio: ratio of the initial mass to the final mass of the rocket

$r_b =$ radius of the rocket at burnout with respect to the center of the earth

$r_{max} =$ maximum radius achieved by the rocket measured with respect to the center of the earth

$t_b =$ burning time: time it takes after ignition for all the rocket fuel to be burned

v_0 = exhaust velocity of the burned gases from the tail of the rocket, measured with respect to the rocket

v_b = vertical velocity of the rocket with respect to the surface of the earth at burnout

z_b = height of the rocket above the ground at burnout

z_{max} = maximum height achieved by the rocket with respect to the ground

chapter 6

Motion of a particle in a plane

This chapter deals with the motion of a particle in two dimensions. In particular, the theory will be developed for the orbits of a particle moving in an inverse square law central field. This theory will be useful in the study of the motion of planets and satellites. Some of the concepts developed with this theory will be useful in analyzing the motion of electrons in the atom, even though classical mechanics does not apply to this system without modification.

6.1 MOTION IN A CIRCLE. Suppose we attach a stone to a string and whirl it around by hand in a circular path at constant speed. We feel the stone pulling outward on our hand away from the center of the circle. Therefore the hand must be exerting a force via the string on the stone *toward* the center of the circle. If the string exerts the only force on the stone, then the stone must be accelerating since $\mathbf{F} = m\mathbf{a}$. Yet the stone is moving with *constant speed* around its circular path. How can it be accelerated and still maintain a constant speed?

Look more closely at the stone in its orbit. What is the instantaneous velocity of the stone? Following Section 3.4, we define the instantaneous velocity of the particle at any instant as the velocity which the particle will assume if all forces are removed from it at that instant. If we cut the string, the stone will fly along a path which is a straight line tangent to the circle at the point where the stone was when the string was cut. Therefore the instantaneous velocity of the stone in its circular path must be tangent to the circle as shown in Fig. 6-1.

Now the force exerted on the stone by the string is pointed toward the center of the circle. Hence it is always perpendicular to the instantaneous velocity of the stone. Thus the force does not change the *magnitude* of the

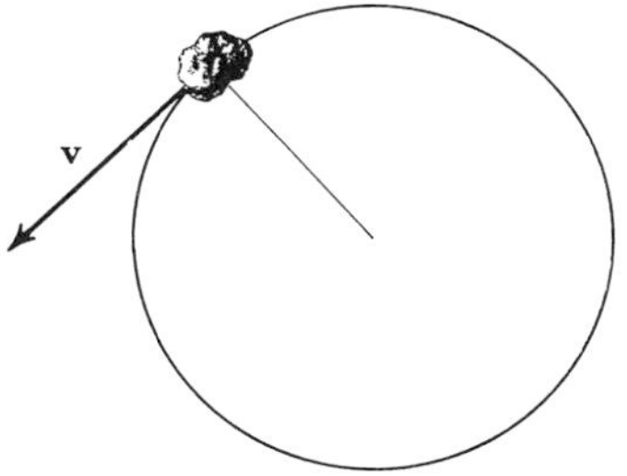

Fig. 6-1. Stone on a circular path.

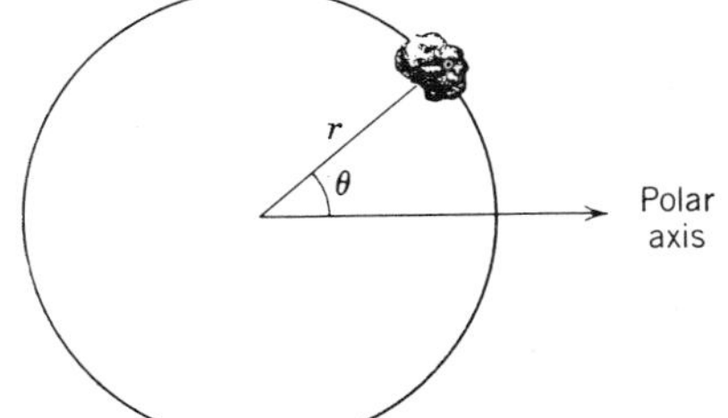

Fig. 6-2. Angle θ specifies the particle position on the circle of radius r.

velocity (the speed) but rather changes its direction. Before this can be discussed in detail, we must consider how motion in a circle is described mathematically.

One way to describe the position of a particle on a circle is to choose a fixed radius, called a *polar axis*, and measure the angle θ formed at the center of the circle by the polar axis and the radius connecting the particle to the center of the circle (Fig. 6-2). Then two quantities specify the position of the particle: the *radius* of the circle on which the particle lies (i.e., the *distance* from the origin to the particle) and the *angle* made with the polar axis by the radius to the particle.

The symbols r and θ may be used to determine the position of any point in the plane. They are called *polar coordinates*. The distance r is called the *radius vector* and the angle θ is called the *polar angle*.

6.2 RADIAN MEASURE. The angle θ may be measured in degrees. Another method more often used in science is *radian measure* (Fig. 6-3). With this method the angle θ is measured as follows: Measure the length of the radius r. Measure the length s of the arc intercepted by the angle θ. Then by definition

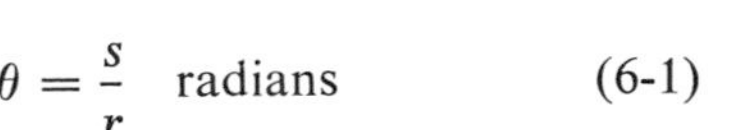

$$\theta = \frac{s}{r} \quad \text{radians} \qquad (6\text{-}1)$$

Fig. 6-3. Radian measure.

When $s = r$, then θ equals 1 radian (abbreviation rad). In other words, an arc of one radius length subtends an angle of 1 radian. Since the circumference of a circle is 2π times its radius, a complete revolution of the particle carried it through an angle of 2π radians. Thus 1 radian is equal to an angle of $360/2\pi \approx 57.3°$.

When moving along a circle through a radian angle θ, a particle moves a distance $s = r\theta$. If the radius is a constant (no radial motion of the particle), the tangential speed of the particle is given by

$$v_T = \frac{ds}{dt} = r\,\frac{d\theta}{dt} \tag{6-2}$$

where $d\theta/dt$ is the rate at which the angle θ is changing with time. Its units are radians per second. It is usually designated by the Greek letter ω (omega) and is called the *angular speed.*

$$\omega = \frac{d\theta}{dt} \qquad \text{definition} \tag{6-3}$$

so that

$$v_T = r\omega \tag{6-4}$$

We can go one step further. If the tangential speed v_T is not constant, the tangential acceleration is

$$a_T = \frac{dv_T}{dt} = r\,\frac{d\omega}{dt} = r\,\frac{d^2\theta}{dt^2} = r\alpha \tag{6-5}$$

where $\alpha = d\omega/dt$ is the *angular acceleration* and is measured in radians per second squared.

Question

6-1 An automobile supercharger is used to force more air into the cylinders. A given supercharger rotates at 16,000 rpm. How many radians per second is this? If the rotor is 5 cm in diameter, what is the tangential velocity of the edge of this rotor?

6.3 RADIAL ACCELERATION. Suppose that a stone on a string is swung in a circular path in such a way that its tangential speed is constant. Then the tangential acceleration a_T is zero. However, the *radial* acceleration is not zero. In order to keep the stone moving in a circle, a radial force must be applied. At any instant $\mathbf{F}_r = m\mathbf{a}_r$, where $\mathbf{F}_r$ and $\mathbf{a}_r$ represent the radial force on the stone and the radial acceleration of the stone respectively. What is the magnitude of this radial acceleration? Consider the tangential velocities at two instants separated by a time dt in Fig. 6-4. In this time the particle has moved through an angle $d\theta$ given by $d\theta = \omega\,dt$. If we draw the two velocity vectors from a common point as in the upper part of Fig. 6-4, it is clear that the angle between them is also $d\theta$. (Can you prove this from plane geometry?) Now by vector addition it is clear from the figure that

$$\mathbf{v}_2 = \mathbf{v}_1 + d\mathbf{v}$$

or

$$d\mathbf{v} = \mathbf{v}_2 - \mathbf{v}_1$$

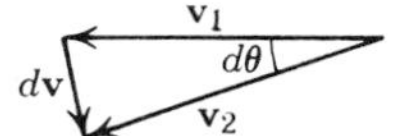

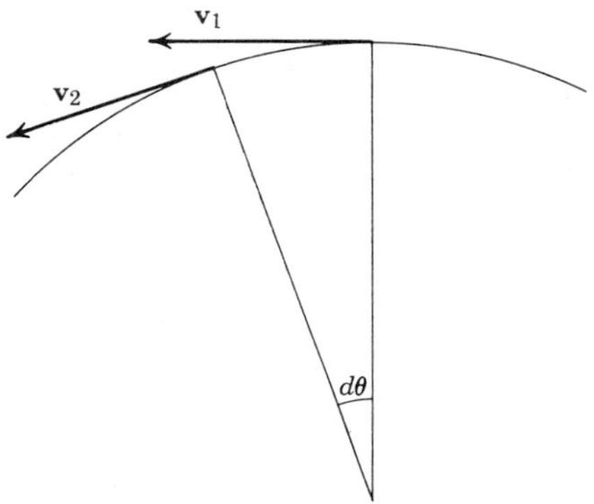

Fig. 6-4. Calculating radial acceleration.

Note that $d\mathbf{v}$ points toward the center of the circle. The magnitude of $d\mathbf{v}$ is very nearly equal to the length of arc connecting the end of $\mathbf{v}_1$ and $\mathbf{v}_2$ with their common point as center. Since dv is very small, this approximation is very good.

$$dv = v_T \, d\theta \tag{6-6}$$

where dv is the magnitude of $d\mathbf{v}$ and v_T is the magnitude of either of the tangential velocities $\mathbf{v}_1$ or $\mathbf{v}_2$. If we divide both sides of Eq. (6-6) by the time increment dt between the two velocities, the radial acceleration is seen to have the magnitude

$$a_r = \frac{dv}{dt} = v_T \frac{d\theta}{dt} = v_T \omega \tag{6-7}$$

The direction of $\mathbf{a}_r$ is toward the center of the circle. This radial acceleration toward the center of the circle is called the *centripetal acceleration.*

Question

6-2 Show that vector $d\mathbf{v}$ in Fig. 6-4 points toward the center of the circle.

The radial force on the stone necessary to hold it in a circular orbit has the magnitude

$$F_r = ma_r = mv_T\omega$$

Since $v_T = r\omega$, we can write F_r in terms of either v_T or ω alone

$$F_r = mr\omega^2 = \frac{m{v_T}^2}{r} \tag{6-8}$$

The direction of $\mathbf{F}_r$ is toward the center of the circle. This radial force toward the center of the circle is called the *centripetal force.*

Questions

6-3 Show that the right side of Eq. (6-8) has the units of force.

6-4 If the blades of an automobile supercharger rotate at 16,000 rpm, what is the force accelerating 1 g of blade toward the center if this gram is situated 5 cm from the axis of rotation?

6.4 CIRCULAR ORBITS IN A CENTRAL GRAVITATIONAL FIELD.

In order to keep a particle in a circular orbit it is necessary to apply a constant force, given by Eq. (6-8), toward the center of the circle.

$$F_r = \frac{m{v_T}^2}{r} = mr\omega^2 \tag{6-8}$$

This force can be supplied the force of gravity between a satellite and its mother planet or sun. From Eq. (5-4),

$$F_g = \frac{GMm}{r^2}$$

where m is the mass of the satellite, M is the mass of the mother planet, r is the distance from the satellite to the center of the planet or sun around which the satellite is orbiting.

In order that a circular orbit be achieved, the force of gravity must provide the exact amount of force necessary to keep the satellite in orbit: no more, no less. In equation form,

$$\frac{\not{m}{v_T}^2}{r} = \frac{GM\not{m}}{r^2}$$

or

$$r = \frac{GM}{{v_T}^2} \tag{6-9}$$

For a given tangential velocity this is the radius of a circular orbit. Notice that this radius does not depend on the mass of the satellite.

Circular orbits are not the only possible orbits in a central inverse square law gravitational field. The most general closed orbit is elliptical with one focus at the center of attraction. We shall study these and other general orbits in Section 6-10.

Questions

6-5 What assumption concerning the relative masses of the satellite and the mother planet is made in the analysis above?

6-6 What tangential velocity is necessary to establish a satellite in a circular orbit 400 km above the surface of the earth?

6-7 Demonstrate that the path of a particle acted on by any central force field will lie in a plane.

6-8 From Eq. (6-9) show that the square of the time required for one revolution about the circle is proportional to the cube of the radius of the circle. This is Kepler's Third Law of Planetary Motion applied to a circular orbit.

6-9 It is desired to establish a communication satellite in such an orbit that it will remain constantly vertically above a particular city on the equator of the earth. At what distance above the city will this orbit be? What is the tangential velocity of the satellite in this orbit? Why must the city be on the equator?

6-10 Show that the equation for the radius of a circular orbit of a charged particle in a central inverse square law electrostatic field is

$$r = \frac{-q_1 q_2}{4\pi\epsilon_0 m {v_T}^2} \tag{6-10}$$

6.5 ENERGY OF CIRCULAR ORBITS. Consider a satellite in a stable circular orbit. From Eq. (6-9),

$$v^2 = \frac{GM}{r}$$

so the kinetic energy of the satellite is

$$T = \tfrac{1}{2}mv^2 = \frac{1}{2}\frac{GMm}{r}$$

Now, from Eq. (5-12), the gravitational potential energy of the satellite is given by

$$V = -\frac{GMm}{r}$$

Therefore the *total* energy is

$$E = T + V = \frac{1}{2}\frac{GMm}{r} - \frac{GMm}{r} = -\frac{1}{2}\frac{GMm}{r}$$

or

$$E = -\frac{1}{2}\frac{GMm}{r} = -\tfrac{1}{2}mv^2 \tag{6-11}$$

Thus, for a circular orbit in a gravitational field, the total energy is equal to the *negative* of the kinetic energy.

It should be no surprise that the total energy of the satellite is negative. This is the result of choosing the zero of potential energy with the satellite at infinity. The satellite in a circular orbit is in effect "trapped" in a *potential well.* If more energy can be given to the satellite, it will be able to "climb farther out" of the potential well.

Question

6-11 Show that the velocity which a particle must have in order to escape to infinity from a distance r is equal to $\sqrt{2}$ times the velocity for a stable circular orbit at a distance r.

6.6 TORQUE AND ANGULAR MOMENTUM. A particle in a central gravitational or electrostatic field can move in a circular orbit, as has been shown. However, there are other possible orbits for a particle in these fields. In order to study these orbits it will be necessary to develop an understanding of two new mechanical concepts, namely *torque* and *angular momentum.*

Torque. If we wish to spin a wheel, we can do so by exerting a tangential force on the rim of the wheel. Experience shows that a force of a given magnitude is less effective in spinning the wheel if it is applied at some angle from the tangential direction or if it is applied nearer the axis of the wheel than the rim. A measure of the effectiveness of a force in causing rotation is given by the *torque.* Since the effectiveness of a force in causing rotation depends on the direction of this force, the torque must be a vector. Torque will also depend on the distance from the axis of the wheel at which the force is applied and, of course, on the magnitude of the force. In Chapter 8 we shall deal with rotating wheels. For the present we shall define the torque on a particle. Suppose that the position of a particle with respect to the origin O of a coordinate system is indicated by the vector $\mathbf{r}$ and that at some particular instant the resultant force on the particle is given by the vector $\mathbf{F}$. The *torque* about O which this force exerts on the particle at this instant is defined by the vector cross product

$$\text{Torque} = \mathbf{n} = \mathbf{r} \times \mathbf{F} \tag{6-12}$$

Torque is given the symbol $\mathbf{n}$ or $\mathbf{N}$. As the equation shows, torque is a vector which is perpendicular to both $\mathbf{r}$ and $\mathbf{F}$. The magnitude of $\mathbf{n}$ is given by the expression

$$|\mathbf{n}| = |\mathbf{r}|\,|\mathbf{F}| \sin \theta \tag{6-13}$$

where θ is the angle between the positive directions of the vectors $\mathbf{r}$ and $\mathbf{F}$.

The units of torque are newton-meters. Torque is sometimes called the *moment of force.*

Questions

6-12 A wrench is used to tighten a nut. A force of 600 N is applied perpendicular to the handle of the wrench a distance of $\frac{1}{3}$ m from the axis of the nut. What torque does this force exert about the axis of the nut? What is the direction of this torque? How can this torque be increased without increasing the magnitude of the force used?

6-13 Show that the magnitude of the torque of a force **F** about O is equal to the magnitude of **F** times the perpendicular distance between O and the straight line along which **F** lies.

6-14 Torque has the units of newton-meters. So does energy. How may the two be distinguished?

6-15 Show that the torque of a force **F** about O will be equal to zero if *any one* of the following conditions obtains.

(*a*) $\mathbf{F} = 0$
or (*b*) the particle is at point O
or (*c*) **F** is parallel (or antiparallel) to **r**.

Angular momentum. If **r** is the position vector of a particle with respect to the origin O of a coordinate system and if $\mathbf{p} = m\mathbf{v}$ is the momentum vector of the particle in the same coordinate system, the *angular momentum* of the particle about O is defined as

$$\text{Angular momentum} = \mathbf{l} = \mathbf{r} \times \mathbf{p} \qquad \text{definition} \tag{6-14}$$

Angular momentum is given the symbol **l** or **L**. As the equation shows, angular momentum is a vector which is perpendicular to both **r** and **p**. The magnitude of **l** is given by the expression

$$|\mathbf{l}| = |\mathbf{r}|\,|\mathbf{p}| \sin \phi \tag{6-15}$$

where ϕ is the angle between the positive directions of the vectors **r** and **p**. The units of angular momentum are kilogram-meters squared per second. Angular momentum is sometimes called the *moment of momentum.*

Questions

6-16 A particle of mass m moves with a vector velocity **v** which is constant in magnitude and direction. A point O lies a perpendicular distance b from the path of the particle. Show that the angular momentum of the particle about O is a constant.

6-17 Show that the magnitude of the angular momentum about O of a particle with momentum **p** is equal to the magnitude of **p** times the perpendicular distance between O and the straight line along which **p** lies.

6-18 Show that the angular momentum of a particle about a point O will be equal to zero if *any one* of the following conditions obtains.

(*a*) $\mathbf{p} = 0$

or (*b*) the particle is at point O

or (*c*) $\mathbf{p}$ is parallel (or antiparallel) to $\mathbf{r}$.

6.7 THE TORQUE LAW. CONSERVATION OF ANGULAR MOMENTUM. Let us see what the law of motion has to say about the relation between the torque on a particle and its angular momentum. If the coordinate system we have chosen in which to measure $\mathbf{n}$ and $\mathbf{l}$ is an inertial coordinate system, the law of motion of the particle is

$$\mathbf{F} = m\ddot{\mathbf{r}} = \dot{\mathbf{p}}$$

If we cross $\mathbf{r}$, the position vector of the particle, into both sides of this equation, we have

$$\mathbf{r} \times \mathbf{F} = \mathbf{r} \times \dot{\mathbf{p}} \tag{6-16}$$

The left side of this equation is simply the torque $\mathbf{n}$ on the particle. What is the right side of the equation? Forget this problem for a minute and consider the following time derivative (see Eq. 4-42).

$$\begin{aligned}\frac{d}{dt}(\mathbf{r} \times \mathbf{p}) &= \dot{\mathbf{r}} \times \mathbf{p} + \mathbf{r} \times \dot{\mathbf{p}} \\ &= \dot{\mathbf{r}} \times m\dot{\mathbf{r}} + \mathbf{r} \times \dot{\mathbf{p}}\end{aligned}$$

The first term on the right side of the last equation must be zero because $\dot{\mathbf{r}}$ is parallel to itself; so $\dot{\mathbf{r}} \times m\dot{\mathbf{r}} = 0$ from the theory of cross products. Therefore

$$\frac{d}{dt}(\mathbf{r} \times \mathbf{p}) = \mathbf{r} \times \dot{\mathbf{p}}$$

Substituting this into Eq. (6-16), we have

$$\mathbf{r} \times \mathbf{F} = \mathbf{n} = \frac{d}{dt}(\mathbf{r} \times \mathbf{p})$$

But $\mathbf{r} \times \mathbf{p}$ is the angular momentum $\mathbf{l}$ of the particle, so the equation becomes

$$\mathbf{n} = \frac{d\mathbf{l}}{dt}$$

or

$$\mathbf{n} = \dot{\mathbf{l}} \tag{6-17}$$

This equation says that the torque on a particle is equal to the rate of change of its angular momentum. We shall call this the *torque law* for a particle.

If for any reason the torque on the particle is equal to zero, $\mathbf{l} = 0$ or $\mathbf{l}$ is a constant vector. In other words, *if the torque on a particle about the origin of any inertial coordinate system is equal to zero, then the angular momentum remains constant in that coordinate system.* This statement is called the *law of conservation of angular momentum* for a particle.

6.8 ANGULAR MOMENTUM IN A CENTRAL FORCE FIELD. Consider a particle moving under the influence of a force which acts toward the origin of some inertial coordinate system. Such a force could be gravitational or electrical or a force of contact (such as a string or spring attaching the particle to the origin). Since $\mathbf{F}$ is antiparallel to $\mathbf{r}$, the torque exerted on the particle by this force is equal to zero because $\mathbf{n} = \mathbf{r} \times \mathbf{F}$. If the torque on the particle is zero, its angular momentum must be conserved. This means that, *when the only force on a particle is due to a central force field, the angular momentum of the particle about the source of that field is a constant.*

Questions

6-19 Show that this result holds also for a particle under the influence of a force which repels it from the origin of an inertial reference system.

6-20 Show that angular momentum is *not* necessarily conserved about an origin other than the source of the central field.

6.9 THE CONIC SECTIONS. Using the laws of conservation of momentum and conservation of energy, we shall show in the next section that a particle moving in an attractive inverse square law central force field will move along a path that can be described as a conic section. That is to say, this path will be one of the following: a circle, an ellipse, a parabola, or a hyperbola. Let us review briefly the definition of a conic section and the form of its equation in polar coordinates.

Definition.* A conic section is the locus of a point which moves in a plane so that the numerical value of the ratio of its distance from a fixed point to its distance from a fixed line is a constant.

The fixed point is called a *focus*. The fixed line is called the *directrix*. The constant value of the ratio is called the *eccentricity* and is given the symbol e. Figure 6-5 illustrates this definition. Point O is at the focus. The straight line which passes through the points labeled S and T is the directrix. The straight line which passes through the points T and O

* Taken from *First Year of College Mathematics* by Henry J. Miles, John Wiley and Sons, Inc., New York, 1941.

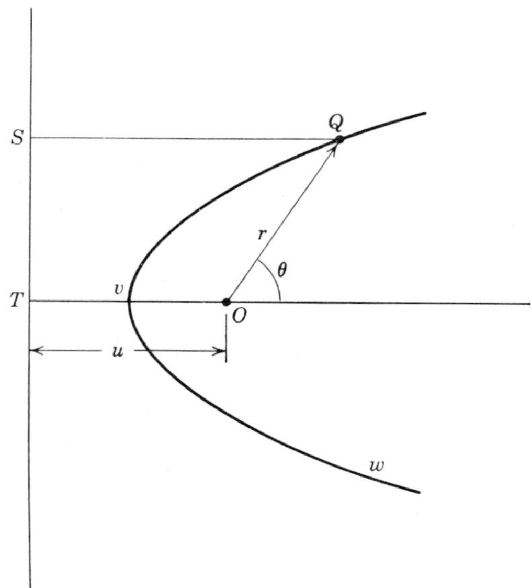

Fig. 6-5. Definition of a conic section.

perpendicular to the directrix is called the *major axis* of the conic section. If $\overline{OQ}$ is the distance between the focus and a point on the curve Qvw and if $\overline{QS}$ is the perpendicular distance between the directrix and the same point Q, then every point Q on the curve will satisfy the relation $\overline{OQ}/\overline{QS} = e$, where e, the eccentricity, is a constant.

If the value of e is greater than one, the curve is a hyperbola.
If the value of e is equal to one, the curve is a parabola.
If the value of e is between zero and one, the curve is an ellipse.
If the value of e is equal to zero, the curve is a circle.

Question

6-21 What is the distance between the focus and the directrix when the curve is a circle?

If we take the origin of a polar coordinate system at the focus, with the polar axis pointing along the major axis and away from the directrix, the equation of a conic section in polar coordinates is given by the following expression.

$$r = \frac{ue}{1 - e\cos\theta} \tag{6-18}$$

where u is the perpendicular distance between the focus and the directrix.

Questions

6-22 Show how Eq. (6-18) is simplified for a circular orbit in the light of your answer to the last question.

6-23 Show that the distance from the central point of an ellipse to the farthest point of the ellipse is given by $ue/(1 - e^2)$. This is called the *semimajor axis* of the ellipse.

6-24 For an ellipse show that

$$e = \frac{r_{max} - r_{min}}{r_{max} + r_{min}} \tag{6-19}$$

where r_{max} is the distance from a focus to the farthest point on the ellipse and r_{min} is the distance from the focus to the nearest point on the ellipse.

6.10 GENERAL SATELLITE ORBITS. Consider a particle moving with respect to an inertial polar coordinate system. The position of the particle in the plane is given by polar coordinates r and θ (Fig. 6-6). In this general case the velocity vector **v** of particle one need not be tangent to the circle of radius r. The velocity vector may be resolved into radial and tangential components. Using Eq. (6-4) and the Pythagorean theorem, we may write

$$v^2 = \dot{r}^2 + r^2\dot{\theta}^2 \tag{6-20}$$

Suppose that the particle is attracted to the origin of the coordinate system by a central gravitational force. We shall assume that the body at the origin which causes this attraction has very much more mass than the particle so that the body at the origin can be considered to be at rest.

Question

6-25 Show that, if the body at the origin does not have much more mass than the particle, the coordinate system determined by the central

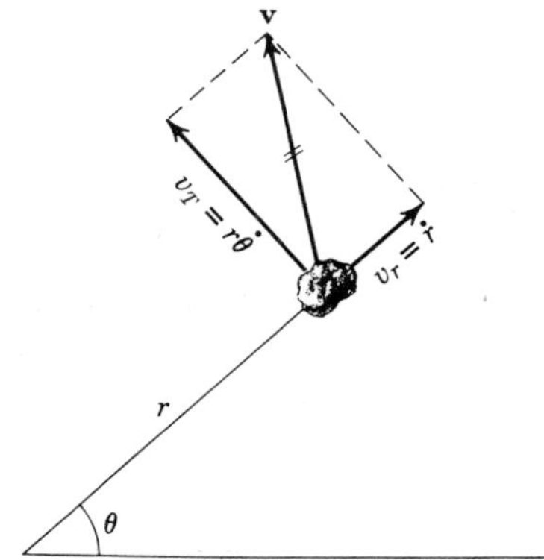

Fig. 6-6. Motion of a particle in a plane.

body is not inertial. What difficulties will this cause in the analysis of the motion of the particle?

If no external forces act on the two particles of this system, then the angular momentum of the system is conserved. Particle one is the only part of the system which can have angular momentum because it is the only part which is moving. The magnitude of the angular momentum of particle one about the origin is given by the expression

$$l = mr^2\dot{\theta} \tag{6-21}$$

where l is a constant.

If there are no frictional or dissipative forces acting on the system the total energy is conserved. The kinetic energy of the particle is given by $T = \frac{1}{2}mv^2 = \frac{1}{2}m(\dot{r}^2 + r^2\dot{\theta}^2)$. The potential energy is given by Eq. (5-12): $V = -GMm/r$, where m is the mass of the particle, M is the mass of the body at the origin, and G is the gravitational constant. The total energy of the particle is given by

$$E = T + V = \tfrac{1}{2}m(\dot{r}^2 + r^2\dot{\theta}^2) - \frac{GMm}{r} \tag{6-22}$$

where E is a constant.

Using Eqs. (6-21) and (6-22), we shall now show that particle one moves along a path which is a conic section.

Solve Eq. (6-21) for $\dot{\theta}$.

$$\dot{\theta} = \frac{l}{mr^2} = \frac{d\theta}{dt} \tag{6-23}$$

Substitute this into Eq. (6-22).

$$E = \tfrac{1}{2}m\left[\dot{r}^2 + r^2\left(\frac{l}{mr^2}\right)^2\right] - \frac{GMm}{r}$$

Solve this equation for $\dot{r} = dr/dt$.

$$\frac{dr}{dt} = \sqrt{\frac{2E}{m} + \frac{2GM}{r} - \frac{l^2}{m^2r^2}} \tag{6-24}$$

Equations (6-23) and (6-24) tell us how r and θ change in a small increment of time dt. In a time dt, r will change by an amount dr and θ will change by an amount $d\theta$. In any given time interval dt the relation between the changes dr and $d\theta$ can be calculated from Eqs. (6-23) and (6-24).

$$dt = \frac{dr}{\sqrt{2E/m + 2GM/r - l^2/m^2r^2}} = \frac{mr^2\,d\theta}{l}$$

or, after some manipulation,

$$d\theta = \frac{l\,dr}{r\sqrt{2mEr^2 + 2GMm^2r - l^2}} \tag{6-25}$$

We can find a relation between θ and r by integrating this equation.

$$\int_{\theta_1}^{\theta} d\theta = \int_{r_1}^{r} \frac{l\,dr}{r\sqrt{2mEr^2 + 2GMm^2r - l^2}}$$

where r_1 and θ_1 are the values of r and θ at some initial time. The left side of this equation is easily integrated to give $\theta - \theta_1$. The right side is an integral whose form we have not encountered before. It is necessary to consult a table of integrals.* The solution gives

$$\theta - \theta_1 = \arcsin \frac{GMm^2r - l^2}{r(G^2M^2m^4 + 2mEl^2)^{1/2}}\Bigg|_{r_1}^{r}$$

The symbol arcsin A means "the angle whose sine is A."

Questions

6-26 Carry out the steps between the last two equations, using a table of integrals.

6-27 Show that sin (arcsin A) = A.

Evaluating the right side of the last equation at the limits,

$$\theta - \theta_1 = \arcsin \frac{GMm^2r - l^2}{r(G^2M^2m^4 + 2mEl^2)^{1/2}} - \arcsin \frac{GMm^2r_1 - l^2}{r_1(G^2M^2m^4 + 2mEl^2)^{1/2}} \tag{6-26}$$

Equation (6-26) gives the relation between θ and r for the orbit of a particle in a central gravitational field once the initial position and velocity of the particle are known. Given these initial conditions, θ_1 on the left of Eq. (6-26) and the second arcsine term on the right of this equation both remain constant as r and θ vary. In choosing the initial conditions the initial angle θ_1 is arbitrary, since it merely determines the direction of the polar axis in the plane of the orbit. Equation (6-18) for the conic section was derived for the case in which the polar axis of the coordinate system lies along the axis of the conic section. Equation (6-26) will reduce to the same form if we *choose the initial angle θ_1 to be equal to the second arcsine term on the right of Eq. (6-26) minus $\pi/2$.* With this

* For example, *Tables of Integrals and Other Mathematical Data* by Herbert B. Dwight, The Macmillan Company, New York, 1957, Formula 380.111.

substitution into Eq. (6-26) the two constant arcsine terms will cancel to give

$$\theta - \left(-\frac{\pi}{2}\right) = \arcsin \frac{GMm^2r - l^2}{r(G^2M^2m^4 + 2mEl^2)^{1/2}}$$

Take the sine of both sides of this equation.

$$\sin\left(\theta + \frac{\pi}{2}\right) = \cos\theta = \frac{GMm^2r - l^2}{r(G^2M^2m^4 + 2mEl^2)^{1/2}}$$

We can now multiply both sides of this equation by the denominator of the right side and solve for r.

$$l^2 = r[GMm^2 - (G^2M^2m^4 + 2mEl^2)^{1/2}\cos\theta]$$

or

$$r = \frac{l^2/GMm^2}{1 - (1 + 2l^2E/G^2M^2m^3)^{1/2}\cos\theta} \tag{6-27}$$

Comparing this to Eq. (6-18), we can see that this is the equation of a conic section in which

$$e = \left(1 + \frac{2l^2E}{G^2M^2m^3}\right)^{1/2} \tag{6-28}$$

and

$$ue = \frac{l^2}{GMm^2} \tag{6-29}$$

It is possible to tell in any individual case whether the path of particle one is a hyperbola or an ellipse, etc., by calculating e and by using the criteria given in Sec. 6.9.

Questions

6-28 From Eq. (6-28) show that if the total energy E is positive the orbit is a hyperbola; if E is zero the orbit is a parabola; and if E is negative the orbit is an ellipse. Interpret these results in terms of the concept of a "potential well" introduced in Sec. 6.5. Under what circumstances is the orbit a circle?

6-29 A vehicle is launched into an orbit around the sun. As it leaves the orbit of the earth (radius 149.5×10^6 km), it has a velocity of 40 km/sec in a direction which makes an angle of 60° with the radius vector from the sun to the position of the vehicle. Calculate the angle θ_1 in Eq. (6-26) under the assumptions later derived for this angle. Draw a diagram to show what physical meaning this angle has. Will the path of the vehicle be an ellipse, a parabola, or a hyperbola? Neglect effects due to the presence of the earth or other planets.

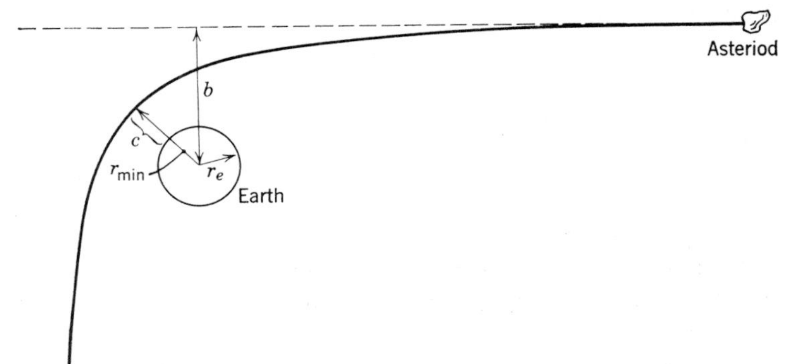

Fig. 6-7.

The following example illustrates how the equations in this section can be used to solve astronomical problems.

Example. An asteroid is observed to be approaching the earth. When first seen, it is a distance of 1,000,000 km and is traveling with a velocity of 10 km/sec in a direction which, if extended, would pass a perpendicular distance of 20,000 km from the center of the earth. What will be the minimum distance between the asteroid and the earth? Will the asteroid return toward the earth again? Neglect the influence of the sun and moon on the path of the asteroid, and assume that the center of the earth constitutes the origin of an inertial coordinate system.

Solution. The motion of the asteroid is shown in Fig. 6-7, not drawn to scale. We wish to find the distance c, which can be calculated if we know r_{min} and r_e, the radius of the earth. The kinetic energy of the asteroid is $\frac{1}{2}mv_1^2$, where $v_1 = 10^4$ m/sec. The potential energy of the asteroid is $-GMm/r_1$, where $r_1 = 10^9$ m and M is the mass of the earth. The total energy is a constant. That is to say, both r and v will change, but always in such a way as to satisfy the equation

$$E = \tfrac{1}{2}mv_1^2 - \frac{GMm}{r_1} = \tfrac{1}{2}mv^2 - \frac{GMm}{r}$$

The angular momentum is also a constant. Its initial value is given by

$$l = m\,|\mathbf{r}_1 \times \mathbf{v}_1| = mbv_1$$

where b is 2×10^7 m. Substituting these expressions into the expression for the eccentricity e, we have

$$e = \left[1 + \frac{2m^2b^2v_1^2(\frac{1}{2}mv_1^2 - GMm/r_1)}{G^2M^2m^3}\right]^{1/2}$$

$$= \left[1 + \frac{b^2v_1^2}{GM}\left(\frac{v_1^2}{GM} - \frac{2}{r_1}\right)\right]^{1/2}$$

Substituting the values

$$\begin{aligned} b &= 2 \times 10^7 \text{ m} \\ v_1 &= 10^4 \text{ m/sec} \\ r_1 &= 10^9 \text{ m} \\ G &= 6.67 \times 10^{-11} \text{ N-m}^2/\text{kg}^2 \\ M &= 5.98 \times 10^{24} \text{ kg} \end{aligned}$$

we obtain $e \cong (1 + 25)^{1/2} = 5.1$, so the path of the particle is a hyperbola and it will never return once it passes the earth. Of course, if the gravitational fields of the sun and moon were taken into account, this result might be different.

Now a look at Eq. (6-18) shows that r has its minimum value when $\theta = \pi$. In this case,

$$r_{\min} = \frac{l^2/GMm^2}{1 + e} = \frac{b^2 v_1{}^2}{GM(1 + e)}$$

Substituting values from above, we find that

$$r_{\min} \cong 16.4 \times 10^6 \text{ m}$$

Since the radius of the earth is 6.37×10^6 m, this means that the asteroid will pass at a minimum distance of about 10,000 km from the surface of the earth.

Questions

6-30 Show that the equation of the path of a charged particle in a central inverse square law electrostatic field can be found by replacing GM in Eqs. (6-22) and (6-27) by $-(1/4\pi\epsilon_0)(q_1 q_2/m)$. If the two charges are of the same sign, show that only hyperbolic orbits are possible.

6-31 Show that a particle initially at a very great distance from the earth with a small initial velocity will describe a parabolic path as it falls toward the earth.

6-32 From Eq. (6-28) for the eccentricity, show that the energy of an orbit is given by the expression

$$E = \frac{G^2 M^2 m^3}{2l^2}(e^2 - 1) = \frac{GMm}{2ue}(e^2 - 1) \tag{6-30}$$

For circular orbits show that this agrees with Eq. (6-11).

6-33 Show that the velocity of a particle at any point in its orbit is given by the equation

$$v^2 = GM\left[\frac{1}{ue}(e^2 - 1) + \frac{2}{r}\right] \tag{6-31}$$

6.11 THE ELLIPTIC ORBIT. The elliptic orbit is of particular interest to man because the earth and the planets move in elliptic orbits about the sun. This interest has been stimulated by man's increasing ability to launch his packages and himself into elliptic orbits about celestial bodies. Various astronomical terms are used to describe points on an elliptic orbit. The point on an elliptic orbit which is nearest the center of attraction is called the *lower apsis* (Fig. 6-8). The point on the orbit which is farthest from the center of attraction is called the *higher apsis*. In the particular case in which the orbit is about the sun, these two points are called the *perihelion* and the *aphelion* respectively (Greek: *Helios* means sun). In the particular case in which the orbit is about the earth, these two points are called the *perigee* and *apogee* respectively. The plural of apsis is *apsides* (rhymes with "rhapsodies").

Question

6-34 Show that at the apsides of an elliptic orbit the speed of the satellite is given by the equation

$$v^2 = \frac{GM}{ue}(e \pm 1)^2 \tag{6-32}$$

The discovery by Johannes Kepler (1571–1630) that planetary orbits are ellipses was one of the turning points of modern science. Kepler is remembered for his three laws of planetary motion:

I. Every planet moves in an elliptical path, with the sun at one focus.

II. An imaginary line drawn from a planet to the sun sweeps over equal areas in equal times.

III. The squares of the periods of the different planets about the sun are proportional to the cubes of the respective semimajor axes of their orbits.

In this statement, the third law has been refined from Kepler's original version which spoke of the "mean distances" of the planets from the sun instead of the semimajor axes of their orbits.

Kepler did not recognize the central importance of these three laws among all his other results. In addition, he did not understand the function

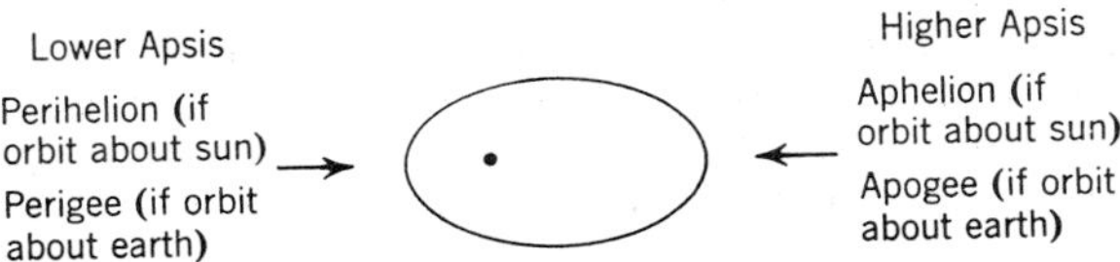

Fig. 6-8. Apsides of an elliptic orbit.

of gravity in determining the planetary orbits. For this reason the three laws remained three separate and unrelated empirical results. It was Newton who recognized the importance of these three laws, extracted them from Kepler's writings, and showed that they all could be derived from the laws of motion and the inverse square law of gravitational force, as we are doing in this chapter.*

We have already demonstrated Kepler's first law.

Question

6-35 Using Eq. (6-23), show that the incremental area dA swept out in an incremental time dt by the radius vector to a satellite from the center of attraction is a constant for elliptic, parabolic, and hyperbolic orbits. Generalize this result to include larger than incremental time intervals. Show that this result is true for *any* central force field, not only the inverse square field.

Now let us consider how much time it takes a satellite to move from one point to another on its path. This can be found by integrating the time- and θ-dependent parts of Eq. (6-23), using Eq. (6-18).

$$dt = \frac{mr^2\, d\theta}{l} = \frac{mu^2e^2\, d\theta}{l(1 - e\cos\theta)^2}$$

$$\int_{t_1}^{t} dt = t - t_1 = \frac{mu^2e^2}{l}\int_{\theta_1}^{\theta} \frac{d\theta}{(1 - e\cos\theta)^2}$$

Once again it is necessary to use a table of integrals to evaluate the right side.† We shall solve the equation for elliptic orbits ($e < 1$). The answer is

$$t - t_1 = \frac{mu^2e^2}{l}\left[\frac{+e\sin\theta}{(1 - e^2)(1 - e\cos\theta)} + \frac{1}{1 - e^2}\frac{2}{\sqrt{1 - e^2}}\arctan\frac{(1 + e)\tan(\theta/2)}{\sqrt{1 - e^2}}\right]_{\theta_1}^{\theta} \qquad (6\text{-}33)$$

* See Arthur Koestler, *The Watershed*, Anchor Books, Doubleday and Co., Inc., Garden City, N.Y., 1960, p. 223: "Not the least achievement of Newton was to spot the three Laws in Kepler's writings, hidden away as they were, like forget-me-nots in a tropical flower bed." This excellent little paper-back biography of Kepler presents a remarkable vignette of an important step in the birth of modern science and several examples of the chaotic way in which scientific discoveries are in fact made as opposed to the logical way they are usually presented in articles, and in textbooks such as this one.

† Dwight, *op. cit.*, Formulas 446.03 and 446.00.

where t_1 and θ_1 are initial values, while t and θ are later values. The symbol arctan B means "the angle whose tangent is B."

Two cases of time of flight are of particular interest. One is the time required for a complete revolution about the orbit. This time is called the period and is given the symbol T. If we set $t_1 = 0$, $\theta_1 = 0$, and $\theta = \pi$, Eq. (6-33) will give the time for half a period.

$$t = \frac{T}{2} = \frac{mu^2e^2}{l} \frac{2}{(1 - e^2)^{3/2}} \frac{\pi}{2}$$

We can eliminate either u or l from this equation by using Eq. (6-29).

$$ue = \frac{l^2}{GMm^2} \tag{6-29}$$

If we eliminate u, the equation for the period becomes

$$T = \frac{2\pi}{G^2M^2} \frac{l^3}{m^3} \frac{1}{(1 - e^2)^{3/2}} \tag{6-34}$$

If we eliminate l, the equation for the period becomes

$$T = \frac{2\pi}{\sqrt{GM}} \left(\frac{ue}{1 - e^2}\right)^{3/2} \tag{6-35}$$

From Question 6-23 we know that $ue/(1 - e^2)$ is the length of the semi-major axis of the ellipse. If both sides of this equation are squared, the result is a mathematical statement of Kepler's Third Law.

Questions

6-36 In determining the period of a satellite in an elliptic orbit, why cannot we determine the length of half a period of a satellite orbit by setting $t_1 = 0$, $\theta_1 = -\pi/2$, and $\theta = +\pi/2$ in Eq. (6-33)?

6-37 Show that the period of an elliptic orbit can be written in the form

$$T = \frac{2\pi GM}{(-2E/m)^{3/2}} \tag{6-36}$$

This form is sometimes more convenient for computation.

Another case of particular interest is the time of flight of a ballistic rocket from one point to another point on the surface of the earth. A ballistic rocket is one that reaches burnout shortly after takeoff, so that all but a small part of its flight is unpowered, as if it had been shot from a cannon. Air resistance is neglected in these calculations. This path of

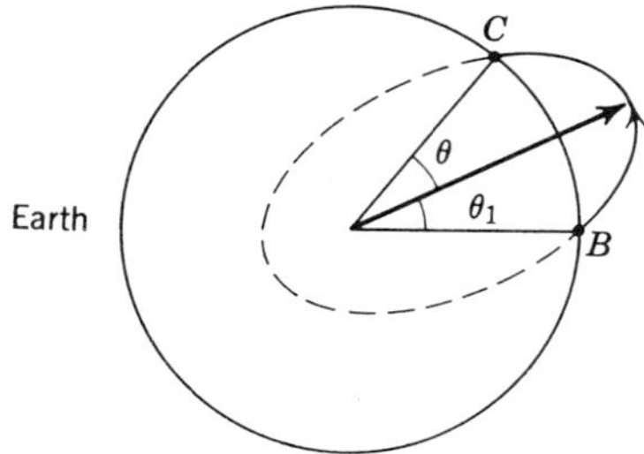

Fig. 6-9. Path of a ballistic rocket.

the ballistic rocket will be that portion of an ellipse which lies above the surface of the earth, as from B to C in Fig. 6-9. From the symmetry of the path it can be seen that for an earth of spherical symmetry the initial and final polar angles satisfy the equation $\theta_1 = -\theta$. Putting this condition into Eq. (6-33), the time of flight will be given by the expression

$$t = A\left[\frac{+e\sin\theta}{(1-e^2)(1-e\cos\theta)} + \frac{2}{(1-e^2)^{3/2}}\arctan\left\{\frac{(1+e)\tan(\theta/2)}{\sqrt{1-e^2}}\right\}\right] \tag{6-37}$$

where

$$A = \frac{2l^3}{G^2M^2m^3} = \frac{2(ue)^{3/2}}{\sqrt{GM}}$$

The best way to use this equation is to obtain first an equation for the orbit from the initial conditions or other data. In order to find the angle θ between the major axis of the ellipse and the point of impact, it may be necessary to solve Eq. (6-18) for $\cos\theta$ after setting r equal to the radius of the earth. Then the values of θ, e, and ue can be substituted into Eq. (6-37).

These equations hold only for an inertial coordinate system which is *not* rotating with the earth. A coordinate system fixed in the earth is not inertial, so satellites do not appear to move in ellipses when seen from the surface of the earth. In solving problems which deal with ballistic rockets or satellites it may be necessary to transform back and forth between an inertial coordinate system and a rotating coordinate system fixed in the earth. The following example will show how this may be accomplished.

Example. A ballistic rocket is launched at the equator in an easterly direction, at an angle of 60° from the horizontal. Its initial speed is 6 km/sec measured with respect to the (rotating) earth. What will be the distance along the earth from the point of launch to the point of impact?

Solution. The rotating earth does not constitute an inertial frame. Our first job will be to find the velocity of the rocket in an inertial frame. With respect to the earth, the initial velocity is $V_1 = 6$ km/sec, the horizontal component of this velocity is $V_h = V_1 \cos 60° = 6$ km/sec $\times \frac{1}{2}$ $= 3$ km/sec. The vertical component is $V_v = V_1 \sin 60° = 6$ km/sec $\times$ $0.866 = 5.196$ km/sec. Now the earth rotates once in approximately 24 hours or 86,400 sec. Hence its angular velocity ω is $2\pi/86{,}400$ radians/sec. Since the radius of the earth is approximately $r_e = 6371$ km, the tangential velocity of a point on the equator is $V_t = r_e\omega = 6371 \times 2\pi/86{,}400$ km/sec $= 0.4634$ km/sec. Since the earth rotates toward the east, the total horizontal velocity component v_T of the ballistic rocket with respect to an inertial frame will be the *sum* of V_h and V_t.

$$v_T = V_h + V_t = 3.00 + 0.4634 = 3.4634 \text{ km/sec}$$

The vertical component of the velocity in the inertial frame is the same as in the frame rotating with respect to the earth: $v_v = V_v = 5.196$ km/sec. The total velocity v in the inertial frame is

$$v = \sqrt{v_v^2 + v_T^2} = \sqrt{38.995} \text{ km/sec} = 6.245 \text{ km/sec}$$

Now we calculate the angular momentum l and the total energy E of the rocket. The magnitude of the angular momentum is equal to the mass m of the rocket times the radius of the earth times the tangential component of the velocity of the rocket. Let us use meters instead of kilometers.

$$\begin{aligned} l = mr_e v_T &= m \times 6.371 \times 10^6 \text{ m} \times 3.4634 \times 10^3 \text{ m/sec} \\ &= 2.2065 \times 10^{10} \text{ m}^2/\text{sec} \times m \end{aligned}$$

Now the total energy of the rocket is given by

$$E = m\left[\tfrac{1}{2}v^2 - \frac{GM}{r_e}\right]$$

where v is the total velocity of the rocket in the inertial frame computed earlier, M is the mass of the earth and is equal to 5.983×10^{24} kg, G is the gravitational constant and is equal to 6.67×10^{-11} N-m^2/kg^2. Using these values yields energy equal to

$$E = -4.3185 \times 10^7 \text{ m}^2/\text{sec}^2 \times m$$

Using these numerical values for angular momentum and total energy, we can calculate the eccentricity of the orbit from Eq. (6-28).

$$e = \left[1 + \frac{2l^2E}{G^2M^2m^3}\right]^{1/2}$$

The mass m of the rocket will cancel in this expression. The result is

$$e = (0.7343)^{1/2} = 0.8571$$

Also, from Eq. (6-29),

$$ue = \frac{l^2}{GMm^2} = 1.220 \times 10^6 \text{ m}$$

Now the equation of the orbit of the ballistic rocket above the earth is given by

$$r = \frac{ue}{1 - e \cos \theta}$$

By setting the radius equal to the radius of the earth, we can find the angle θ in Fig. 6-9 which is the half-angle subtended at the origin of the inertial reference frame between the point of launch and the point of impact. Solving this equation for $\cos \theta$ and substituting values, we have

$$\cos \theta = \left[\frac{r_e - ue}{er_e}\right] = 0.94335$$

or

$$\theta = 19^\circ\ 23'$$

and

$$2\theta = 38^\circ\ 46' = 0.6777 \text{ radian}$$

The great circle distance s covered by the rocket is found from the equation

$$2\theta = \frac{s}{r_e}$$

from which

$$s = 2\theta r_e = 4.317 \times 10^6 \text{ m}$$

This is equal to the distance around the earth covered by the rocket with respect to the inertial frame. Since the earth is rotating, it will move under the rocket during the flight. We can calculate the distance which the surface of the earth moves at the equator during the flight if we know the time the flight takes. This time can be found from Eq. (6-37), using the following values from the calculations above,

$$\begin{aligned}
(ue)^{3/2} &= 1.345 \times 10^9 \text{ m}^{3/2} \\
(GM)^{1/2} &= 1.997 \times 10^7 \text{ m}^{3/2}/\text{sec} \\
\sin \theta &= 0.33189 \\
\tan (\theta/2) &= 0.17093 \\
(1 - e^2) &= 0.2657 \\
(1 - e \cos \theta) &= 0.1915
\end{aligned}$$

From these values the time of flight is found to be

$$t = 781 \text{ sec or about 13 min}$$

During the time the rocket is traveling eastward in its orbit the earth is also rotating eastward, so that the point of impact for the rotating system will be west of the point of impact for the inertial system. The distance S' which the surface of the earth moves at the equator in a time t is given by $S' = V_t t$, where V_t is the tangential velocity of the surface of the earth and was calculated earlier to be 0.4634×10^3 m/sec. Hence, while the rocket is in the air, the surface of the earth at the equator will have moved a distance

$$S' = 0.4634 \times 10^3 \times 781 \text{ m} = 0.362 \times 10^6 \text{ m}$$

Finally, the actual distance D on the earth covered by the rocket is given by

$$D = s - S' = 4.317 \times 10^6 - 0.362 \times 10^6 \text{ m}$$
$$D = 3.955 \times 10^6 \text{ m} = 3955 \text{ km} \quad \textit{Answer}$$

EXERCISES

6-1 Show that the energy of an elliptic orbit can be written

$$E = -\frac{GMm}{r_{\text{min}} + r_{\text{max}}}$$

6-2 A comet approaches the sun on an elliptical orbit. Its nearest point of approach is 1.60×10^{11} m from the center of the sun. Its velocity at the nearest point is 4.00×10^4 m/sec. Predict the approximate number of years which will elapse before the comet will return to the same point. Neglect any effects due to the planets.

6-3 It is desired to place a weather observation satellite in a circular orbit at an altitude of 425 miles (0.684×10^6 m) above the surface of the earth. Suppose that the altitude at burnout is exactly 425 miles and that the speed at burnout is exactly correct for a circular orbit at this altitude. What angular deviation of the direction of the burnout velocity from the tangential direction will result in an orbit whose minimum and maximum distances from the surface of the earth are 415 miles (0.668×10^6 m) and 435 miles (0.700×10^6 m) respectively?

6-4 A space probe is launched from the earth into the same orbit as the earth about the sun but far from the earth in this orbit. It is desired to place this probe into the orbit of Mars. This is done as follows. The rocket engines are turned on, and the tangential velocity of the probe is increased to the perihelion value of velocity of an elliptic orbit whose aphelion is in the orbit of Mars. This impulse of the rocket engines can be assumed to occur in negligible time, so that this increase in velocity follows the laws for linear acceleration of a rocket. The rocket engines are turned off, and the probe "coasts" into the orbit of Mars along the elliptic orbit. Now the rocket motors are again turned on to give the probe enough additional tangential velocity to stay in the circular orbit of Mars. Mars itself is not approached. Then the motors are employed in reverse to slow down the probe to the aphelion velocity of an elliptic orbit whose perihelion lies in the orbit of the earth. Upon arrival at the earth orbit the motors are again employed to slow down the probe to a tangential orbital velocity equal to that of the earth. Return to the gravitational field of the earth is arranged by other means.

Using a rocket exhaust velocity of 3500 m/sec calculate the mass ratio required for each of the impulses used in the previous round trip. Assume that the earth and Mars both move in circular orbits which lie in the same plane. What is the over-all mass ratio for the entire trip? What is the approximate minimum time for the round trip?

6-5 Suppose that you are in one of two satellites in the same circular orbit about the earth. The other satellite is a kilometer or so ahead of you. You wish to project a small object in such a way that it can be caught by the occupants of the other satellite. If you project the object directly toward the other satellite, the object will go into an elliptic orbit with the point of projection at perigee. This means that to you the object will appear to move away from the earth and backward with respect to your direction of motion. How should you project the object so that it can be caught by the other satellite?

6-6 It is proposed to catapult payloads off the moon by constructing a horizontal track along the surface of the moon and accelerating the payloads to escape velocity along this track. Such a device would have the advantage that rocket fuel for launch does not have to accompany the payload. Using algebraic symbols, find an expression for the length of such a track necessary to allow the payload to reach escape velocity with constant acceleration. Also find an expression for the maximum useful power which must be supplied to the payload during launch. Assume that the moon is a perfect sphere, and neglect the rotation of the moon on its axis, its revolution about the earth, and the gravitational field of the earth.

Assuming a payload of 10 metric tons (10,000 kg) and a constant acceleration of 10 g (98 m/sec^2) along the track, give your opinion as to whether or not such a device is feasible. Comment on the additional difficulties which would exist in using a similar device for launching payloads from the earth. In making your judgment you may find the following figures useful: The electrical power demand in a small industrial city is about $\frac{1}{2}$ kW per person of the population. The Atlas missile booster has a thrust of 360,000 lb force (1.6×10^6 N), and the Saturn booster has a thrust of 1.3×10^6 lb of force (5.8×10^6 N).

6-7 Consider a rocket far from the earth but in the same orbit as the earth about the sun. It is desired to drop this rocket into the sun. One way to do this is to use the rocket engines to reduce the orbital velocity of the rocket about the sun (about 30 km/sec) to zero, after which the rocket will fall into the sun. A more economical way to achieve the same result follows. The rocket engines are used to *increase* the orbital velocity of the rocket. This puts the rocket into an elliptical orbit of higher eccentricity than the orbit of the earth. When the rocket arrives at the aphelion of this new orbit, it is moving slower than it was in its original orbit. Now the rockets are used to reduce this smaller tangential velocity to zero, after which the rocket falls into the sun. Work out the total change in velocity of this second procedure, and compare it to stopping the rocket in the original orbit. Find the second orbit for which the total change in velocity is a minimum, and calculate the approximate time for one-half of this orbit. Assume that all rocket firings are done in short bursts.*

* See *American Journal of Physics*, **28,** 497 (1960).

PROJECT IV. THE HARMONIC OSCILLATOR*

Consider a particle held in equilibrium between two fixed walls by the action of two springs as shown in Fig. IV-1. Since we have assumed that the particle is at rest, the two springs exert no net force on the particle. Choose the origin of an inertial coordinate system such that the particle is initially at rest at the position $x = 0$. If the particle is displaced a distance x from its position of equilibrium toward one wall, experiment shows that the springs exert a force proportional to this displacement in a direction opposite to the displacement. If a direction is chosen for positive displacement and force, then the net force exerted on the particle by the springs is represented by

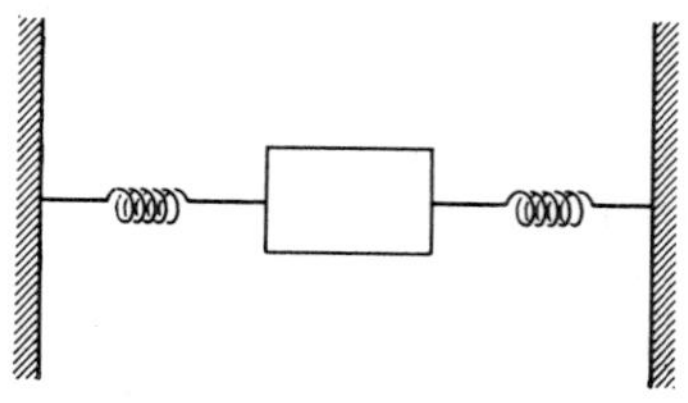

Fig. IV-1.

$$F \propto -x$$

or, putting in a constant of proportionality k,

$$F = -kx$$

where the value of k depends on the springs used. This system is called a *harmonic oscillator*, and the motion of the particle when released is said to be *harmonic motion*. Under these circumstances, and neglecting any forces due to gravity or friction, carry out the following demonstrations and answer the accompanying questions.

IV-1 Show that, if the particle is released from a position other than the equilibrium position, its equation of motion is

$$m\ddot{x} = -kx$$

or

$$\ddot{x} = -\frac{k}{m}x \qquad \text{(IV-1)}$$

where m is the mass of the particle. The mass of the springs is to be neglected in the following calculations.

IV-2 Show that the solution

$$x = A \cos \omega t \qquad \text{(IV-2)}$$

* In this project it is assumed that the student has learned how to differentiate sine and cosine functions.

satisfies Eq. (IV-1) provided the constant ω satisfies the equation

$$\omega = \sqrt{k/m} \tag{IV-3}$$

The quantity ω is referred to as the angular frequency. What are the units of ω? What are the units of A? Mathematically what values can A have? *Physically* what values can A have in this problem? What happens if A exceeds the physically permissible values? Does Eq. (IV-1) hold for this case?

IV-3 Describe the motion of the particle represented by Eq. (IV-2). What equation gives the velocity of the particle as a function of time? What is this velocity when $x = A$? when $x = -A$? when $x = 0$? What is the acceleration of the particle when $x = A$? when $x = -A$? when $x = 0$?

IV-4 The *period* T of a harmonic oscillator is defined as the longest interval of time during which the motion of the oscillator does not repeat itself. Show that the period of this harmonic oscillator is given by the expression $T = 2\pi/\omega = 2\pi\sqrt{m/k}$.

IV-5 Show that the solution

$$x = B \sin \omega t \tag{IV-4}$$

also satisfies Eq. (IV-1) for the same value of ω. What mathematical and physical values can B have? Answer Question IV-3 concerning Eq. (IV-4).

IV-6 Show that the solution

$$x = A \cos \omega t + B \sin \omega t \tag{IV-5}$$

also satisfies Eq. (IV-1). Show that Eq. (IV-5) can also be written

$$x = C \cos (\omega t + \phi) \tag{IV-6}$$

Find expressions for C and ϕ in terms of A and B. What are the *physical* meanings of C and ϕ?

IV-7 Consider the following four separate sets of initial conditions. For each case determine which of Eqs. (IV-2), (IV-4), (IV-5), and (IV-6) can be used to describe the motion of the particle (more than one of these equations can be used in each case). For the appropriate equations determine A, B, C, and/or ϕ in terms of the initial conditions given.

Case I:	at	$t = 0,$	$x = x_1,$	$\dot{x} = 0$
Case II:	at	$t = 0,$	$x = 0,$	$\dot{x} = v_1$
Case III:	at	$t = 0,$	$x = x_1,$	$\dot{x} = v_1$
Case IV:	at	$t = t_1$	$x = x_1,$	$\dot{x} = v_1$

Equations (IV-5) and (IV-6) are called the *general solutions* to Eq. (IV-1). In what way are they more general than the solutions in Eqs. (IV-2) and (IV-4)?

IV-8 Show that the work done by an external force in displacing the particle very slowly from its equilibrium position ($x = 0$) to a position x is given by

$$W = \tfrac{1}{2}kx^2$$

Call this work the *potential energy* of the particle V.

$$V = \tfrac{1}{2}kx^2$$

Now show that during the motion of a harmonic oscillator in the absence of external forces (other than the springs) the sum of the kinetic and the potential energy of the particle is constant. What is the form of this energy when $x = 0$? when $x = C$? when $x = -C$?

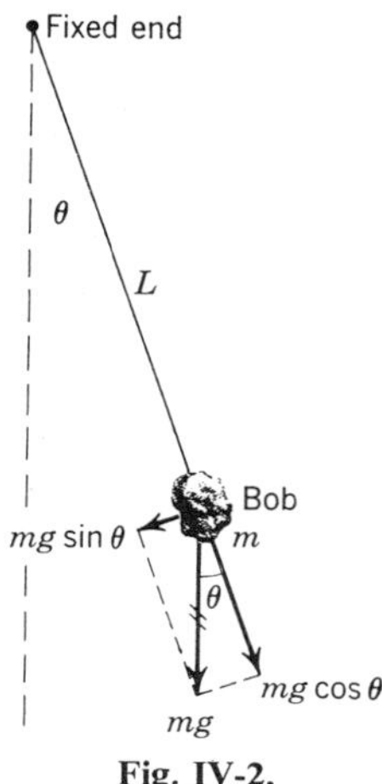

Fig. IV-2.

Consider a *simple pendulum* in a uniform gravitational field. The simple pendulum consists of a particle called a bob attached to an inextensible string of length L the other end of which is attached to a fixed point (Fig. IV-2). The mass of the string is considered to be negligible. If now the bob is drawn back from its equilibrium position as shown in the figure, one component of the force of gravity on the bob will act toward the equilibrium position.

IV-9 If the bob is released from a position other than the equilibrium position, show that its equation of motion will be given by

$$mL\ddot{\theta} = -mg \sin \theta \tag{IV-7}$$

IV-10 Now look in a table of $\sin \theta$ in which θ is expressed in radians. Note that $\sin \theta$ is approximately equal to θ if the angle is small enough. What is the maximum radian angle for which $\sin \theta$ differs from θ by less than 1 percent? What is the approximate value of this angle in degrees?

IV-11 If θ is small enough that $\sin \theta$ is approximately equal to θ, show that Eq. (IV-7) can be rewritten in the approximate form

$$\ddot{\theta} = -\frac{g}{L}\theta \tag{IV-8}$$

Show that the form of Eq. (IV-8) is mathematically identical with the form of Eq. (IV-1) and hence the simple pendulum vibrating with small amplitudes is a harmonic oscillator. Show that the general solution to Eq. (IV-8) has the form

$$\theta = D \sin (\omega t + \psi) \tag{IV-9}$$

provided $\omega = \sqrt{g/L}$. What are the units of ψ? What are the units of D? What are the physical limits on the value of D? What happens when these limits are exceeded? Does Eq. (IV-8) apply in this case?

IV-12 Show that the kinetic energy of the bob at any instant is given by the expression

$$T = \tfrac{1}{2}mL^2\dot{\theta}^2$$

Show that the potential energy is given by the expression

$$V = \tfrac{1}{2}mgL\theta^2$$

Show that this is equal to mgh, where h is the height through which the bob has been raised in drawing it away from the position of equilibrium. Show that the sum of the kinetic and the potential energy of the bob remains a constant during its motion.

IV-13 Show that the period of the simple pendulum of small amplitude is given by the expression

$$T = 2\pi/\omega = 2\pi\sqrt{L/g}$$

Is this equation true at the surface of the moon as well as at the surface of the earth? If $g = 9.8$ m/sec^2, what is the length of a simple pendulum with a period of one second? Does the mass of the bob enter this calculation? Why or why not? Construct a "one-second pendulum" and check your results.

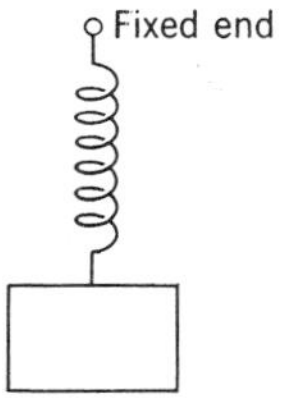

Fixed end

Fig. IV-3.

IV-14 Consider a particle hanging vertically from a spring in a uniform gravitational field (see Fig. IV-3). Show that, if the particle is pulled vertically downward and then released, it will execute simple harmonic motion provided the force exerted by the spring is given by $F = -kz$, where z is the extension of the spring. Show that the angular frequency ω is given by Eq. (IV-3). Neglect the mass of the spring.

PROJECT V. THE UNINTENTIONAL BALLISTIC MISSILE

An earth satellite is launched from 28° 28′ north latitude, 80° 28′ west longitude. The launching vehicle goes off course because of a malfunction of the guidance system. At burnout the last stage has components of velocity as follows: 3.10701×10^3 m/sec vertically, 5.38065×10^3 m/sec to the north, and 2.57000×10^3 m/sec to the east with respect to the surface of the rotating earth. Will the last stage fall on a major city?

Assume: That the gravitational constant is exactly $G = 6.67 \times 10^{-11}$ N-m^2/kg^2; that the earth is a sphere of exact radius $r_e = 6371$ km; that the mass of the earth is exactly $M = 5.983 \times 10^{24}$ kg; that the earth rotates once on its axis in exactly 23.9333 h; that gravitational effects of the sun and the moon can be neglected, as well as effects due to the motion of the earth about the sun; that burnout is achieved very near the surface of the earth; and that air resistance can be neglected. Do *not* neglect the rotation of the earth.

Hint: Relations in a Spherical Triangle. If a spherical triangle has sides which are great circles, and if A, B, and C are the three angles, a, b, and c are the respective opposite sides (expressed in terms of angle subtended at the center of the sphere), then

$$\frac{\sin A}{\sin a} = \frac{\sin B}{\sin b} = \frac{\sin C}{\sin c}$$

$$\cos a = \cos b \cos c + \sin b \sin c \cos A$$

Check points: In the *inertial* system: the eccentricity of the orbit is $\frac{1}{2}$, the initial speed is approximately 6.9 km/sec, and the sine of the angle between the initial velocity vector and the local vertical is approximately 0.89.

PROJECT VI. THE BOHR ATOM AND THE HYDROGEN SPECTRUM

Elementary particles which make up atoms, such as protons and electrons, are not *particles* according to our definition of particles, because they are too small to be visible to the unaided human eye. For this reason we should be very suspicious of theories of atomic structure which use classical mechanics and treat electrons and protons as particles. Experiment shows this suspicion to be well justified. Nevertheless, when the atom was first being studied, the laws of classical mechanics were the only laws of motion known. Therefore they were applied to the atom rather uncritically. Niels Bohr showed that the addition of a few simple assumptions to the laws of classical mechanics allowed one to describe a large class of experimental results concerning atoms. The model of the atom which arises from the use of these assumptions is called the *Bohr model of the atom*, or simply the *Bohr atom*. The Bohr atom fails to account for many atomic phenomena. The explanation of these phenomena and the origins of the assumptions which Bohr introduced can be found in the more advanced subject of *quantum mechanics*. In this project we shall study the Bohr atom and the hydrogen spectrum.

When atoms are heated or placed in an electric discharge, they emit light. If the light from a gaseous sample of one kind of atom is passed through a slit and then through a prism, the spectrum produced will be made up of discrete parallel lines. This is called a *line spectrum*. Each of these lines is due to light of a different wavelength.

At the turn of the twentieth century it was known that hydrogen was the simplest atom. Therefore there was some interest to see if the wavelengths in the line spectrum of hydrogen could be expressed in a simple equation. It was found possible to separate these lines analytically into several sets or *series*. The lines in three of these series (named for their discoverers) have wavelengths given by the following formulas.

Lyman series: $$\frac{1}{\lambda} = R\left[\frac{1}{1^2} - \frac{1}{n^2}\right] \qquad n = 2, 3, 4, \ldots$$

Balmer series: $$\frac{1}{\lambda} = R\left[\frac{1}{2^2} - \frac{1}{n^2}\right] \qquad n = 3, 4, 5, \ldots$$

Paschen series: $$\frac{1}{\lambda} = R\left[\frac{1}{3^2} - \frac{1}{n^2}\right] \qquad n = 4, 5, 6, \ldots$$

where R is an experimental constant, called the *Rydberg constant*, which has the value $R = 1.097 \times 10^7\ \mathrm{m}^{-1}$.

Show that, as n increases, the difference in wavelength between adjacent spectral lines in any given series decreases. Show that, as n becomes very large, the wavelength approaches a minimum. This is called the *limit of the series*.

In 1913 Niels Bohr showed that the observed wavelengths could be accounted for if it was assumed that the electron moves in a circular path about the proton which constitutes the nucleus of the hydrogen atom and if the following two postulates are satisfied.

I. The only permitted orbits for the electron are those for which its angular momentum about the nucleus is some integer multiple of $h/2\pi$, where h is *Planck's constant*, whose numerical value is known from other experiments to be 6.625×10^{-34} joule-sec.

II. When an electron jumps from an orbit of larger radius to an orbit of smaller radius, it emits a flash of light (a *photon*) of frequency ν given by the expression

$$h\nu = E_2 - E_1$$

where E_2 is the total energy of the initial orbit, E_1 is the total energy of the final orbit, and h is Planck's constant.

Set up the expression for the total energy of an electron of charge $-e$ and mass m in a circular orbit about a proton of charge $+e$. Assume that the proton is fixed in an inertial frame, and neglect all but electrostatic forces between the particles. Now introduce the requirement of Bohr's first postulate. Find an expression for the energies of the resulting quantized orbits. Using Bohr's second postulate and the expression $\nu\lambda = c$ for the relation between the frequency, wavelength, and velocity for light of a given wavelength, show how the various spectral series can be accounted for. Draw a diagram with arrows illustrating which electron transitions are involved in each spectral series. Can you predict the existence of a fourth series? What equation will give the wavelengths of the lines in this series? (This is called the *Brackett series*.) Using the numerical values for the mass and charge of the electron and the speed of light, show that your theoretical value for the Rydberg constant corresponds to the experimental one. You have just derived a fundamental physical constant from theory.

PROJECT VII. RUTHERFORD SCATTERING

The Rutherford scattering experiment* demonstrated that the nucleus of an atom is very much smaller than the atom itself. For this reason it is one of the classic experiments of physics. Furthermore, the analysis of Rutherford scattering is similar to the analysis of some modern nuclear scattering experiments.

Figure VII-1 shows the Rutherford scattering experiment schematically. A radioactive source which emits alpha particles is enclosed in a lead shield with a small aperture. Alpha particles are helium nuclei, and they carry a positive charge of twice the magnitude of the charge on the electron. A narrow beam of these alpha particles defined by the aperture is incident on a thin gold foil. The alpha particles are scattered by atoms in the gold foil. These scattered alpha particles are incident on a zinc sulfide screen. Zinc sulfide emits a visible flash of light when struck by an alpha particle. The results of the experiment are expressed in terms of the relative number of alpha particles which are scattered through angles near any given angle ϕ with respect to the direction of the incident beam. In order to prevent the collision of alpha particles with air molecules, the experiment is performed in a vacuum.

We shall use classical mechanics to analyze this experiment. As in the case of the Bohr atom, this analysis will have to be redone later using quantum mechanics, since an alpha particle is not a *visible particle* for which the laws of classical mechanics were derived. In the case of the Bohr atom, the quantum mechanical calculation gives a result rather different from the classical calculation, whereas for Rutherford scattering

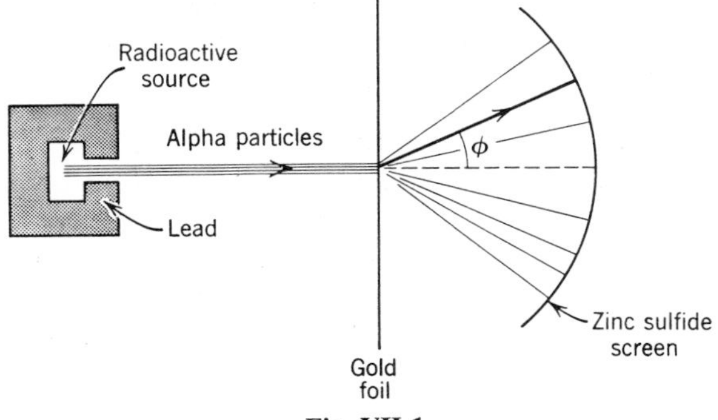

Fig. VII-1.

* Ernest Rutherford, *Philosophical Magazine*, **21**, 669 (1911).

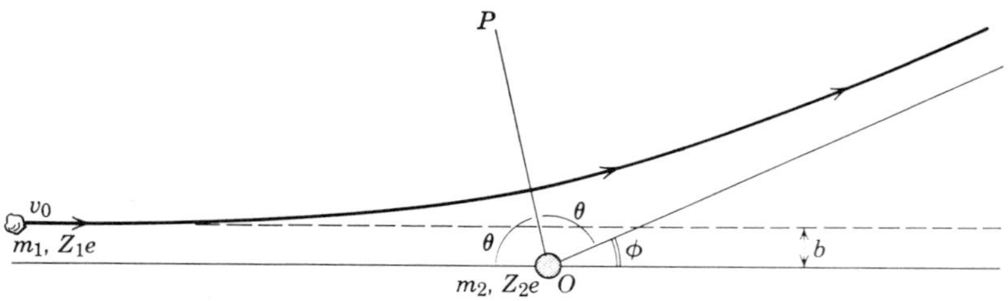

Fig. VII-2.

the quantum mechanical calculation gives the same result as the classical calculation.

Consider an incident nuclear particle of mass m_1 and charge Z_1e, where Z_1 is some integer and e is the magnitude of the charge on the electron (Fig. VII-2). For the alpha particle, $Z_1 = 2$. This incident particle approaches a target nucleus of mass m_2 and charge Z_2e. Z_2 is the atomic number of the target nucleus. Let b be the perpendicular distance between the target nucleus and the extension of the initial line along which the incident particle moves. The distance b is called the *impact parameter*. We make the following assumptions:

Assumption 1. The target nucleus is so much more massive than the incident particle that the target nucleus can be considered to remain fixed during the interaction. (The gold nucleus has about fifty times the mass of the alpha particle.)

Assumption 2. Because most of the deflection of the incident particle occurs when it is closest to the target nucleus and inside the cloud of electrons which surround the target nucleus, the presence of these electrons can be neglected.

Assumption 3. The interacting particles can be considered to be uniform spheres of charge, and the distance between them is always greater than the sum of the radii of the two particles.

Assumptions 2 and 3 mean that Eq. (5-5) is valid for the force between the particles where $q_1 = Z_1e$ and $q_2 = Z_2e$. We shall introduce one more assumption below.

Using Assumption 1, take the target nucleus to be the origin of an inertial coordinate system. In Question 6-30 you showed that under the preceding conditions the path of the incident particle is a hyperbola. Let OP in Fig. VII-2 be the major axis of this hyperbola. Use Eq. (6-18) to show that the angle θ in the figure is given by

$$\cos\theta = \frac{1}{e} \qquad \text{(VII-1)}$$

If v_0 is the speed of the incident particle before deflection, show that the angular momentum and energy of the incoming particle are given by the equations

$$l = m_1 v_0 b \tag{VII-2}$$

$$E = \tfrac{1}{2} m_1 v_0^2 \tag{VII-3}$$

Show that this energy and angular momentum will remain constant during the interaction. From the results of Question 6-30 show that the eccentricity of the orbit is given by

$$e = \left[1 + \frac{m_1^2 v_0^4 b^2 (4\pi\epsilon_0)^2}{Z_1^2 Z_2^2 e^4}\right]^{1/2} \tag{VII-4}$$

Define the constant

$$K = \frac{Z_1 Z_2 e^2}{4\pi\epsilon_0 m_1} \tag{VII-5}$$

so that Eq. (VII-4) becomes

$$e = \left[1 + \frac{v_0^4 b^2}{K^2}\right]^{1/2} \tag{VII-6}$$

Using Eqs. (VII-6) and (VII-1) and trigonometric identities, show that

$$\tan\theta = \frac{v_0^2 b}{K} \tag{VII-7}$$

From Fig. VII-2 show that the angle of deflection ϕ is given by

$$\phi = \pi - 2\theta = \pi - 2\arctan\frac{v_0^2 b}{K} \tag{VII-8}$$

Divide both sides of Eq. (VII-8) by 2, take the tangent of both sides, and show by trigonometric identities that the result is

$$\tan\frac{\phi}{2} = \frac{K}{v_0^2 b} \tag{VII-9}$$

This equation gives the angle of deflection ϕ as a function of the initial velocity v_0 of the incident particle, the impact parameter b, and (through K) the charges on the two particles and the mass of the incident particle.

There are two reasons why Eq. (VII-9) cannot be compared directly with the results of a Rutherford scattering experiment. The first reason is that experimentally one is shooting a beam of alpha particles at a small area of a gold foil which consists of many gold nuclei; there is no direct way to measure the impact parameter b for each collision. Thus Eq. (VII-9) contains two unknowns, only one of which can be measured experimentally, so that the experiment cannot be used to verify Eq. (VII-9) directly. The second difficulty is related to the first. Since the actual impact parameters for a given set of collisions will almost always be different for each collision, two incident particles will almost never be deflected through exactly the same angle ϕ. For this reason the results of an actual scattering experiment are expressed in terms of the relative number of particles deflected through a small *range of angles* $d\phi$ around a particular average angle ϕ. Equation (VII-9) must be put in such a form that it can be compared with experimental results expressed in this way. We now consider these two difficulties.

Suppose that the beam of incident particles has a cross section of area A, that N_0 particles pass down this beam during an experiment, and that these N_0 particles are distributed uniformly over the area A. Consider a single scattering nucleus in the center of this beam. Suppose that a fraction dN/N_0 of the incident particles in the beam passes through a ring of radius b and thickness db before being deflected by the target nucleus (Fig. VII-3). All these particles will be deflected through approximately the same angle. Show that the fraction of the area of the beam taken up by the ring is $2\pi b\, db/A$, so that the fraction of the particles in the beam which pass through the ring is given by

$$\frac{dN}{N_0} = \frac{2\pi b\, db}{A} \tag{VII-10}$$

Show from Eq. (VII-9) that

$$b\, db = -\frac{1}{2}\frac{K^2}{v_0^{\,4}}\frac{\cos(\phi/2)}{\sin^3(\phi/2)}\, d\phi \tag{VII-11}$$

where the minus sign arises from the fact that smaller values of b give larger values of ϕ. Suppressing this minus sign, show that Eq. (VII-10) becomes

$$\frac{dN}{N_0} = \frac{\pi K^2 \cos(\phi/2)\, d\phi}{v_0^{\,4} A \sin^3(\phi/2)} \tag{VII-12}$$

Equation (VII-12) gives the fraction of the incident particles in the beam which will be deflected through a range of angles $d\phi$ near the average angle ϕ *by a single scattering nucleus at the center of the beam of incident particles.*

Now consider Assumption 2. Deflection is assumed to take place inside the cloud of electrons which surround the nucleus. The width of the beam of incident particles, on the other hand, is of the order of a millimeter or so—very, very much wider than the diameter of the inner shell of electrons in an atom. Since the incident particle must pass very close to a target nucleus in order to be deflected, this means that a target nucleus can be anywhere in the beam and Eq. (VII-12) will still apply. If the target foil

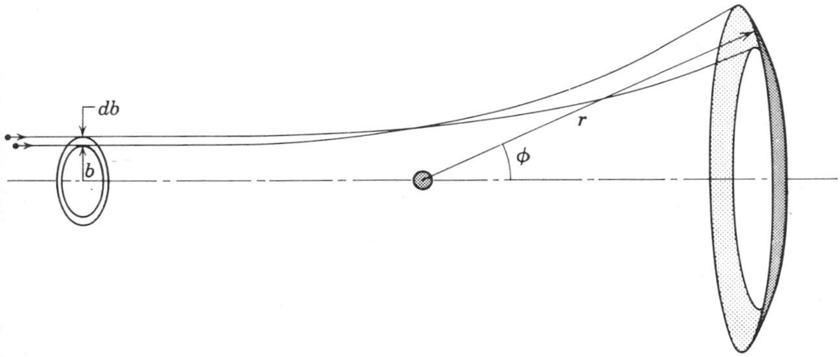

Fig. VII-3.

has a thickness s and contains n atoms per unit volume of target material, then the number of target atoms in a beam of area A is nsA.

Show that the total number of particles scattered into the range of angles $d\phi$ around angle ϕ by all the target nuclei is given by the equation

$$dN = \frac{\pi N_0 ns K^2 \cos(\phi/2)\, d\phi}{v_0^4 \sin^3(\phi/2)} \tag{VII-13}$$

$$= \frac{N_0 ns Z_1^2 Z_2^2 e^4 \cos(\phi/2)\, d\phi}{64\pi\epsilon_0^2(\frac{1}{2}m_1 v_0^2)^2 \sin^3(\phi/2)} \tag{VII-14}$$

provided that we make the following additional assumption:

Assumption 4. As an incident particle passes through the target foil it will come near enough to *not more than one target nucleus* to be deflected by it. In other words, the observed deflections are the result of *single* interactions.

According to Eq. (VII-14) the number of particles scattered into a small range of angles, $d\phi$, is

(1) directly proportional to the thickness s of the foil,
(2) directly proportional to the *square* of the atomic number Z_2 of the target nucleus,
(3) inversely proportional to the *square* of the kinetic energy of the incident particles.

Geiger and Marsden* verified these predictions experimentally, together with the variation of dN with angle ϕ. The atomic number of the target nucleus was varied by using target foils made of elements other than gold.

* H. Geiger and E. Marsden, *Philosophical Magazine*, **25**, 604 (1913).

One more modification is necessary to put Eq. (VII-14) into the form in which it is usually presented. This equation gives the number of particles scattered into a spherical ring of width $r\,d\phi$ which subtends a half-angle ϕ at the target. The more conventional expression gives the number of particles scattered into a unit of *solid angle*. The solid angle is defined as follows.

A radian angle $d\phi$ in two dimensions was defined in Sec. 6.2 as the ratio dS/r, where dS is the arc length intercepted by the angle on a circle of radius r centered at the apex of the angle. The unit of ϕ is the *radian*. In a similar manner, the *solid angle* $d\Omega$ is defined as the ratio dA/r^2, where dA is the area intercepted by the solid angle on the surface of a sphere of radius r centered at the apex of the solid angle. The unit of Ω is the *steradian* (abbreviation: sr). Show that the total solid angle subtended by a sphere is 4π steradians. Now show that the spherical ring of Eq. (VII-14) into which the particles are scattered has the area dA given by

$$dA = (2\pi r \sin\phi)(r\,d\phi)$$

so that the solid angle subtended by this ring at the target point is

$$d\Omega = 2\pi \sin\phi\, d\phi = 4\pi \sin\frac{\phi}{2}\cos\frac{\phi}{2}\, d\phi$$

and Eq. (VII-14) can be written to give the number of particles, dN', scattered into a solid angle $d\Omega$ at an angle ϕ.

$$dN' = \frac{N_0 n s Z_1{}^2 Z_2{}^2 e^4\, d\Omega}{256\pi^2\epsilon_0{}^2(\frac{1}{2}m_1 v_0{}^2)^2 \sin^4(\phi/2)} \qquad \text{(VII-15)}$$

Equation (VII-15) is the one used by Geiger and Marsden. In their experiment a zinc sulfide screen of small area mounted on a microscope was moved around the circumference of the circle shown in Fig. VII-1 and the number of flashes on this screen was counted as a function of the deflection angle ϕ. Since this screen subtended a constant solid angle, Eq. (VII-15) is more useful in interpreting the results of this method than is Eq. (VII-14).

Suppose that Eqs. (VII-14) and (VII-15) are verified experimentally. Show carefully to what extent this supports the model of the atom which has a very small but massive central nucleus. Equation (VII-9) may be useful in this demonstration. To what extent does this demonstration fail to exclude all other possible models of the atom? Does it exclude the "plum pudding model" in which the electrons are distributed randomly like plums in a pudding made up of a uniform cloud of mass and positive charge the size of the atom?

Summary of Symbols

A = area of beam of incident particles

b = impact parameter: perpendicular distance between target nucleus and the extension of the line along which the incident particle moves initially

e = magnitude of the electrical charge of an electron or proton
$Z_1 e$ = charge on the incident particle ($Z_1 = 2$ for an alpha particle)
$Z_2 e$ = charge on the target nucleus (Z_2 = atomic number of the target nucleus = 79 for the gold nucleus)
$K = \dfrac{Z_1 Z_2 e^2}{4\pi\epsilon_0 m_1}$ [Eq. (VII-5)]
m_1 = mass of the incident particles
m_2 = mass of the target nucleus (Assumption 1, that the target nucleus does not move during the interaction, is equivalent to assuming that m_2 is infinite.)
n = number of target nuclei per unit volume of the target foil
N_0 = number of incident particles
dN = number of incident particles deflected through a range of angles $d\phi$ near ϕ [Eq. (VII-14)]
dN' = number of incident particles deflected into a solid angle $d\Omega$ near ϕ [Eq. (VII-15)]
s = thickness of the target foil
v_0 = initial velocity of the incident particles
ϵ_0 = a constant used in the force law between charged particles [See Eq. (5-5).]
ϕ = the angle of deflection of the incident particle
$d\Omega$ = an increment of solid angle

chapter 7

The mechanics of a system of particles

7.1 INTRODUCTION. A particle is a material body which is visible to the unaided human eye and whose position in space is accurately enough described by a geometrical point. In the preceding chapters we have applied the mechanics of a particle to a tin can, a piece of cheese, an apple, an automobile, a rocket ship, and even a planet. All these objects were considered to be small enough with respect to the scale of the experiments in which they were involved that their positions were accurately enough described by a point. Yet, for experiments which demand sufficiently accurate measurements of position, any one of these objects could be considered too big to be called a particle. Even if we could designate one particular point of a body to specify the position of that body, such as the center of a spherical planet, our present equations of motion would not be able to describe the rotation of that body about an axis which passes through this point.

Using the laws of mechanics already derived, it is possible to predict the behavior of bodies which are too large to be called particles. This is done by considering these larger bodies to be made up of much smaller parts, each of which is small enough, considering the scale of the experiment, to be called a particle. The laws of particle mechanics are applied to these smaller parts. When the motion of these parts is known, the over-all motion of the larger body is thereby determined. The larger body does not need to be a rigid structure of unchanging shape. The same kind of analysis will apply to a set of particles which are grouped together in almost any way at all. We shall call any such set a *system of particles.*

If the system of particles is not a rigid body, then a complete description of its motion might have to include a description of the motion of each separate particle. To avoid this complication it is convenient to describe the motion of a system of particles in terms of an average position of the system called the *center of mass*. The term *center of mass* will be defined in Sec. 7.3.

Question

7-1 By demanding an accurate enough measurement of position, we can make almost any object appear too large to be called a particle. Even the smaller parts into which the object is divided for analysis might be considered too big to be called particles. How far can this subdivision continue and still allow us to make use of the laws of motion for particles? Reread the definition of a particle which begins this section.

7.2 FORCES ON A SYSTEM OF PARTICLES. Consider a system of particles. These particles can be small elements of mass in a larger body, or they can be physically separated from each other, or they can make up a combination of these two cases. The particles may be interconnected with springs or strings or rods or by the forces of cohesion in a solid, or they may attract or repel one another as the result of electrostatic or gravitational forces; they may interact with any combination of these forces, or they may not exert any forces on each other at all. A great many actual systems could be particular examples of this general system of particles.

We shall make only two assumptions about the forces with which any two particles in the system act on each other. These assumptions are that:

1. the forces exerted on each other by any two particles in the system are equal in magnitude and opposite in direction;
2. the forces exerted on each other by any two particles in the system lie parallel to the straight line which joins the two particles.

In other words if $\mathbf{F}_{12}$ is the force exerted on particle one by particle two and $\mathbf{F}_{21}$ is the force exerted on particle two by particle one, then the first assumption states that $\mathbf{F}_{12} = -\mathbf{F}_{21}$. More generally, if $\mathbf{F}_{ij}$ is the force exerted on particle i by particle j and if $\mathbf{F}_{ji}$ is the force exerted on particle j by particle i, then $\mathbf{F}_{ij} = -\mathbf{F}_{ji}$. The second assumption says that $\mathbf{F}_{ij}$ and $\mathbf{F}_{ji}$ both lie parallel to the straight line joining particle i and particle j, as shown in Fig. 7-1. The forces between particles in most (but not all) physical systems of interest to physicists satisfy these two assumptions.

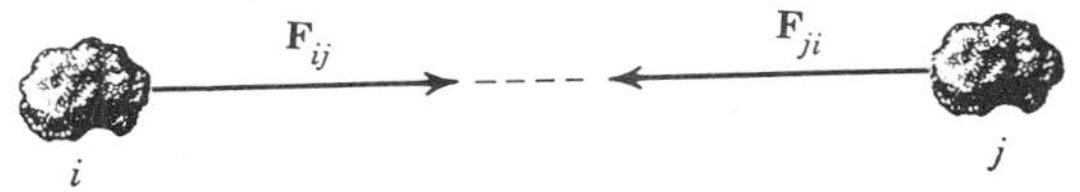

Fig. 7-1. Assumptions about the forces between particles in the system of particles.

Now suppose that there are forces due to external causes which act on the particles of our system. These external forces may be due to any cause or causes and may act on all the particles of the system or on only a few particles of the system or may act with different magnitude on different particles of the system. What will be the total force on any one particle of the system due to all causes, internal and external?

Consider particle i of the system of particles. Particle i may be any one of the particles in the system. Particle i is acted on, first of all, by forces due to other particles of the system. The sum of these forces is given by the expression $\sum_j \mathbf{F}_{ij}$, where $\mathbf{F}_{ij}$ is the force exerted on particle i by particle j and the symbol $\sum_j$ means that these forces are to be summed over all other particles j. Note that this is a *vector sum*.

Question

7-2 In the same notation, what would $\mathbf{F}_{33}$ mean? Show that in general $\mathbf{F}_{ii}$ is equal to zero. Show that the summation over j above can be extended to *all* particles in the system including particle i.

Particle i is also acted on by external forces. Let $\mathbf{F}_i^e$ be the resultant force on particle i due to all external sources. We may write the total resultant force $\mathbf{F}_i$ on particle i (due to both internal and external sources) in the form

$$\mathbf{F}_i = \sum_i \mathbf{F}_{ij} + \mathbf{F}_i^e \tag{7-1}$$

This expression gives the total force on particle i due to both internal and external sources.

7.3 MOTION OF THE CENTER OF MASS. CONSERVATION OF LINEAR MOMENTUM. How will particle i move under the influence of the total force given by Eq. (7-1)? According to the laws of motion of a particle, the resultant force on particle i is equal to the product of its mass and its acceleration. If $\mathbf{r}_i$ represents the vector position of particle i with respect to the origin of some inertial coordinate system, its acceleration will be given by $\ddot{\mathbf{r}}_i$ (see Sec. 4.15), so that

$$\mathbf{F}_i = m_i\ddot{\mathbf{r}}_i = \sum_j \mathbf{F}_{ij} + \mathbf{F}_i^e \tag{7-2}$$

The total mass M of the system of particles is given by the summation

$$M = \sum_i m_i$$

We *define* the *center of mass* $\mathbf{R}$ of a system of particles by the expression

$$\mathbf{R} = \frac{\sum_i m_i \mathbf{r}_i}{\sum_i m_i} = \frac{\sum_i m_i \mathbf{r}_i}{M} \qquad \text{definition} \qquad (7\text{-}3)$$

with respect to the origin of a given coordinate system.

Questions

7-3 A system consists of two particles of equal mass located at points $\mathbf{r}_1 = 0$, $\mathbf{r}_2 = 2\hat{k}$ meters. Where is the center of mass?

7-4 Three particles of mass 1, 2, and 3 kg are located at the points $\mathbf{r}_1 = 1\hat{\imath} + 2\hat{\jmath} + 3\hat{k}$, $\mathbf{r}_2 = 3\hat{\imath} + 2\hat{\jmath} - 1\hat{k}$, $\mathbf{r}_3 = 2\hat{\imath} - 3\hat{\jmath} + 1\hat{k}$, respectively. All distances are in meters. Where is the center of mass of the system located?

7-5 From Eq. (7-3) show that X, Y, and Z, the x, y, and z components of the center of mass respectively, are given by the equations

$$X = \frac{\sum_i m_i x_i}{M}$$

$$Y = \frac{\sum_i m_i y_i}{M} \qquad (7\text{-}4)$$

$$Z = \frac{\sum_i m_i z_i}{M}$$

where x_i, y_i, and z_i are the coordinates of any particle i of the system of particles.

7-6 Two particles of equal mass move according to the equations $\mathbf{r}_1 = t\hat{\imath} + 2t^2\hat{\jmath} + 4\hat{k}$ and $\mathbf{r}_2 = 3t^3\hat{\imath} - t\hat{\jmath} + t^4\hat{k}$. Find the position $\mathbf{R}$, the velocity $\dot{\mathbf{R}}$, and the acceleration $\ddot{\mathbf{R}}$ of the center of mass as a function of time.

Since the second derivative of a sum is the sum of the second derivatives and since the masses of the individual particles are assumed to be constant, the acceleration of the center of mass $\ddot{\mathbf{R}}$ will have the value

$$\ddot{\mathbf{R}} = \frac{\sum_i m_i \ddot{\mathbf{r}}_i}{M}$$

or

$$M\ddot{\mathbf{R}} = \sum_i m_i \ddot{\mathbf{r}}_i$$

The right side of this equation will be equal to the left side of Eq. (7-2) if both sides of Eq. (7-2) are summed over all particles i.

$$\sum_i m_i \ddot{\mathbf{r}}_i = M\ddot{\mathbf{R}} = \sum_i \sum_j \mathbf{F}_{ij} + \sum_i \mathbf{F}_i^e \tag{7-5}$$

The sum $\sum_i \mathbf{F}_i^e$ is simply the total (vector sum) of the external forces acting on all the particles of the system. Let this total have the symbol $\mathbf{F}^e$, so that $\sum_i \mathbf{F}_i^e = \mathbf{F}^e$. Now Eq. (7-5) becomes

$$M\ddot{\mathbf{R}} = \sum_i \sum_j \mathbf{F}_{ij} + \mathbf{F}^e \tag{7-6}$$

The first term on the right of this equation is equal to zero under the assumptions we have made about the nature of the internal forces between the particles of the system. This will be shown in the following paragraph.

Question

7-7 Consider a system made up of three interacting particles. Write out the double sum in Eq. (7-6) for this case. Using the assumptions in the second paragraph of Sec. 7.2, show that this double sum is equal to zero.

The symbols i and j in the double sum merely represent a set of numbers (each number corresponding to a particle in the system). We could just as well have used two other symbols, p and q for example, to represent these numbers. Since i and j represent the *same* set of numbers, there is no reason why we should not interchange the symbols i and j, using the symbol i for the jth set of numbers and using the symbol j for the ith set of numbers. This interchange of symbols will merely change the appearance of the double summation sign, but it would not change the actual summation if it were written out. From this argument it follows that the first term on the right of Eq. (7-6) can be written in either of the following two ways:

$$\sum_i \sum_j \mathbf{F}_{ij} = \sum_j \sum_i \mathbf{F}_{ji} \tag{7-7}$$

Now the double sum in this equation can be taken in either order. It makes no difference whether the sum is taken first over the i and then each term summed over the j or vice-versa. Hence Eq. (7-7) can just as well be written

$$\sum_i \sum_j \mathbf{F}_{ij} = \sum_i \sum_j \mathbf{F}_{ji} \tag{7-8}$$

This expression will be true no matter what the relation is between $\mathbf{F}_{ij}$ and $\mathbf{F}_{ji}$. However, we have assumed that

$$\mathbf{F}_{ij} = -\mathbf{F}_{ji}$$

for every pair of particles in the system. Hence if we sum both sides of the last equation over both *i* and *j*, the two sides of the resulting equation will still be equal.

$$\sum_i \sum_j \mathbf{F}_{ij} = \sum_i \sum_j (-\mathbf{F}_{ji})$$
$$= -\sum_i \sum_j \mathbf{F}_{ji} \tag{7-9}$$

Comparing Eq. (7-9) with Eq. (7-8), we see that the left side is the same in both cases but the right side in Eq. (7-9) is the negative of the right side in Eq. (7-8). The only vector which is equal to its own negative is the zero vector. Hence

$$\sum_i \sum_j \mathbf{F}_{ij} = 0 \qquad \text{QED}$$

Another way to prove this result is to demonstrate that the double sum is made up of two kinds of terms, namely terms of the form $\mathbf{F}_{pp}$ and pairs of terms of the form $\mathbf{F}_{pq} + \mathbf{F}_{qp}$. Once you have convinced yourself of this fact, then the result follows immediately because $\mathbf{F}_{pp}$ represents the net force which particle p exerts on itself, which must be zero; and, since $\mathbf{F}_{pq} = -\mathbf{F}_{qp}$, it follows that $\mathbf{F}_{pq} + \mathbf{F}_{qp} = 0$. Therefore the double sum is equal to zero.

Since the double summation is zero, Eq. (7-6) becomes

$$M\ddot{\mathbf{R}} = \mathbf{F}^e \tag{7-10}$$

Equation (7-10) is quite a remarkable result. It says that no matter what goes on between the particles in the system the center of mass will move as if it were a single particle of mass M to which are applied all the external forces which act on the individual particles of the system. This is true no matter what the internal forces between particles in the system are, as long as the forces exerted by two particles in the system on each other are equal in magnitude and opposite in direction.

Questions

7-8 Consider a system made up of two particles of equal mass, both initially at rest at the origin. Particle one is subjected to no forces and remains at the origin. Particle two is subjected to a constant force **F** in the x-direction. Find an equation for the motion of the center of mass of the system. Show that Eq. (7-10) is satisfied.

7-9 Was Assumption 2 in the second paragraph of Sec. 7.2 used in the proof of Eq. (7-10)?

7-10 The trajectory of an artillery shell is a parabola in a uniform vertical gravitational field. If the shell explodes in mid-air, show that the center of mass of the shell will continue on the parabolic path undisturbed.

Neglect air resistance. When does the center of mass cease to follow a parabola?

If there are no external forces on the system of particles, Eq. (7-10) reads $M\ddot{\mathbf{R}} = 0$ or

$$M\dot{\mathbf{R}} = \sum_i m_i \dot{\mathbf{r}}_i = \text{const} \tag{7-11}$$

Now $m_i \dot{\mathbf{r}}_i$ is equal to $\mathbf{p}_i$, the momentum of the ith particle. The summation over i results in the total vector sum of the momenta of the separate particles in the system. By definition this is equal to the total momentum of the system. Equation (7-11) says that *for a system of particles free of external forces the total linear momentum remains constant.* This is called the *law of conservation of momentum* for a system of particles. Equation (7-11) says also that this total linear momentum is equal to the linear momentum of the center of mass. Notice carefully that the law of conservation of momentum deals with measurements made with respect to an *inertial* reference frame.

Question

7-11 Consider the earth as a system of particles. With respect to an inertial reference frame, is the linear momentum of the earth conserved? Consider the solar system as a system of particles. Is the linear momentum of the solar system conserved?

7.4 ANGULAR MOMENTUM. THE TORQUE LAW. CONSERVATION OF ANGULAR MOMENTUM. The linear momentum of particle i is given by $\mathbf{p}_i = m_i \dot{\mathbf{r}}_i$. Therefore Eq. (7-2) may be written

$$\dot{\mathbf{p}}_i = \sum_j \mathbf{F}_{ij} + \mathbf{F}_i^e \tag{7-12}$$

The *angular* momentum of particle i is defined as $\mathbf{l}_i = \mathbf{r}_i \times \mathbf{p}_i$ (see Sec. 6.6). The time derivative of this angular momentum is given by $\dot{\mathbf{l}}_i = \mathbf{r}_i \times \dot{\mathbf{p}}_i + \dot{\mathbf{r}}_i \times m_i \dot{\mathbf{r}}_i$. But $\dot{\mathbf{r}}_i \times \dot{\mathbf{r}}_i$ is equal to zero by the laws of the cross product. Hence $\dot{\mathbf{l}}_i = \mathbf{r}_i \times \dot{\mathbf{p}}_i$. Now take the cross product of $\mathbf{r}_i$ with both sides of Eq. (7-12).

$$\dot{\mathbf{l}}_i = \mathbf{r}_i \times \dot{\mathbf{p}}_i = \sum_j \mathbf{r}_i \times \mathbf{F}_{ij} + \mathbf{r}_i \times \mathbf{F}_i^e$$

The term $\mathbf{r}_i \times \mathbf{F}_i^e$ on the right is the torque on particle i due to the resultant external force on particle i (see Sec. 6.6). Call this torque $\mathbf{n}_i^e$. The equation becomes

$$\dot{\mathbf{l}}_i = \sum_j \mathbf{r}_i \times \mathbf{F}_{ij} + \mathbf{n}_i^e \tag{7-13}$$

The *total angular momentum* of the system of particles is defined as the vector sum

$$\mathbf{L} = \sum_i \mathbf{l}_i \qquad \text{definition} \tag{7-14}$$

Equation (7-13) may be summed over i to read

$$\dot{\mathbf{L}} = \sum_i \dot{\mathbf{l}}_i = \sum_i \sum_j \mathbf{r}_i \times \mathbf{F}_{ij} + \sum_i \mathbf{n}_i^e$$

The second term on the right of this equation is simply the resultant torque on the system of particles due to all external forces. Call this resultant torque $\mathbf{N}^e$.

$$\mathbf{N}^e = \sum_i \mathbf{n}_i^e \qquad \text{definition} \tag{7-15}$$

so that

$$\dot{\mathbf{L}} = \sum_i \sum_j \mathbf{r}_i \times \mathbf{F}_{ij} + \mathbf{N}^e \tag{7-16}$$

Under the assumptions we have made about the internal forces of the system, the double sum in this equation is equal to zero. The proof proceeds in much the same way as the similar proof in the last section. The i and j symbols are interchanged.

$$\begin{aligned}\sum_i \sum_j \mathbf{r}_i \times \mathbf{F}_{ij} &= \sum_j \sum_i \mathbf{r}_j \times \mathbf{F}_{ji} \\ &= \sum_i \sum_j \mathbf{r}_j \times \mathbf{F}_{ji}\end{aligned} \tag{7-17}$$

But, since $\mathbf{F}_{ij} = -\mathbf{F}_{ji}$, the left side of this equation also satisfies the equation

$$\sum_i \sum_j \mathbf{r}_i \times \mathbf{F}_{ij} = -\sum_i \sum_j \mathbf{r}_i \times \mathbf{F}_{ji} \tag{7-18}$$

Add the two sides of Eq. (7-17) and Eq. (7-18):

$$\begin{aligned}2\sum_i \sum_j \mathbf{r}_i \times \mathbf{F}_{ij} &= \sum_i \sum_j (\mathbf{r}_j \times \mathbf{F}_{ji} - \mathbf{r}_i \times \mathbf{F}_{ji}) \\ &= \sum_i \sum_j (\mathbf{r}_j - \mathbf{r}_i) \times \mathbf{F}_{ji}\end{aligned}$$

But from Fig. 7-2 it can be seen that $\mathbf{r}_j - \mathbf{r}_i$ is simply the vector which connects particles i and j. Since $\mathbf{F}_{ji}$ is assumed to lie parallel to this line,

$$(\mathbf{r}_j - \mathbf{r}_i) \times \mathbf{F}_{ji} = 0$$

by the theory of cross products. Therefore the double sum is equal to zero. Equation (7-16) becomes

$$\dot{\mathbf{L}} = \mathbf{N}^e \tag{7-19}$$

This equation says that the rate of change of the total angular momentum of a system of particles is equal to the resultant torque exerted by all external forces which act on the system. We shall call it the *torque law* for a system of particles.

If no external torque acts on the system of particles, then $\dot{\mathbf{L}}$ equals zero so $\mathbf{L}$ is constant. The *law of conservation of angular momentum* says that *in the absence of external torques the angular momentum of a system of particles remains constant.* Notice carefully that the law of conservation of angular momentum deals with measurements made with respect to an *inertial* reference frame.

The particles in the system do not have to be "rotating" about the origin in any obviously ordered way for these expressions to be true. A dust cloud in space will follow these equations just as well as a phonograph turntable.

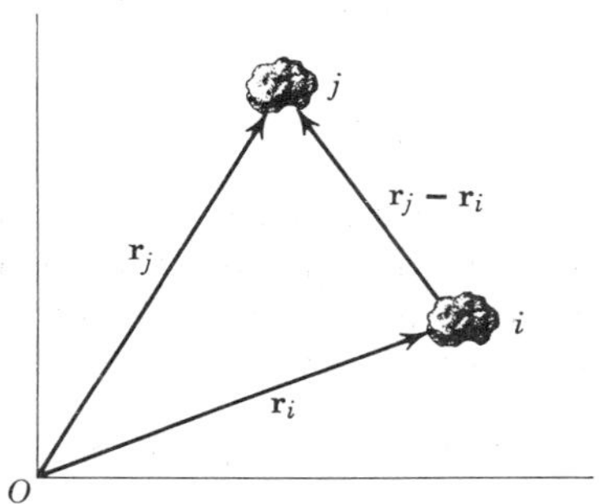

Fig. 7-2. Determination of $\mathbf{r}_j - \mathbf{r}_i$.

Questions

7-12 Is it possible for $\mathbf{N}^e$ to be equal to zero if $\mathbf{F}^e$ is not equal to zero?

7-13 Will Eq. (7-19) necessarily be valid if the particles in the system interact with magnetic forces? Will Eq. (7-10) necessarily be valid?

7.5 ANGULAR MOMENTUM WITH RESPECT TO A MOVING POINT. Consider the following three physical systems: (*a*) a uniform cylindrical disk rolling down an inclined plane, (*b*) the tire of an automobile rotating as the car accelerates along a smooth straight road, (*c*) a jet turbine rotor spinning as the airplane flies along. All these physical systems have in common a rigid body rotating about *an axis which is moving with respect to an inertial reference frame.* How can we analyze the rotation of these bodies with respect to moving axes? The equations of motion derived thus far hold only with respect to points which are at rest with respect to an inertial reference frame. Nevertheless under certain circumstances the laws of motion about moving axes will have the same form as that about an axis at rest in an inertial reference system. We shall return to rigid body motion in the next chapter. We investigate here the following more general question: Under what circumstances will the torque law in which measurements are made with respect to an arbitrarily moving point give the same result as the torque law in which measurements are made with respect to a point which is stationary in an inertial coordinate system?

The coordinate system of Fig. 7-3 with origin at point O is an inertial coordinate system. The location of particle i, which represents any one of

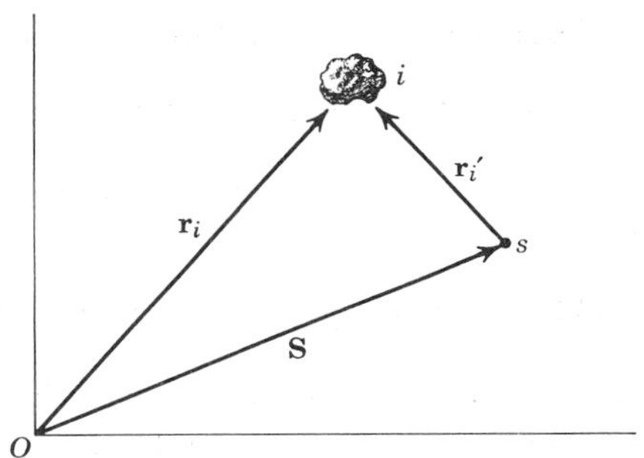

Fig. 7-3. Position of particle i with respect to a moving point s.

the particles in the system of particles, is given by the vector $\mathbf{r}_i$. Point s is some arbitrary point whose location is determined by the vector $\mathbf{S}$. Point s may move in any arbitrary manner with respect to point O. The velocity of point s with respect to point O may be large or small and may change direction or magnitude with time, but point s does not jump discontinuously from one position to another or from one velocity to another. In other words, point s behaves no more erratically than a particle behaves. We now ask, What would be the laws of motion of the system of particles if point s were taken as the origin?

Let $\mathbf{r}_i'$ be the vector which locates particle i with respect to point s. From Fig. 7-3,

$$\mathbf{r}_i = \mathbf{S} + \mathbf{r}_i' \tag{7-20}$$

from which it follows that

$$\dot{\mathbf{r}}_i = \dot{\mathbf{S}} + \dot{\mathbf{r}}_i' \tag{7-21}$$

In the inertial coordinate system the total angular momentum of the system of particles about O is defined by the equation

$$\mathbf{L} = \sum_i \mathbf{r}_i \times m_i\dot{\mathbf{r}}_i \tag{7-22}$$

Substitute into this equation from Eqs. (7-20) and (7-21).

$$\mathbf{L} = \sum_i (\mathbf{S} + \mathbf{r}_i') \times m_i(\dot{\mathbf{S}} + \dot{\mathbf{r}}_i')$$

Expand the separate cross products.

$$\mathbf{L} = \sum_i \mathbf{S} \times m_i\dot{\mathbf{S}} + \sum_i \mathbf{S} \times m_i\dot{\mathbf{r}}_i' + \sum_i \mathbf{r}_i' \times m_i\dot{\mathbf{S}} + \sum_i \mathbf{r}_i' \times m_i\dot{\mathbf{r}}_i' \tag{7-23}$$

The last term has the same form as the right side of Eq. (7-22) with $\mathbf{r}_i$ replaced by $\mathbf{r}_i'$. This term is by definition the angular momentum of the system of particles about the point s. Call this angular momentum $\mathbf{L}_s$.

$$\mathbf{L}_s = \sum_i \mathbf{r}_i' \times m_i\dot{\mathbf{r}}_i' \qquad \text{definition} \tag{7-24}$$

Substitute this into Eq. (7-23). The other terms can be rewritten so that the equation reads

$$\mathbf{L} = (\sum_i m_i)\mathbf{S} \times \dot{\mathbf{S}} + \mathbf{S} \times (\sum_i m_i\dot{\mathbf{r}}_i') + (\sum_i m_i\mathbf{r}_i') \times \dot{\mathbf{S}} + \mathbf{L}_s \tag{7-25}$$

Now consider the summations in this equation. The first one is simply the total mass M of all the particles in the system.

$$\sum_i m_i = M$$

If we were to find the location $\mathbf{R}'$ of the center of mass of the system of particles with respect to point s (see Fig. 7-4), its location would be defined as (see Eq. 7-3)

$$\mathbf{R}' = \frac{\sum_i m_i\mathbf{r}_i'}{M} \qquad \text{definition} \tag{7-26}$$

so that the sum $\sum_i m_i\mathbf{r}_i'$ in the third term on the right of Eq. (7-25) is

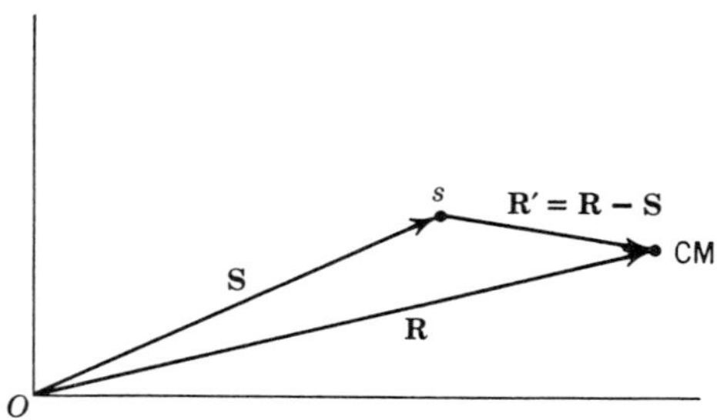

Fig. 7-4. Position of center of mass with respect to point s.

simply $M\mathbf{R}'$. But, from Fig. 7-4, $\mathbf{R}' = \mathbf{R} - \mathbf{S}$, where $\mathbf{R}$ is the location of the center of mass with respect to point O. Hence

$$\sum_i m_i \mathbf{r}_i' = M\mathbf{R}' = M(\mathbf{R} - \mathbf{S})$$

If we take the time derivative of both sides of this equation we have

$$\sum_i m_i \dot{\mathbf{r}}_i' = M(\dot{\mathbf{R}} - \dot{\mathbf{S}})$$

which is the summation found in the second term on the right of Eq. (7-25).

With these substitutions, Eq. (7-25) becomes

$$\begin{aligned} \mathbf{L} &= M\mathbf{S} \times \dot{\mathbf{S}} + \mathbf{S} \times M(\dot{\mathbf{R}} - \dot{\mathbf{S}}) + M(\mathbf{R} - \mathbf{S}) \times \dot{\mathbf{S}} + \dot{\mathbf{L}}_s \\ &= \cancel{M\mathbf{S} \times \dot{\mathbf{S}}} + M\mathbf{S} \times \dot{\mathbf{R}} - \cancel{M\mathbf{S} \times \dot{\mathbf{S}}} + M(\mathbf{R} - \mathbf{S}) \times \dot{\mathbf{S}} + \mathbf{L}_s \\ \mathbf{L} &= M\mathbf{S} \times \dot{\mathbf{R}} + M(\mathbf{R} - \mathbf{S}) \times \dot{\mathbf{S}} + \mathbf{L}_s \qquad (7\text{-}27) \end{aligned}$$

Equation (7-27) relates the angular momentum of the system of particles about the inertial point O to the angular momentum of the system of particles about the arbitrary point s. The result shows that in general the two are not equal.

Question

7-14 Prove that $\mathbf{L} = \mathbf{L}_s$ provided that at least one of the following conditions is satisfied.

(1) $\mathbf{S} = 0$ or
(2) $\dot{\mathbf{R}} = 0$ or
(3) $\mathbf{S}$ is parallel to $\mathbf{R}$

and provided at least one of the following conditions is satisfied.

(1)′ $\mathbf{R} = \mathbf{S}$ or
(2) $\dot{\mathbf{S}} = 0$ or
(3) $(\mathbf{R} - \mathbf{S})$ is parallel to $\dot{\mathbf{S}}$.

Describe some motions of point s which would satisfy both of these criteria.

We wish to find the circumstances, if any exist, under which Eq. (7-19)

$$\mathbf{N}^e = \dot{\mathbf{L}} \qquad (7\text{-}19)$$

for motion about O is also valid for motion about s:

$$\mathbf{N}_s^e \overset{?}{=} \dot{\mathbf{L}}_s$$

where $\mathbf{N}_s^e$ is the net external torque measured about point s. To do this we take the time derivative of both sides of Eq. (7-27).

$$\begin{aligned}\dot{\mathbf{L}} &= M\dot{\mathbf{S}} \times \dot{\mathbf{R}} + M\mathbf{S} \times \ddot{\mathbf{R}} + M(\dot{\mathbf{R}} - \dot{\mathbf{S}}) \times \dot{\mathbf{S}} \\ &\quad + M(\mathbf{R} - \mathbf{S}) \times \ddot{\mathbf{S}} + \dot{\mathbf{L}}_s \\ &= M\dot{\mathbf{S}} \times \dot{\mathbf{R}} + \mathbf{S} \times M\ddot{\mathbf{R}} + M(\dot{\mathbf{R}} \times \dot{\mathbf{S}}) \\ &\quad - M(\dot{\mathbf{S}} \times \dot{\mathbf{S}}) + M(\mathbf{R} - \mathbf{S}) \times \ddot{\mathbf{S}} + \dot{\mathbf{L}}_s \qquad (7\text{-}28)\end{aligned}$$

Now, since $\dot{\mathbf{S}} \times \dot{\mathbf{R}} = -\dot{\mathbf{R}} \times \dot{\mathbf{S}}$ from the laws of cross products, the first and third terms in Eq. (7-28) cancel. Also, since $\dot{\mathbf{S}}$ is clearly parallel to itself, $\dot{\mathbf{S}} \times \dot{\mathbf{S}} = 0$. Hence

$$\dot{\mathbf{L}} = \mathbf{S} \times M\ddot{\mathbf{R}} + M(\mathbf{R} - \mathbf{S}) \times \ddot{\mathbf{S}} + \dot{\mathbf{L}}_s \qquad (7\text{-}29)$$

Question

7-15 What conditions must be satisfied in order that $\dot{\mathbf{L}} = \dot{\mathbf{L}}_s$? Are these conditions different from those in the last question?

The torque about O due to external forces is defined as

$$\mathbf{N}^e = \sum_i \mathbf{r}_i \times \mathbf{F}_i^e \qquad (7\text{-}30)$$

In order to relate this torque to the torque about point s, we substitute from Eq. (7-20) for $\mathbf{r}_i$.

$$\begin{aligned}\mathbf{N}^e &= \sum_i (\mathbf{S} + \mathbf{r}_i') \times \mathbf{F}_i^e \\ &= \sum_i \mathbf{S} \times \mathbf{F}_i^e + \sum_i \mathbf{r}_i' \times \mathbf{F}_i^e \\ \mathbf{N}^e &= \mathbf{S} \times (\sum_i \mathbf{F}_i^e) + \sum_i \mathbf{r}_i' \times \mathbf{F}_i^e \qquad (7\text{-}31)\end{aligned}$$

But the first summation on the right is simply the net external force $\mathbf{F}^e$ on all particles of the system.

$$\sum_i \mathbf{F}_i^e = \mathbf{F}^e \qquad (7\text{-}32)$$

The second term on the right of Eq. (7-31) is by definition the net external torque about point s. Call this $\mathbf{N}_s^e$.

$$\sum_i \mathbf{r}_i' \times \mathbf{F}_i^e = \mathbf{N}_s^e \qquad \text{definition} \qquad (7\text{-}33)$$

Therefore Eq. (7-31) becomes

$$\mathbf{N}^e = \mathbf{S} \times \mathbf{F}^e + \mathbf{N}_s^e \qquad (7\text{-}34)$$

From Eq. (7-10)

$$\mathbf{F}^e = M\ddot{\mathbf{R}}$$

so that Eq. (7-34) becomes

$$\mathbf{N}^e = \mathbf{S} \times M\ddot{\mathbf{R}} + \mathbf{N}_s^e \qquad (7\text{-}35)$$

This equation relates the net external torque on the system of particles about point O to the net external torque about point s.

Now Eq. (7-19) says that

$$\mathbf{N}^e = \dot{\mathbf{L}} \tag{7-19}$$

about point O since this point is at rest in an inertial reference frame. Substitute into this equation from Eqs. (7-29) and (7-35).

$$\mathbf{S} \times M\ddot{\mathbf{R}} + \mathbf{N}_s^{\,e} = \mathbf{S} \times M\ddot{\mathbf{R}} + M(\mathbf{R} - \mathbf{S}) \times \ddot{\mathbf{S}} + \dot{\mathbf{L}}_s$$

or

$$\boxed{\mathbf{N}_s^{\,e} = M(\mathbf{R} - \mathbf{S}) \times \ddot{\mathbf{S}} + \dot{\mathbf{L}}_s} \tag{7-36}$$

This equation relates the torque about point s to the rate of change of angular momentum about point s. The equation shows that

$$\mathbf{N}_s^{\,e} = \dot{\mathbf{L}}_s \tag{7-37}$$

provided that at least one of the following conditions is satisfied.

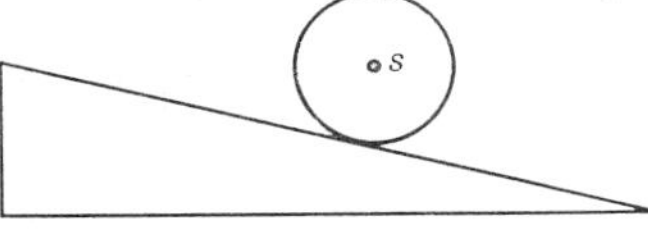

Fig. 7-5.

(1) $\mathbf{R} = \mathbf{S}$, that is, point s is at the center of mass, or

(2) $\ddot{\mathbf{S}} = 0$, that is, point s moves with constant velocity or zero velocity with respect to the inertial frame, or

(3) $(\mathbf{R} - \mathbf{S})$ is parallel to $\ddot{\mathbf{S}}$.

Example. A uniform circular disk rolls down an inclined plane (see Fig. 7-5). Show that Eq. (7-37) holds if s is at the center of the disk.

Solution. Since the disk is uniform, the center of mass must be at the center of the disk. Hence $\mathbf{R} = \mathbf{S}$ and Eq. (7-37) holds.

Questions

7-16 Show that Eq. (7-37) holds for the other two physical systems which were described at the beginning of this section provided that point s is on the axis of rotation in each case. Will Eq. (7-37) hold in each case if point s moves *along* the axis of rotation?

7-17 Does Eq. (7-37) apply to the rotation of the earth about a point on its axis? Is the angular momentum of the earth about such a point a constant?

7.6 KINETIC ENERGY WITH RESPECT TO A MOVING POINT.

The kinetic energy T_i of particle i is

$$T_i = \tfrac{1}{2} m_i v_i^{\,2} = \tfrac{1}{2} m_i \dot{r}_i^{\,2} = \tfrac{1}{2} m_i \dot{\mathbf{r}}_i \cdot \dot{\mathbf{r}}_i$$

The total kinetic energy T of the system of particles is

$$T = \sum_i T_i = \tfrac{1}{2} \sum_i m_i \dot{\mathbf{r}}_i \cdot \dot{\mathbf{r}}_i \tag{7-38}$$

With respect to Fig. 7-3, let $\dot{\mathbf{r}}_i = \dot{\mathbf{S}} + \dot{\mathbf{r}}_i'$ so that

$$\begin{aligned} T &= \tfrac{1}{2} \sum_i m_i(\dot{\mathbf{S}} + \dot{\mathbf{r}}_i') \cdot (\dot{\mathbf{S}} + \dot{\mathbf{r}}_i') \\ &= \tfrac{1}{2} \sum_i m_i \dot{\mathbf{S}} \cdot \dot{\mathbf{S}} + \tfrac{1}{2} \sum_i m_i \dot{\mathbf{S}} \cdot \dot{\mathbf{r}}_i' \\ &\quad + \tfrac{1}{2} \sum_i m_i \dot{\mathbf{r}}_i' \cdot \dot{\mathbf{S}} + \tfrac{1}{2} \sum_i m_i \dot{\mathbf{r}}_i' \cdot \dot{\mathbf{r}}_i' \end{aligned}$$

$$T = \tfrac{1}{2}\left(\sum_i m_i\right)\dot{\mathbf{S}} \cdot \dot{\mathbf{S}} + \dot{\mathbf{S}} \cdot \left(\sum_i m_i \dot{\mathbf{r}}_i'\right) + \tfrac{1}{2} \sum_i m_i \dot{\mathbf{r}}_i' \cdot \dot{\mathbf{r}}_i' \tag{7-39}$$

but, as before (see Fig. 7-4),

$$\sum_i m_i = M$$

$$\sum_i m_i \dot{\mathbf{r}}_i' = M\dot{\mathbf{R}}' = M \frac{d}{dt}(\mathbf{R} - \mathbf{S})$$

and the last summation on the right of Eq. (7-39) is the kinetic energy with respect to motion about point s. Call this kinetic energy T_s.

$$T_s = \tfrac{1}{2} \sum_i m_i \dot{\mathbf{r}}_i' \cdot \dot{\mathbf{r}}_i' \qquad \text{definition} \tag{7-40}$$

With these substitutions Eq. (7-39) becomes

$$T = \tfrac{1}{2} M\dot{S}^2 + M\dot{\mathbf{S}} \cdot \left[\frac{d}{dt}(\mathbf{R} - \mathbf{S})\right] + T_s \tag{7-41}$$

Equation (7-41) relates the kinetic energy of the system of particles about the inertial point O to the kinetic energy of the system of particles about the arbitrary point s. This equation becomes simplified under some circumstances. First of all, if $\dot{\mathbf{S}} = 0$, that is, if point s is fixed in space, then

$$T = T_s \tag{7-42}$$

On the other hand, even if $\dot{\mathbf{S}} \neq 0$, the second term on the right of Eq. (7-41) will be equal to zero if at least one of the following conditions is satisfied.

(1) $\mathbf{R} - \mathbf{S} = 0$, that is, if point s is at the center of mass, or

(2) $\mathbf{R} - \mathbf{S}$ is a constant, that is, if the vector from point s to the center of mass is constant in magnitude and direction, or

(3) $(d/dt)(\mathbf{R} - \mathbf{S})$ is perpendicular to $\dot{\mathbf{S}}$.

In this case Eq. (7-41) becomes

$$T = \tfrac{1}{2}M\dot{S}^2 + T_s \tag{7-43}$$

This very important equation says that, under the conditions described above, the kinetic energy consists of two parts: the kinetic energy obtained if all the mass of the system were concentrated at point s and the kinetic energy of the system about point s.

Question

7-18 Suppose that point s lies on the axis of rotation of each of the three physical systems which were described at the beginning of Sec. 7.5. Under these circumstances will Eq. (7-43) hold for each of these systems? Will Eq. (7-43) hold in each case if point s moves *along* the axis of rotation?

7.7 MOTION WITH RESPECT TO THE CENTER OF MASS. The equations derived in the last two sections take on a particularly simple form if point s coincides with the center of mass of the system of particles, i.e., if $\mathbf{R} = \mathbf{S}$.

Let the subscript cm represent a measurement with respect to the center of mass. Thus $\mathbf{N}_{\text{cm}}{}^e$ represents the resultant external torque measured with respect to the center of mass, and so on. If point s is at the center of mass, Eqs. (7-27), (7-29), (7-34), (7-36), and (7-41) become

$$\mathbf{L} = \mathbf{L}_{\text{cm}} + M\mathbf{R} \times \dot{\mathbf{R}} \tag{7-44}$$

$$\dot{\mathbf{L}} = \dot{\mathbf{L}}_{\text{cm}} + M\mathbf{R} \times \ddot{\mathbf{R}} \tag{7-45}$$

$$\mathbf{N}^e = \mathbf{N}_{\text{cm}}{}^e + \mathbf{R} \times \mathbf{F}^e = \mathbf{N}_{\text{cm}}{}^e + M\mathbf{R} \times \ddot{\mathbf{R}} \tag{7-46}$$

$$\mathbf{N}_{\text{cm}}{}^e = \dot{\mathbf{L}}_{\text{cm}} \tag{7-47}$$

$$T = T_{\text{cm}} + \tfrac{1}{2}M\dot{R}^2 \tag{7-48}$$

These results will be very useful in the next chapter.

Questions

7-19 If Q represents any of the quantities $\mathbf{L}$, $\dot{\mathbf{L}}$, $\mathbf{N}^e$, or T in Eqs. (7-44) through (7-48), show that all these equations are of the form

[Q calculated with respect to the inertial point O] equals [Q calculated with respect to the center of mass]

plus [Q calculated with respect to the inertial point O for a particle of mass M located at the center of mass]

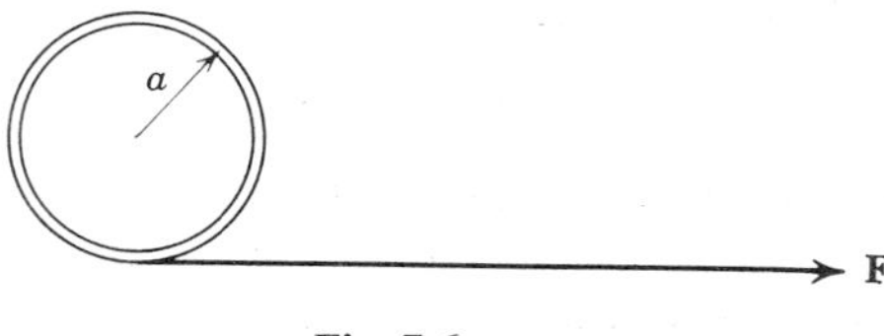

Fig. 7-6.

7-20 Enumerate the conditions which must be satisfied in each case if the following equations are to be true.

$$\mathbf{L} = \mathbf{L}_{cm}$$
$$\dot{\mathbf{L}} = \dot{\mathbf{L}}_{cm}$$
$$\mathbf{N}^e = \mathbf{N}_{cm}{}^e$$
$$T = T_{cm}$$

7-21 An inextensible string of negligible mass is wrapped tightly around the rim of a thin circular hoop of mass M and radius a. The center of the hoop is placed at rest at the origin O of an inertial coordinate system, and a constant linear force **F** is applied to the string in a direction which lies in the plane of the hoop as shown in Fig. 7-6. Write equations for the displacement and rotation of the hoop while the string is unwinding.

In this chapter we have derived some laws which interrelate some of the average properties of the motion of a system of particles. These average properties include the acceleration of the center of mass, the total angular momentum and its time derivative, the total kinetic energy, the net external force, and the net external torque. Knowledge of these average properties can be very useful, but they do not describe the motion of the system completely. The position and velocity of every particle in the system are not derivable from these laws. A complete description will depend on the detailed way in which the particles are interconnected. We shall treat one type of interconnection between particles in the next chapter.

EXERCISES

7-1 An artillery shell explodes in mid-air over level ground. Describe qualitatively the motion of the center of mass until the center of mass comes to rest.

7-2 Consider a system of particles made up of the earth and the moon revolving about each other as they proceed together around the sun. Is there a point in this system of particles about which angular momentum is conserved? If it exists, find the position of this point. Do not assume that the moon has negligible mass compared with the mass of the earth, and do not assume that the path of the system around the sun is a circle.

7-3 Consider the system of particles which is made up of the turbine rotor of the single jet engine of an airplane which is banking in a horizontal circular turn. Assume that the center of mass of the rotor lies on its axis of rotation and that the center of the circle around which the airplane moves is at rest in an inertial reference system. Does the net external torque on the rotor about any arbitrary point on its axis of symmetry equal the rate of change of angular momentum about that point? If not, is there any single point on the axis of symmetry about which the net external torque equals the rate of change of angular momentum?

7-4 A uniform sphere rolls from rest down an inclined plane (see Fig. 7-7). Consider the straight line traced out by the center of the sphere. An imaginary point s moves along this straight line with constant acceleration g. Does the torque on the sphere measured with respect to point s equal the rate of change of angular momentum of the sphere measured with respect to point s?

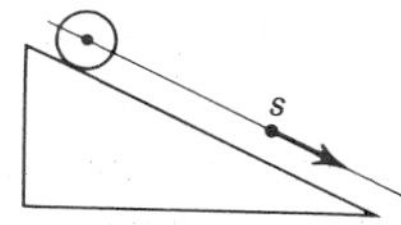

Fig. 7-7.

7-5 The gravitational field of the moon attracts the oceans of the earth, causing tides. The friction of the tides against the land exerts a torque on the earth which gradually slows down the rotation of the earth about its axis. At the same time the radius of the path of the moon about the earth is observed to increase slowly with time. Using the conservation of angular momentum, show qualitatively how these two observations can be related. Is mechanical energy conserved in this process? Predict the ultimate result of this process. Your qualitative answer to this question will not be affected if you assume that the center of mass of the moon follows a circular path about the center of mass of the earth and that the center of mass of the earth is fixed in an inertial reference frame. You may wish to consider the problem with these assumptions relaxed.

7-6 The *center of gravity* of a system of particles is defined as that point about which gravitation forces exert no net torque. Show that in a uniform gravitational field the center of gravity of a system of particles coincides with the center of mass.

chapter 8

The rigid body

8.1 INTRODUCTION. The equations for a system of particles derived in the last chapter have very wide application in physics. They are used in studying the motion of galaxies, the motions in our solar system, geological occurrences on the earth, the machines men use, and, with considerable modification, the motions of elementary particles in the atom and the nucleus. The ratio of the diameter of our galaxy to the diameter of the nucleus is roughly 10^{34}. This is a very wide range for the usefulness of any physical law.

One of the most useful special cases of a system of particles is the rigid body. Roughly speaking, a rigid body is one which does not change its size or shape during a given experiment. The earth, a baseball, a gear wheel, a steel beam are all objects which may be called rigid bodies. Strictly speaking, the concept of a rigid body is an idealization which is never rigorously realized in practice. The earth is covered with oceans which move, a baseball is distorted at the moment of impact with a bat, a steel beam may bend or vibrate under a load. In fact, all solid matter is made up of atoms which are continually agitated by thermal vibrations. Nevertheless the concept of rigid body can be a very useful one in practice. The earth does not change diameter by as much as two parts in a million because of tides, a baseball is nearly rigid after leaving the bat, and the thermal vibrations are too small to affect parts of a rigid body large enough to be visible to the unaided eye. A physical "rigid body" must be sufficiently rigid, with respect to the scale and accuracy of the experiment, that its departure from rigidity does not influence the experimental results beyond some permissible limit of error.

The individual particles which make up the idealized rigid body are always the same fixed distance from one another. This constitutes a rigorous definition of a rigid body. In mathematical language, if $\mathbf{r}_i$ is the position vector of a particle i in a body and $\mathbf{r}_j$ is the position vector of another particle j in the body, then the body is rigid by definition if the scalar quantity

$$|\mathbf{r}_j - \mathbf{r}_i| = c_{ij} \tag{8-1}$$

is constant for every pair of particles in the body. The symbol c_{ij} is a scalar, in general different for every pair of particles in the body, but constant in time for any particular pair of particles.

Questions

8-1 Show that another way of expressing Eq. (8-1) is

$$(\mathbf{r}_j - \mathbf{r}_i) \cdot (\mathbf{r}_j - \mathbf{r}_i) = c_{ij}^2 \tag{8-2}$$

where the dot implies a dot product.

8-2 Show that $c_{ij} = c_{ji}$.

How will a rigid body move under the action of forces and torques? To begin with, the results derived in the last chapter for a system of particles will apply to the special case of a rigid body. Thus the center of mass of a rigid body which is acted on by several forces will move in the same way that a particle of mass equal to the total mass of the rigid body would move if acted on by the same forces. Also, the vector rate of change of angular momentum of the rigid body about any point fixed in an inertial coordinate frame is equal to the net torque on the body about that point. The rules concerning angular momentum and kinetic energy with respect to a moving point and with respect to the center of mass (Sec. 7.5 through 7.7) hold for the special case of the rigid body.

The laws derived in Chapter 7 for a system of particles can be used to describe the motion of the center of mass of a rigid body. However they do not describe completely the *orientation* of the rigid body about the center of mass. This orientation cannot be described completely from a knowledge of the total angular momentum and kinetic energy measured with respect to the center of mass.

A complete description of the rotation of a rigid body about its center of mass can be derived from the laws of motion, but this description is quite complicated and is best accomplished by using more advanced mathematical methods. Fortunately, most of the practical problems involving rotating rigid bodies deal either with rotation about a fixed axis or with rotation about an axis which moves parallel to itself (such as the rotation of the wheel of an automobile which is driven along a straight road). For these cases the description of rotation is greatly simplified.

In the next section we shall treat the case of a rigid body rotating about a fixed axis. In Sec. 8.10 the treatment will be extended to include rotation about an axis which moves parallel to itself.

Question

8-3 Find a very unsymmetrical rigid body. There are not too many of these about in this age of manufacture, but a stone or bent stick will do. Throw this unsymmetrical rigid body into the air several times, twisting it in a different way each time you let go of it. Do you wonder that the complete description of this kind of motion is rather complicated?

8.2 RIGID BODY ROTATING ABOUT A FIXED AXIS. THE MOMENT OF INERTIA. Consider a rigid body rotating about an axis as shown in Fig. 8-1. We shall assume that this axis is fixed in the body and that the ends of this axis are also fixed with respect to an inertial coordinate system so that the only motion of the body is rotation about the axis. We shall assume also that the origin of the inertial coordinate system is chosen to lie at some point O on the axis of rotation.

Consider a volume element of the rigid body which has a mass m_i. Call this volume element "particle i." The vector $\mathbf{r}_i$ in Fig. 8-1 represents the position of particle i with respect to the origin at O. It will be convenient to describe the position of particle i in a somewhat different way. Draw the z-axis of a Cartesian coordinate system along the axis of rotation starting at point O. The x- and y-axes will be mutually perpendicular and

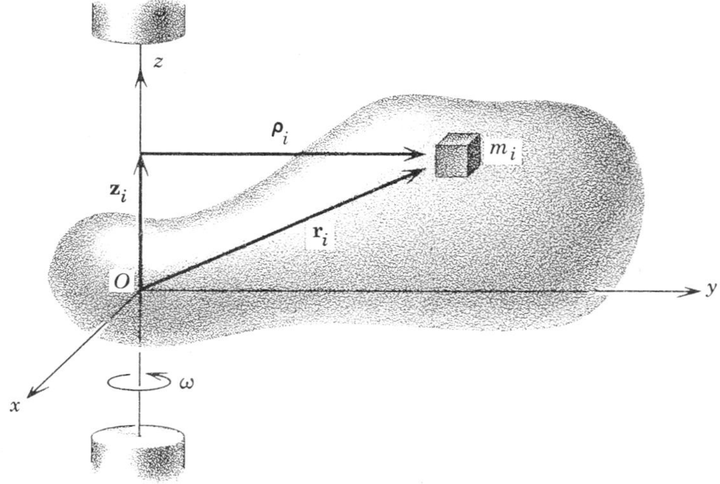

Fig. 8-1. Rigid body rotating about a fixed axis.

perpendicular to the z-axis through O. We shall describe the position of particle i by the two vectors $\mathbf{z}_i$ and $\boldsymbol{\rho}_i$ (Fig. 8-1). The vector $\mathbf{z}_i$ represents the perpendicular height of particle i above the xy plane. The vector $\boldsymbol{\rho}_i$ represents the perpendicular distance from the z-axis to particle i. The vector $\mathbf{z}_i$ will always be vertical, while the vector $\boldsymbol{\rho}_i$ will always lie parallel to the xy plane. From Fig. 8-1 the position of vector $\mathbf{r}_i$ can be expressed in terms of $\mathbf{z}_i$ and $\boldsymbol{\rho}_i$.

$$\mathbf{r}_i = \mathbf{z}_i + \boldsymbol{\rho}_i \tag{8-3}$$

from which it follows that

$$\dot{\mathbf{r}}_i = \dot{\mathbf{z}}_i + \dot{\boldsymbol{\rho}}_i \tag{8-4}$$

and

$$\ddot{\mathbf{r}}_i = \ddot{\mathbf{z}}_i + \ddot{\boldsymbol{\rho}}_i \tag{8-5}$$

Questions

8-4 Show that, if particle i were not part of a rigid body but moved along an arbitrary path in space, $\dot{\mathbf{z}}_i$ and $\ddot{\mathbf{z}}_i$ would always be parallel to the z-axis and $\dot{\boldsymbol{\rho}}_i$ and $\ddot{\boldsymbol{\rho}}_i$ would always lie parallel to the xy plane.

8-5 For every particle i in the rotating rigid body of Fig. 8-1 show that $\dot{\mathbf{z}}_i = 0$, $\ddot{\mathbf{z}}_i = 0$, $|\boldsymbol{\rho}_i| =$ constant and that the tip of the vector $\boldsymbol{\rho}_i$ describes a circle around the axis of rotation.

Since we are dealing with a rigid body, every particle in the body will rotate about the axis with the same angular velocity. This is proved by the fact that after one revolution every particle in the body returns to its original position. Call this common angular velocity ω. The magnitude of the tangential velocity $\mathbf{v}_i$ of particle i about the axis of rotation is $v_i = \rho_i\omega$, where ρ_i is the magnitude of the vector $\boldsymbol{\rho}_i$. The *direction* of $\mathbf{v}_i$ is into the paper in Fig. 8-2. The angular momentum $\mathbf{l}_i$ of the volume element about the point O is given by

$$\mathbf{l}_i = \mathbf{r}_i \times m_i\mathbf{v}_i \tag{8-6}$$

The direction of this angular momentum is perpendicular to both $\mathbf{r}_i$ and $\mathbf{v}_i$ as shown in the figure. The *total* angular momentum of the rigid body $\mathbf{L} = \sum_i \mathbf{l}_i$ can be found by vector summation of the angular momenta from all volume elements in the rigid body. This total angular momentum will not necessarily lie along the axis of rotation. Even if ω is constant, $\mathbf{L}$ may change direction as the body rotates.

Question

8-6 Consider a long, thin, uniform rigid rod made to rotate about one end at a constant angle with respect to a fixed axis as shown in Fig. 8-3. If the rod is D meters long, weighs M kg, makes an angle θ with respect to

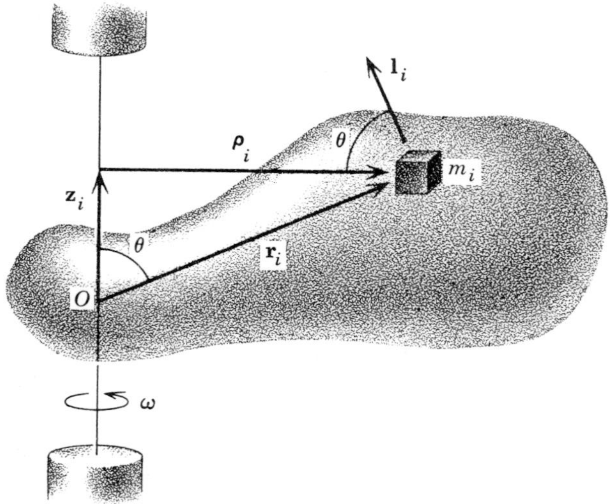

Fig. 8-2. Angular momentum $\mathbf{l}_i$ of particle i.

the axis of rotation, and rotates at a constant angular velocity ω radians/sec, what is the magnitude of the total angular momentum? What is the *direction* of the total angular momentum in the picture, and how does this direction change with time? What does this change of direction tell you about the forces which the bearings exert on the axis of rotation?

A more instructive result is found if we consider the component of $\mathbf{l}_i$ along the axis of rotation. Call this component l_{iz}. From Fig. 8-2 the magnitude of the component of $\mathbf{l}_i$ along the axis is given by $l_i \sin\theta$, or by $l_{iz} = m_i v_i r_i \sin\theta$. But $\rho_i = r_i \sin\theta$ and $v_i = \omega\rho_i$, so that

$$l_{iz} = m_i \rho_i^2 \omega \qquad (8\text{-}7)$$

Question

8-7 Show that the magnitude of l_{iz} does not depend on where the origin O of the coordinate system is chosen so long as this origin is on the axis of rotation.

The component of the total angular momentum of the rotating body along its axis of rotation L_z is given by

$$L_z = \sum l_{iz} = \sum_i m_i \rho_i^2 \omega = (\sum_i m_i \rho_i^2)\omega \qquad (8\text{-}8)$$

The sum $\sum_i m_i \rho_i^2$ is characteristic of the rigid body and of the choice of

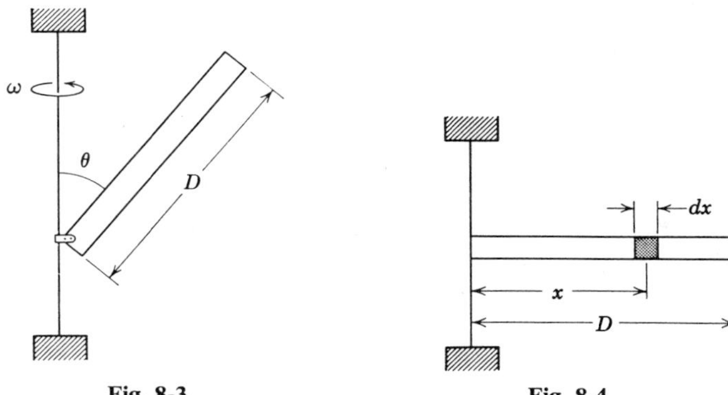

Fig. 8-3. Fig. 8-4.

the axis about which it rotates. This sum is called the *moment of inertia* of the rigid body about the given axis and is given the symbol I.

$$I = \sum_i m_i \rho_i^2 \qquad \text{definition} \tag{8-9}$$

The units of moment of inertia are kilogram-meters².

The moment of inertia of any body about a particular axis is found by taking the product of the mass of each volume element in the body and the square of its perpendicular distance from the axis of rotation and then summing all these products.

Example. What is the moment of inertia of a uniform rod of mass M and length D about an axis perpendicular to the rod through one end of the rod?

Solution. Consider a volume element of the rod of length dx and distance x from the axis (see Fig. 8-4). Since the rod is uniform, its density per unit length is M/D so the mass of this volume element is $(M/D)\,dx$. The summation in Eq. (8-9) becomes an integration.

$$I = \sum_i m_i \rho_i^2 \rightarrow \frac{M}{D} \int_0^D x^2\, dx = \frac{M}{D} \left[\frac{x^3}{3} \right]_0^D = \tfrac{1}{3} M D^2$$

Question

8-8 Show that the moment of inertia of a uniform rod of length D and mass M about an axis perpendicular to its length through the *center* of the rod is given by

$$I = \tfrac{1}{12} M D^2$$

Example. What is the moment of inertia of a uniform circular disk of mass M and radius R about an axis through its center perpendicular to the disk? (See Fig. 8-5.)

Solution. The density of the disk per unit area is given by $M/\pi R^2$. The mass of a thin circular ring of radius r and width dr is given by $(M/\pi R^2)(2\pi r\, dr)$. The moment of inertia of this thin circular ring is given by $r^2(M/\pi R^2)(2\pi r\, dr)$. The total moment of inertia is the sum of the moments of inertia of all such thin circular rings.

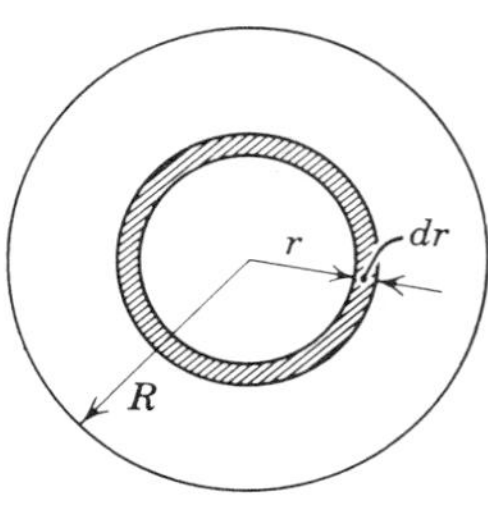

Fig. 8-5.

$$I = \int_0^R r^2\left(\frac{M}{\pi R^2}\right)(2\pi r\, dr)$$

$$= \frac{2M}{R^2}\int_0^R r^3\, dr = \frac{2M}{R^2}\left[\frac{r^4}{4}\right]_0^R$$

$$I = \tfrac{1}{2}MR^2$$

Question

8-9 Show that a uniform cylinder of mass M and radius R also has a moment of inertia about an axis which coincides with its cylindrical axis given by $\frac{1}{2}MR^2$.

Some moments of inertia for rigid bodies of uniform density are summarized in Fig. 8-6.

Questions

8-10 Using Fig. 8-6, find the moment of inertia of a uniform cube of edge length a about an axis which passes through the center of two opposite faces of the cube.

8-11 What is the moment of inertia of the earth about its axis? Assume that the earth is spherical and of uniform density.

With the substitution for I given in Eq. (8-9), Eq. (8-8) now reads

$$L_z = I\omega \tag{8-10}$$

Note the analogy to the equation for linear momentum, $p = mv$.

Question

8-12 What is the numerical value of the angular moment of the earth about its axis? Assume that the earth is spherical and of uniform density.

Now consider the net external torque on the rotating body $\mathbf{N}^e$. This torque will include not only torques exerted on the rotating body by way of

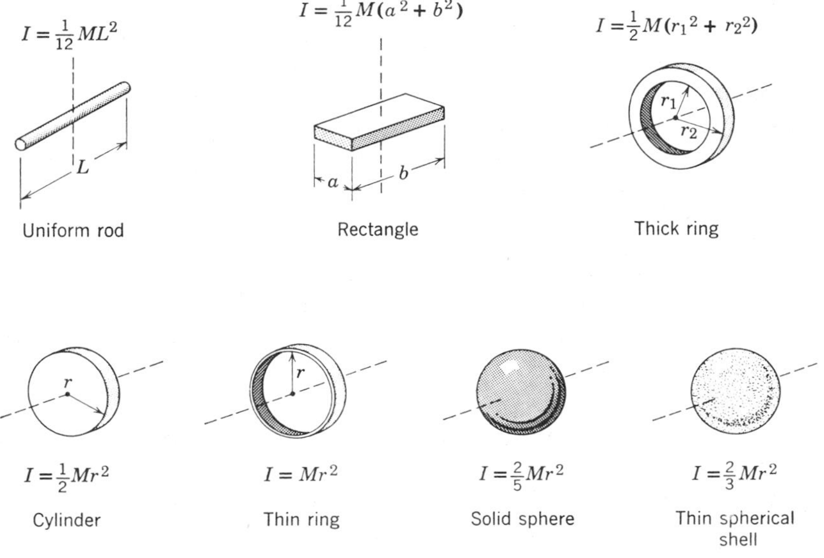

Fig. 8-6. Moments of inertia for several bodies of uniform density.

the axis and its bearings but also torques due to other external forces on the body. The relation between $\mathbf{N}^e$ and $\dot{\mathbf{L}}$ is given by Eq. (7-19).

$$\mathbf{N}^e = \dot{\mathbf{L}} \tag{7-19}$$

If we take components of these two vectors parallel to the axis of rotation, the left side becomes N_z^e and the right side becomes

$$\dot{L}_z = \frac{d}{dt}(I\omega)$$

so that

$$N_z^e = \frac{d}{dt}(I\omega) \tag{8-11}$$

If I is constant, this equation becomes

$$N_z^e = I\dot{\omega} \tag{8-12}$$

Equation (8-12) says that the rate of change of the component of angular momentum along the fixed axis of rotation of a rigid body is equal to the component of the net torque along the same axis. Note the analogy to the equation for linear motion, $F = m\dot{v}$.

Questions

8-13 A flywheel of mass 10^4 kg and radius 2 m is rotated from rest about its central axis by a constant net torque of 10 N-m. What is the angular acceleration of the flywheel in radians per second^2?

8-14 A wheel with moment of inertia I is acted on by a net torque given by $N_z^e = at - bt^3$, where a and b are constants. If the wheel starts with an initial angular velocity $+\omega_1$, find an expression for its angular velocity as a function of time.

8-15 Accurate astronomical observations tell us that it takes 0.0016 sec longer for the earth to rotate once on its axis now than it did one hundred years ago. What single force applied due west at the equator of the earth constantly for that period would be sufficient to cause this decrease in rotation rate?

8.3 CONSERVATION OF ANGULAR MOMENTUM ABOUT A FIXED AXIS. Suppose that no torques N_z^e are exerted on a rigid body rotating about a fixed axis. In this case, according to Eq. (8-11), $I\omega$ is a constant. In other words, the z-component of angular momentum is conserved. This means that, if the moment of inertia I remains constant, ω will remain constant. It is possible, however, for the moment of inertia I to change. This could be accomplished by such a scheme as that represented in Fig. 8-7, where the rigid rods are of negligible mass. If the initial and final moments of inertia are I_1 and I_2 respectively and the initial and final angular velocities are ω_1 and ω_2 respectively, then, since $I\omega$ must remain constant for a torque-free system, it follows that

$$I_1\omega_1 = I_2\omega_2 \tag{8-13}$$

Example. In Fig. 8-7, $m = 1$ kg, $\rho_1 = 1$ m, $\rho_2 = 5$ m, $\omega_1 = 1$ radian/sec. What is ω_2?

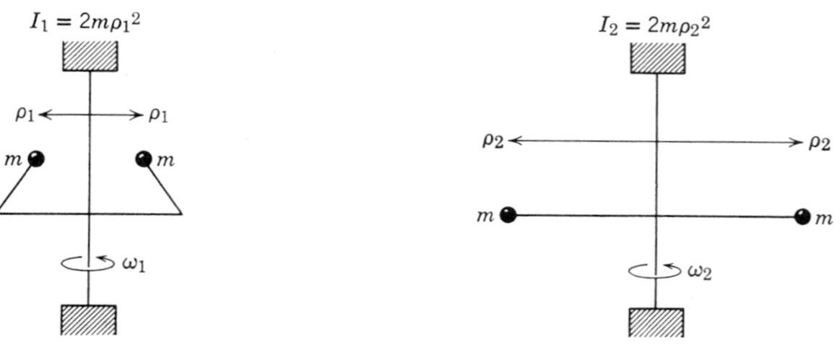

Fig. 8-7. Changing the moment of inertia of a rotating body.

Solution.

$$I_1 = 2m\rho_1^2 = 2(1)(1)^2 = 2 \text{ kg-m}^2$$

$$I_2 = 2m\rho_2^2 = 2(1)(5)^2 = 50 \text{ kg-m}^2$$

$$I_1\omega_1 = 2 \times 1 \text{ kg-m rad/sec} = I_2\omega_2 = 50 \text{ kg-m}^2\, \omega_2$$

so

$$\omega_2 = \tfrac{2}{50} = \tfrac{1}{25} \text{ rad/sec}$$

Questions

8-16 A skater rotating at a rate of one revolution per second on the tip of one skate with arms extended has a moment of inertia I about the axis of rotation. By pulling her arms in she reduces her moment of inertia to $\frac{1}{2}I$. If the torque exerted by the ice on the tip of her skate can be neglected, at how many revolutions per second will she rotate with her arms pulled in?

8-17 A space ship of cylindrical symmetry is rotating about its cylindrical axis. In order to slow the rate of rotation, two strings of negligible mass with particles of equal mass on the ends are let out symmetrically on opposite sides of the space ship. After the strings are let out to full length, the particle on the end of each string rotates about the axis of the ship at the same angular rate as the ship rotates. If each particle has a mass of 10 kg and the moment of inertia of the space ship is 1000 kg-m^2, what must be the length of each string in order that the final angular velocity of the space ship be 1 percent of its initial angular velocity? Assume that the particles were initially a perpendicular distance of 2 m from the axis of the space ship. Is angular momentum conserved if both strings are cut simultaneously?

8.4 THE PARALLEL AXIS THEOREM. The moment of inertia of a rigid body about a fixed axis depends on the position of the axis in the body. For instance, the moment of inertia of a thin uniform rod about an axis perpendicular to the rod through its center is different from the moment of inertia about an axis perpendicular to the rod through one end, as was shown in Sec. 8.2. Sometimes it is easy to calculate the moment of inertia of a symmetrical body about its axis of symmetry (such as the moment of inertia of a circular disk about an axis through its center) but difficult to calculate the moment of inertia about any other axis.

If the moment of inertia of a rigid body about any axis which passes through its center of mass is known, then it is easy to calculate its moment of inertia about any axis parallel to this one.

Consider an axis of rotation perpendicular to the paper which passes through point O' in Fig. 8-8 and also passes through the center of mass of the rigid body. The perpendicular distance and direction from the axis through O' to volume element i is denoted by the vector $\boldsymbol{\rho}_i'$. We wish to find the moment of inertia of the rigid body about an axis which is also perpendicular to the paper through point O. The perpendicular distance and direction from the axis through O to the axis through O' is denoted by the vector $\mathbf{b}$. The perpendicular distance and direction from the axis through O to volume element i is given by $\boldsymbol{\rho}_i$. From the figure,

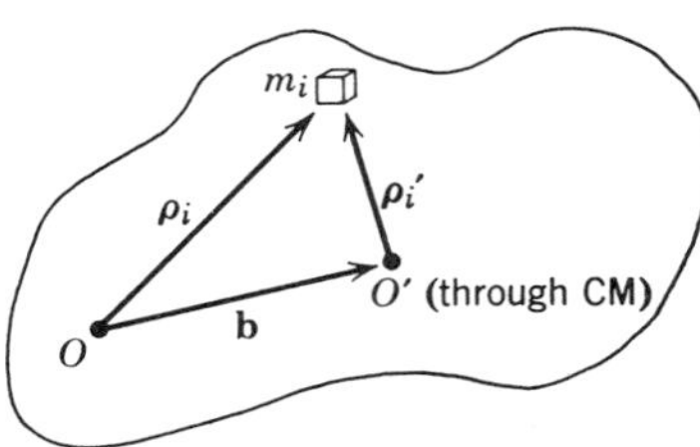

Fig. 8-8. Derivation of the parallel axis theorem.

$$\boldsymbol{\rho}_i = \mathbf{b} + \boldsymbol{\rho}_i' \tag{8-14}$$

Now the moment of inertia about the axis through O is defined by Eq. (8-9).

$$I = \sum_i m_i \rho_i^2 = \sum_i m_i \boldsymbol{\rho}_i \cdot \boldsymbol{\rho}_i$$

Substitute from Eq. (8-14),

$$I = \sum_i m(\mathbf{b} + \boldsymbol{\rho}_i') \cdot (\mathbf{b} + \boldsymbol{\rho}_i')$$

or, expanding,

$$I = \sum_i m_i \mathbf{b} \cdot \mathbf{b} + 2 \sum_i m_i (\mathbf{b} \cdot \boldsymbol{\rho}_i') + \sum_i m_i \boldsymbol{\rho}_i' \cdot \boldsymbol{\rho}_i' \tag{8-15}$$

The last summation on the right,

$$\sum_i m_i \boldsymbol{\rho}_i' \cdot \boldsymbol{\rho}_i' = \sum_i m_i \rho_i'^2$$

is the moment of inertia about the axis through O'. Since this axis passes through the center of mass, call this sum I_{cm}. Now consider the second summation on the right of Eq. (8-15).

$$2 \sum_i m_i (\mathbf{b} \cdot \boldsymbol{\rho}_i') = 2\mathbf{b} \cdot \sum_i m_i \boldsymbol{\rho}_i'$$

By definition $\sum_i m_i \boldsymbol{\rho}_i'$ is simply the total mass M times the perpendicular vector to the center of mass from the axis through O'. But, since the axis through O' passes also through the center of mass, this summation is equal to zero. Therefore the second term on the right of the equation is equal to zero. Setting $\sum_i m_i = M$, the total mass of the rigid body, and $\mathbf{b} \cdot \mathbf{b} = b^2$, Eq. (8-15) becomes

$$I = Mb^2 + I_{\text{cm}} \tag{8-16}$$

This is called the *parallel axis theorem.* It states that the moment of inertia of a rigid body about any fixed axis is equal to the moment of inertia of the total mass concentrated at the center of mass plus the moment of inertia about a parallel axis through the center of mass.

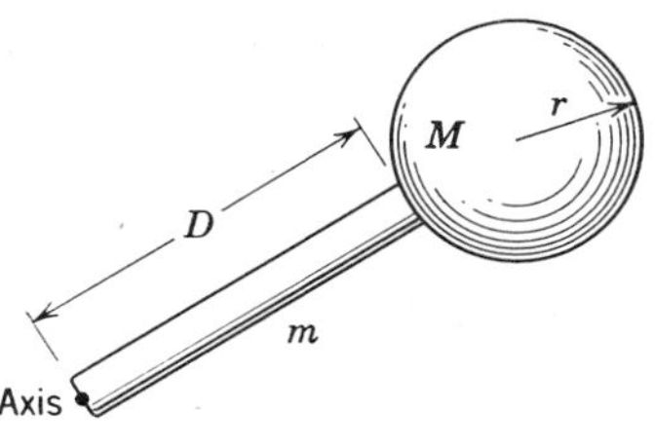

Fig. 8-9.

Questions

8-18 Show that the symbol I_{cm} by itself does not have a unique meaning for the general rigid body. How is the particular I_{cm} to be chosen for Eq. (8-16)?

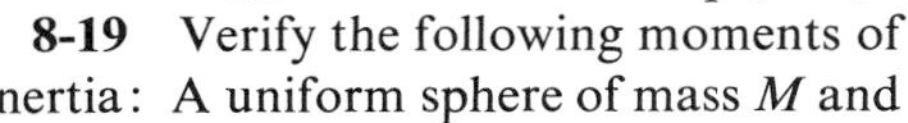

8-19 Verify the following moments of inertia: A uniform sphere of mass M and radius r about a tangent to the sphere: $I = \frac{7}{5}Mr^2$; a uniform cylinder (or disk) of mass M and radius R about a tangent to the cylinder parallel to the cylindrical axis: $I = \frac{3}{2}MR^2$; a uniform sphere attached to a rigid rod about an axis perpendicular to the rod as shown in Fig. 8-9: $I = \frac{1}{3}mD^2 + \frac{2}{5}Mr^2 + M(r + D)^2$.

8.5 KINETIC ENERGY OF ROTATION ABOUT A FIXED AXIS. In Fig. 8-1 the tangential velocity of particle i about the fixed axis is given by $v_i = \rho_i\omega$. The kinetic energy of particle i is thus $T_i = \frac{1}{2}m_iv_i^2 = \frac{1}{2}m_i\rho_i^2\omega^2$. The total kinetic energy T of the rigid body rotating about the axis is given by the sum of the kinetic energy of each particle which makes up the body.

$$T = \sum_i T_i = \sum_i \tfrac{1}{2}m_iv_i^2 = \tfrac{1}{2}\Big(\sum_i m_i\rho_i^2\Big)\omega^2$$

but $\sum_i m_i\rho_i^2 = I$, so that

$$T = \tfrac{1}{2}I\omega^2 \qquad (8\text{-}17)$$

The kinetic energy of a rigid body rotating about a fixed axis is equal to one-half the moment of inertia of the rigid body about that axis times the square of the angular velocity. Note the analogy to the equation $T = \frac{1}{2}mv^2$ for the translational kinetic energy of a particle.

Question

8-20 What is the kinetic energy of a uniform sphere of mass M and radius R rotating about a tangent to the sphere with angular velocity ω?

8.6 WORK AND POWER DEVELOPED BY A TORQUE ABOUT A FIXED AXIS. Suppose that a rigid body initially at rest is rotated about a fixed axis by a torque N_z^e. We suppose that there is negligible bearing friction, so that N_z^e is the net torque acting on the rigid body about the fixed axis. How much work is done by the torque in a time t? Since there is negligible friction, the work done by the torque must appear in rotational kinetic energy of the body.

From Eq. (8-12), $N_z^e = I\dot{\omega}$ or $d\omega = (N_z^e/I)\,dt$. Integrating both sides and setting the initial ω equal to zero, we have

$$\omega = \frac{d\theta}{dt} = \frac{N_z^e}{I}\,t \tag{8-18}$$

Integrate this equation again and set the initial θ equal to zero.

$$\theta = \frac{1}{2}\frac{N_z^e}{I}\,t^2$$

or

$$t = \sqrt{\frac{2I\theta}{N_z^e}}$$

Substitute this into Eq. (8-18).

$$\omega = \frac{N_z^e}{I}\sqrt{\frac{2I\theta}{N_z^e}} = \sqrt{\frac{2N_z^e\theta}{I}} \tag{8-19}$$

Now the final kinetic energy of rotation is given by

$$T = \tfrac{1}{2}I\omega^2$$

Substitute for ω from Eq. (8-19).

$$T = \frac{1}{2}I\left(\frac{2N_z^e\theta}{I}\right) = N_z^e\theta$$

So the work done by the torque in time t is given by

$$W = N_z^e\theta \tag{8-20}$$

where θ is the angular displacement of the rigid body in time t. Note the analogy to the equation $W = Fs$ for linear motion.

Question

8-21 If the rotating body has an initial angular velocity ω_1 and an initial angular displacement θ_1, show that Eq. (8-20) becomes

$$N_z^e(\theta - \theta_1) = \tfrac{1}{2}I\omega^2 - \tfrac{1}{2}I\omega_1^2 \tag{8-21}$$

For a small angle $d\theta$ the work dW done by the torque is given by

$$dW = N_z^e\,d\theta \tag{8-22}$$

Dividing both sides by dt, we find the rate at which the torque N_z^e does work on the rotating body, or the *power* P developed by the torque, to be

$$\frac{dW}{dt} = P = N_z^e \frac{d\theta}{dt}$$

or

$$P = N_z^e \omega \tag{8-23}$$

Note the analogy to the equation $P = Fv$ for the linear motion of a particle.

Question

8-22 The shaft of a motor which is doing work at a rate of 100 hp is rotating at a rate of 1000 rpm. What torque does the shaft exert?

8.7 ANALOGOUS EXPRESSIONS FOR ROTATION ABOUT A FIXED AXIS AND LINEAR MOTION OF A PARTICLE. In the last few sections we have found quite a few expressions concerning rotation of a rigid body about a fixed axis which are similar in form to expressions concerning motion of a particle in a straight line. These expressions are compared in the accompanying table. It is assumed that forces act only

	Particle Moving in a Straight Line	Rigid Body Rotating about a Fixed Axis
Momentum or angular momentum	$p = mv$	$L_z = I\omega$
Equation of motion	$F = m\dot{v} = \dot{p}$	$N_z^e = I\dot{\omega} = \dot{L}_z$
Kinetic energy	$T = \frac{1}{2}mv^2$	$T = \frac{1}{2}I\omega^2$
Work	$W = Fx$	$W = N_z^e\theta$
Power	$P = Fv$	$P = N_z^e\omega$

along the direction of motion of the particle moving in a straight line. It can be seen that one set of expressions can be obtained from the other by interchanging the following symbols.

$$\begin{aligned} m &\leftrightarrow I \\ v &\leftrightarrow \omega \\ p &\leftrightarrow L_z \\ F &\leftrightarrow N_z^e \end{aligned} \tag{8-24}$$

Note particularly that the expressions in the table deal with rigid body rotation *about a fixed axis.* This axis is fixed in the body and fixed with respect to an inertial reference frame. The general motion of a rigid body involves rotation about an axis which changes position and direction in the body and/or position and direction in space. The analysis of this general motion of a rigid body is much more complex, and the results of this analysis do not have the same simple form as the results for rotation about a fixed axis.*

8.8 TORQUE ON A RIGID BODY DUE TO A UNIFORM GRAVITATIONAL FIELD. Before we go on to study some special cases of rigid body rotation about a moving axis, let us take time to analyze the process of comparing masses at the earth's surface using an equal-arm balance. Before we can do this we have to determine the torque on a rigid body resulting from the forces due to a uniform gravitational field.

Consider a rigid body in a uniform gravitational field $\mathbf{g}$. We shall now show that the torque on this rigid body exerted by the gravitational force is the same as that exerted by a single force $M\mathbf{g}$ applied at the center of mass of the rigid body. Here M is the total mass of the rigid body.

Consider an element of mass m_i in the rigid body (Fig. 8-10). Let $\mathbf{r}_i$ represent the position of the element of mass with respect to the origin of an inertial coordinate system. Let $\mathbf{R}$ represent the position of the center of mass of the rigid body with respect to the same coordinate system, and let $\mathbf{r}_i'$ represent the location of the mass element with respect to the center of mass. Hence

$$\mathbf{r}_i = \mathbf{R} + \mathbf{r}_i' \tag{8-25}$$

The external gravitational force on this mass element is given by $m_i\mathbf{g}$. The external torque $\mathbf{n}_i^e$ on particle i about the origin is given by

$$\mathbf{n}_i^e = \mathbf{r}_i \times \mathbf{F}_i^e = \mathbf{r}_i \times m_i\mathbf{g}$$

Substitute from Eq. (8-25).

$$\begin{aligned}\mathbf{n}_i^e &= (\mathbf{R} + \mathbf{r}_i') \times m_i\mathbf{g} \\ &= m_i\mathbf{R} \times \mathbf{g} + m_i\mathbf{r}_i' \times \mathbf{g}\end{aligned} \tag{8-26}$$

The total external torque $\mathbf{N}^e$ on the rigid body about the origin due to the

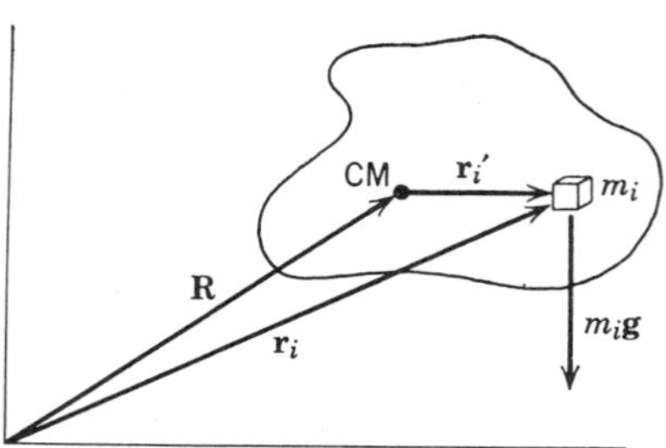

Fig. 8-10. Calculation of the torque exerted on a rigid body by a uniform gravitational field.

* Herbert Goldstein, *Classical Mechanics*, Addison-Wesley Publishing Co., Cambridge, Mass., 1953, Chapter 5.

gravitational forces is found by summing Eq. (8-26) over all elements of mass in the body.

$$\mathbf{N}^e = \sum_i \mathbf{n}_i^e = \sum_i m_i \mathbf{R} \times \mathbf{g} + \sum_i m_i \mathbf{r}_i' \times \mathbf{g}$$

$$= (\sum_i m_i)\mathbf{R} \times \mathbf{g} + (\sum_i m_i \mathbf{r}_i') \times \mathbf{g} \tag{8-27}$$

By definition, the first summation on the right side of Eq. (8-27) is equal to M, the total mass of the rigid body. Also by definition, the second summation is equal to M times the vector position of the center of mass with respect to the center of mass. This vector position is equal to zero since $\mathbf{r}_i'$ is measured with respect to the center of mass. Hence the second term is equal to zero and Eq. (8-27) becomes

$$\mathbf{N}^e = M\mathbf{R} \times \mathbf{g} = \mathbf{R} \times M\mathbf{g} \tag{8-28}$$

But this is the same torque as that due to a single force $M\mathbf{g}$ applied at the center of mass. We have shown that *the torque on a rigid body of mass M due to a uniform gravitational field* $\mathbf{g}$ *is the same as that due to a single force $M\mathbf{g}$ applied to the center of mass of the rigid body.*

Questions

8-23 Show that this result is true for a general system of particles as well as for the special case of a rigid body.

8-24 Why are *internal* forces on particle i due to other particles in the rigid body omitted from the proof?

We already know from Eq. (7-10) in Chapter 7 that the translational motion of the center of mass of a system of particles will be the same as that of a single particle of mass M equal to the total mass of the system when acted on by a force equal to the vector sum of all the external forces which act on the system. This will be true for the special case of the rigid body. The vector sum of the gravitational forces in a uniform gravitational field is equal to $\sum_i m_i \mathbf{g} = M\mathbf{g}$. Combining this with the result for rotation derived above, we see that both the translational and the rotational motion of a rigid body resulting from the forces due to a uniform gravitational field will be the same as if a single force $M\mathbf{g}$ were applied to the center of mass of the rigid body.

Questions

8-25 Show that in a uniform vertical gravitational field a rigid body can be supported at rest without rotation by a force applied to a single

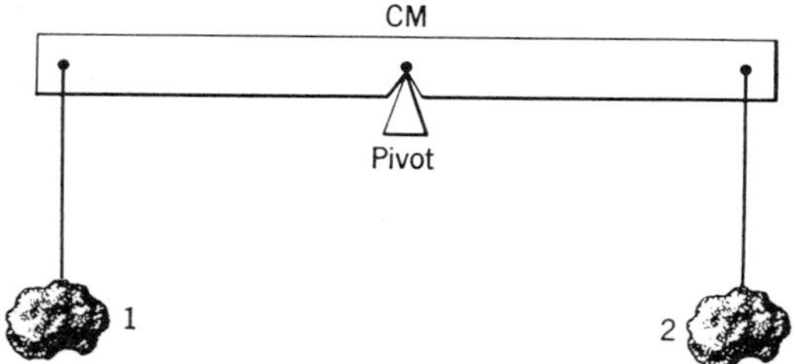

Fig. 8-11. Idealized equal-arm balance.

point of the body if this point lies on a vertical line which passes through the center of mass. Differentiate between points of support above, at, and below the center of mass with regard to stability of the configuration under small rotations of the rigid body.

8-26 Using the results of the previous question, devise an experimental procedure for locating the center of mass of a rigid body. What is the minimum number of steps in this procedure?

8.9 THE COMPARISON OF MASSES WITH AN EQUAL-ARM BALANCE. Consider an idealized equal-arm balance in a uniform gravitational field, as pictured in Fig. 8-11. The balance consists of a uniform rod, called a *beam*, suspended in a horizontal position from its center of mass on a fixed pivot which is designed so that rotation of the beam about the pivot is essentially frictionless. Two particles whose masses are to be compared are hung on strings from points on the rod which are at equal distances from the pivot on either side (hence the name equal-arm balance). When by trial and error two particles are found for which the balance remains at rest when released from rest, the masses of the two particles are said to be equal. Let us see if this conclusion can be justified.

By definition a rigid body is in *equilibrium* when there are no net forces or net torques acting on the body. We wish to show that when the equal-arm balance is in equilibrium the masses of the two particles which hang from the arms are equal.

Figure 8-12 shows the forces acting on each component of the apparatus. For convenience we assume that the strings holding particles one and two have negligible mass. When the system is in equilibrium, the net force on each particle must be zero. Hence the force of gravity on each particle is exactly balanced by the upward force of the string.

Now consider the beam. Since it is in equilibrium, there is no net torque on it about the pivot axis. As shown in the last section, the net force of gravity $M\mathbf{g}$ on the beam has the same effect as it would have if applied to the center of mass. Since the beam is supported at the center of mass, the gravitational forces acting directly on the beam exert no net torque on it. Since the force $\mathbf{F}_p$ due to the pivot is also exerted at the center of mass, this force exerts no torque about this point either. The only other forces on the beam are the reaction forces corresponding to the forces which the strings apply to particles one and two. These two forces exert torques perpendicular to the plane of the diagram. Since these two torque vectors lie along the same line, they can be added like scalars with due regard to sign. Taking the direction into the paper as positive, the torque about the center of mass of the beam due to particle two has the value m_2gd. The torque about the same point due to particle one has the value $-m_1gd$. Particles one and two have been chosen by experiment so that the beam remains in equilibrium when released from rest. Hence there is no net torque on the beam. Therefore

$$m_2gd - m_1gd = 0$$

or

$$m_2gd = m_1gd$$

or

$$m_2 = m_1 \tag{8-29}$$

We have shown that, *when an equal-arm balance is in equilibrium in a uniform gravitational field, the masses of the particles attached to each arm are equal.* In earthbound laboratories this method of comparing masses is more convenient and more accurate than the method outlined in Sec. 3.10. We have just shown that these two methods give the same result.

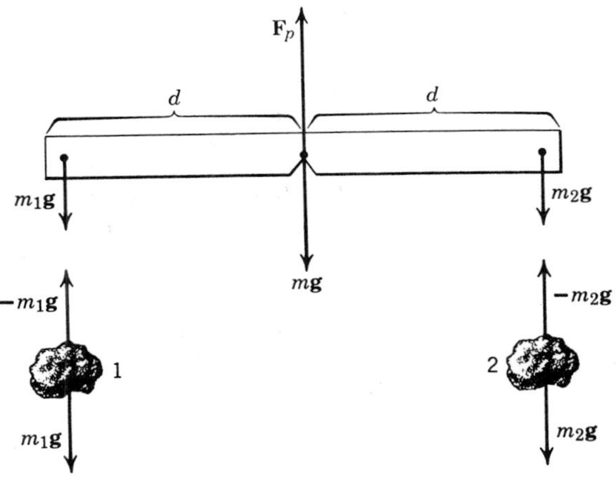

Fig. 8-12. Forces acting on each component of the equal-arm balance.

Questions

8-27 Find an expression for the magnitude of $\mathbf{F}_p$, the force exerted on the beam by the pivot.

8-28 In practical equal-arm balances, the axis of the pivot is at a position vertically above the center of mass of the beam. Show that in this case any rotation of the beam from horizontal is accompanied by a slight gravitational torque tending to return the beam to a horizontal position. Show that for such balances the masses of particles can be compared accurately only if the beam is horizontal after equilibrium has been reached.

8-29 In practical equal-arm balances, trays are suspended from the ends of the beam and the particles to be compared are placed on these trays. Repeat the analysis including the trays, and show what physical conditions the trays must satisfy if the result of the analysis is to be the same.

8-30 When a practical equal-arm balance is used, the particle of unknown mass is placed in, say, the right-hand tray and a series of calibrated masses is added to the left-hand tray in sequence until equilibrium is achieved. First of all, how can these masses be calibrated with respect to a single standard mass? Secondly, how can the sequence of adding calibrated masses to the left-hand tray be carried out with the least waste motion? What is the method of computing the mass of the particle of unknown mass once equilibrium has been achieved? How can the additive property of mass be verified by using an equal-arm balance?

8-31 Show that the method of comparing masses using the equal-arm balance will give the same results on the surface of the moon as on the surface of the earth. How would the analysis above differ for this case?

8-32 Explain carefully the principle of the so-called *triple beam balance* on which masses are moved along one arm to achieve equilibrium. Is this an equal-arm balance? Will the triple beam balance measure mass correctly on the moon if it does so on the earth?

8.10 RIGID BODY ROTATING ABOUT AN AXIS WHICH MOVES PARALLEL TO ITSELF. Suppose that a rigid body rotates about an axis that is fixed in the body but which moves parallel to itself in an inertial coordinate system. A disk rolling down an inclined plane is an example of such motion. The more general case is shown in Fig. 8-13. The coordinate system with origin at O is inertial. Let point s be a point fixed in the rotating body on the axis about which the body is rotating. The condition that the axis of rotation of the rigid body move parallel to itself is expressed by saying that this axis of rotation is always parallel to the z-axis. Aside from this condition, the axis can move in any direction or

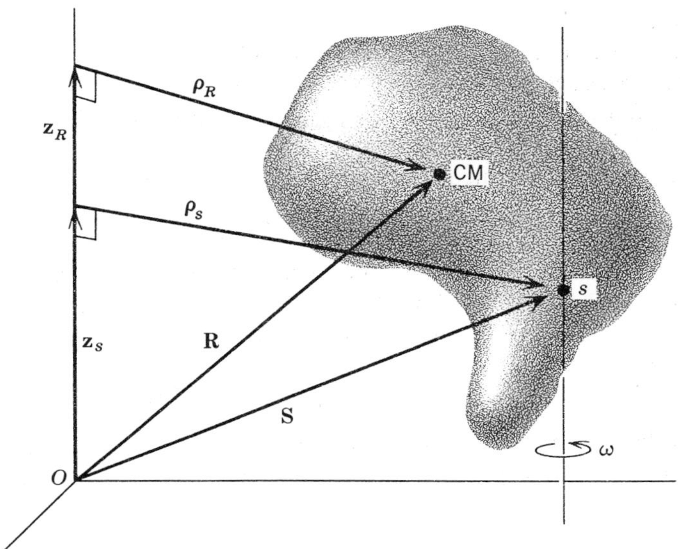

Fig. 8-13. Rigid body rotating about an axis which moves parallel to itself.

sequence of directions with any velocity or acceleration. We now try to answer the question: What is the equation of motion which governs rotation about the moving axis? This question was answered for a general system of particles in Sec. 7.5. The result was given by Eq. (7-36).

$$\mathbf{N}_s^{\,e} = M(\mathbf{R} - \mathbf{S}) \times \ddot{\mathbf{S}} + \dot{\mathbf{L}}_s \tag{7-36}$$

Let us apply this result to the present case. First of all, we are interested in the z-component of the angular momentum of the rotating body. Take the z-component of both sides of Eq. (7-36).

$$N_{sz}^{\,e} = [M(\mathbf{R} - \mathbf{S}) \times \ddot{\mathbf{S}}]_z + \dot{L}_{sz} \tag{8-30}$$

Let

$$\begin{aligned} \mathbf{R} &= \mathbf{Z}_R + \boldsymbol{\rho}_R \\ \mathbf{S} &= \mathbf{Z}_s + \boldsymbol{\rho}_s \end{aligned} \tag{8-31}$$

as shown in Fig. 8-13. Now substitute Eqs. (8-31) into Eq. (8-30) and expand the cross product into separate terms. All cross-product terms involving $\mathbf{Z}_R$ or $\mathbf{Z}_s$ or their time derivatives in this expansion will correspond to vectors which have directions perpendicular to the z-axis. Hence the z-components of these terms will be equal to zero and will not contribute to the z-component of the bracketed term in Eq. (8-30). Hence Eq. (8-30) becomes

$$N_{sz}^{\,e} = [M(\boldsymbol{\rho}_R - \boldsymbol{\rho}_s) \times \ddot{\boldsymbol{\rho}}_s]_z + \dot{L}_{sz} \tag{8-32}$$

Questions

8-33 Carry out the substitution of Eqs. (8-31) into Eq. (8-30). Expand the cross product into separate terms and verify Eq. (8-32).

8-34 Show that the vector $(\boldsymbol{\rho}_R - \boldsymbol{\rho}_s) \times \ddot{\boldsymbol{\rho}}_s$ lies parallel to the z-axis.

Using the result of the last question, Eq. (8-32) becomes

$$N_{sz}^{\ e} = |M(\boldsymbol{\rho}_R - \boldsymbol{\rho}_s) \times \ddot{\boldsymbol{\rho}}_s| + \dot{L}_{sz} \tag{8-33}$$

If I_s is the moment of inertia of the rigid body about the axis of rotation through point s, and ω is the angular velocity of the rotation about this axis, then $L_{sz} = I_s\omega$ and $\dot{L}_{sz} = I_s\dot{\omega}$. With this substitution Eq. (8-33) becomes

$$N_{sz}^{\ e} = |M(\boldsymbol{\rho}_R - \boldsymbol{\rho}_s) \times \ddot{\boldsymbol{\rho}}_s| + I_s\dot{\omega} \tag{8-34}$$

This is the equation of the rotation of a rigid body about its moving axis of rotation. It reduces to the same form as in an inertial system.

$$N_{sz}^{\ e} = I_s\dot{\omega} \tag{8-35}$$

provided the first term on the right side of Eq. (8-34) is equal to zero. This will occur if at least one of the following conditions is satisfied:

(1) $\boldsymbol{\rho}_R = \boldsymbol{\rho}_s$, that is, if the center of mass of the rigid body lies along the axis of rotation; a special case of this condition occurs if point s coincides with the center of mass; or

(2) $\ddot{\boldsymbol{\rho}}_s = 0$, that is, if the axis of rotation is not accelerated in a direction perpendicular to its length.

Questions

8-35 Find the most general motion of point s for which condition 2 above is satisfied. Can point s be accelerating in the z-direction?

8-36 Under what conditions will the work and power expended by $N_{sz}^{\ e}$ be the same as that expended by $N_z^{\ e}$?

8-37 If the center of mass of the rigid body lies on its axis of rotation, use Eq. (7-41) to show that the kinetic energy of the rigid body is given by

$$T = \tfrac{1}{2}m\dot{R}^2 + \tfrac{1}{2}I_s\omega^2 \tag{8-36}$$

8-38 An automobile accelerates forward along a straight smooth road. Is the rate of change of angular momentum about the axis of a wheel on the car equal to the net external torque on the wheel about that axis?

8-39 Suppose that in the last question the road is uneven so that the wheel bounces up and down. Assume that the wheel does not change shape during the bouncing and that the axis of the wheel continues to point in the same direction in space during its up and down motion. In

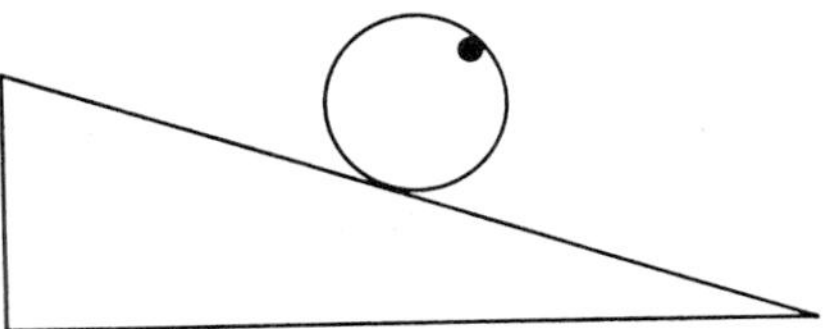

Fig. 8-14.

this case is the rate of change of the angular momentum of the wheel about its axis equal to the net external torque about the axis of the wheel?

8-40 Consider the turbine rotor of a single-jet airplane. This turbine rotor rotates about an axis parallel to the direction of flight of the airplane. As the airplane accelerates forward in straight line flight, does the rate of change of angular momentum of the turbine rotor about its axis of rotation equal the net external torque on the rotor about this axis?

8-41 A circular hoop with a piece of lead glued inside of its rim rolls down a straight inclined plane in a uniform gravitational field (see Fig. 8-14). The axis of the hoop moves parallel to itself, and the hoop remains in contact with the plane at all times. Does the rate of change of angular momentum of the system about the center of the hoop equal the net external torque about this center? Does the rate of change of angular momentum of the system about its center of mass equal the net external torque about the center of mass?

8.11 RIGID BODY WITH AXIAL SYMMETRY. Many of the rigid bodies used in science and commerce are axially symmetric. We define a rigid body to be *axially symmetric* if the z-coordinate axis can be positioned in the stationary body in such a way that for every mass element m_i in the body with coordinates $\mathbf{z}_i + \boldsymbol{\rho}_i$ there will be an element of equal mass at the point $\mathbf{z}_i - \boldsymbol{\rho}_i$. When the z-axis is positioned in this way it is said to lie along an *axis of symmetry* of the rigid body. Many axially symmetric rigid bodies have more than one axis of symmetry. A uniform building brick has three axes of symmetry, whereas a uniform cone has only one.

Questions

8-42 How many axes of symmetry does an automobile tire have? a pencil? a piece of pipe? the human body? Be careful.

8-43 Show that the center of mass of an axially symmetric rigid body must lie on every axis of symmetry.

It is easy to show that when an axially symmetrical rigid body rotates about a fixed axis of symmetry the total angular momentum $\mathbf{L}$ points

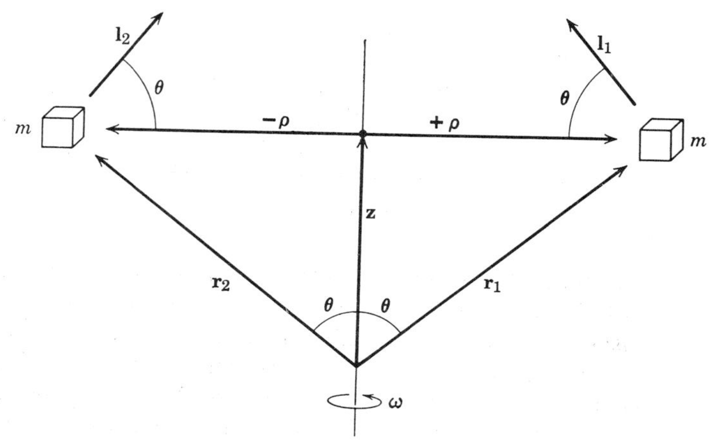

Fig. 8-15. Analysis of angular momentum of an axially symmetric rigid body.

along the axis of rotation. (We saw in Question 8-6 that this is not always true of the general rigid body.) The proof follows from an analysis of Fig. 8-15.

Consider two symmetrical volume elements in the rigid body. Both volume elements lie in a plane common with the axis of symmetry. If the rigid body rotates about its axis of symmetry as shown, it is clear that the components of the two angular momenta perpendicular to the axis of rotation will cancel each other, leaving only the components parallel to the axis of rotation. The z-component of the angular momentum of the right-hand element is given by

$$l_{1z} = (\mathbf{r}_1 \times m\mathbf{v}_1)_z = r_1 mv \sin\theta = m\rho v = m\rho^2\omega$$

The z-component of the left-hand mass element has the same value. If we add $\mathbf{l}_1$ and $\mathbf{l}_2$, all but the z-components will cancel. Hence

$$\mathbf{l}_1 + \mathbf{l}_2 = 2m\rho^2\omega\hat{k} \tag{8-37}$$

where $\hat{k}$ is a unit vector in the z-direction. Since the axially symmetric rigid body is made up entirely of such pairs of symmetrically placed mass elements, the total angular momentum $\mathbf{L}$ must lie along the axis of rotation. QED.

It is convenient to define an *angular velocity vector* $\boldsymbol{\omega}$ as follows. The magnitude of $\boldsymbol{\omega}$ is equal to the angular velocity ω. The direction of $\boldsymbol{\omega}$ is the direction a right-handed screw would advance if rotated in the same way as the rigid body. This is shown in Fig. 8-16*a*. Another way to determine the direction of the vector $\boldsymbol{\omega}$ is given in Fig. 8-16*b*. If the fingers of the right hand are curled around the axis of rotation in the

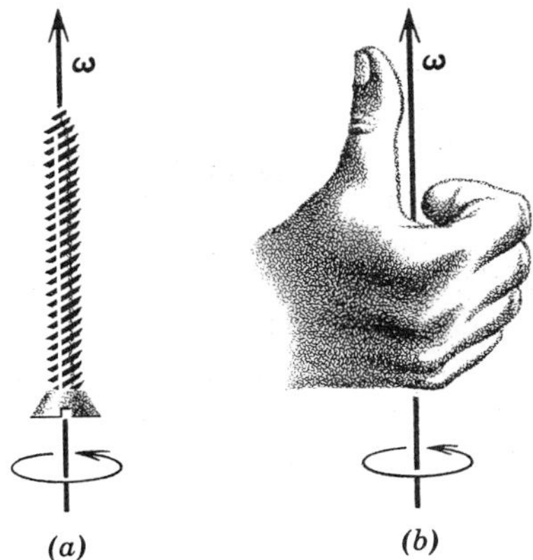

Fig. 8-16. Direction of the vector **ω**.

direction in which the rigid body rotates, the extended thumb will point in the direction of **ω**.

With this substitution Eq. (8-37) becomes

$$\mathbf{l}_1 + \mathbf{l}_2 = 2m\rho^2\boldsymbol{\omega} \tag{8-38}$$

for either sense of rotation of the rigid body about the z-axis. From this the total angular momentum can be found by summing the angular momenta of all such pairs of volume elements in the rigid body.

$$\mathbf{L} = \sum_i m_i\rho_i^{\,2}\boldsymbol{\omega}$$

$$\mathbf{L} = I_{\text{sym}}\boldsymbol{\omega} \tag{8-39}$$

where I_{sym} represents the moment of inertia about the axis of symmetry. Note carefully that Eq. (8-39) was developed for rotation about an axis of symmetry only.

Questions

8-44 An automobile travels due north. In what direction does the angular velocity vector of each wheel point?

8-45 From the equation $\mathbf{l} = \mathbf{r} \times m\dot{\mathbf{r}}$ and the equations $\mathbf{r}_1 = \mathbf{z} + \boldsymbol{\rho}$ and $\mathbf{r}_2 = \mathbf{z} - \boldsymbol{\rho}$ prove Eq. (8-37) with more mathematical rigor.

8.12 THE GYROSCOPE. Consider an axially symmetric rigid body rotating on fixed bearings about an axis of symmetry in interstellar space. We assume that the bearings on which the body rotates have negligible friction. If the axis of rotation remains fixed with respect to an inertial reference frame, it is easy to show that these bearings exert neither a net force nor a net torque on the rotating body. First of all, the body is in interstellar space so that the only forces on it are due to the bearings. Secondly, the center of mass of the body lies on the axis of rotation and thus remains stationary. Hence the bearings do not exert a net force on the body. Thirdly, the direction of the total angular momentum of the body lies along the axis of rotation as Eq. (8-39) shows. Since the direction of the axis of rotation is fixed, the angular momentum does not change direction. Since the bearings are essentially frictionless, ω is constant so that the angular momentum does not change in magnitude. Since the angular momentum of the body does not change in either direction or magnitude, the bearings do not exert a net torque on the body. Thus the bearings exert neither a net force nor a net torque on the rotating body under these conditions.

Question

8-46 Show that, if the fixed bearings are not quite frictionless, the effect of the torque due to this friction will not be to change the direction of the angular momentum.

As the bearings exert neither a net force nor a net torque on the rotating symmetrical body, they are of no use and may be removed without changing the motion of the body at all. The axis of rotation will continue to point in the same direction with respect to an inertial reference frame. Such a rotating body is called a *gyroscope* or *gyro*. The gyroscope is exceedingly useful for indicating fixed directions in all kinds of navigational guidance systems.

At second glance, the property of the gyroscope to indicate a fixed direction may not appear to be so unique. After all, if a straight line is drawn on any rigid body and then the rigid body is placed at rest without rotation in an inertial system, the straight line will also point in a fixed direction as long as the rotating body is free of torques. Why is the gyroscope more useful for indicating direction than this non-rotating rigid body? Here is the difference: if the non-rotating rigid body experiences even the slightest transient torque it will begin to rotate *and this rotation will continue indefinitely*. On the other hand, if the gyroscope experiences a transient torque it may deviate a little from the fixed direction, but, when this torque is removed, *the deviation of the gyroscope will stop*, because a continued torque is necessary to cause a continued change of the angular momentum vector. Since slight transient torques are unavoidable in a practical guidance system, the gyroscope is useful for indicating direction but the non-rotating rigid body is not.

One more refinement must be made before the gyroscope can be useful in practical guidance systems. Rockets and space ships must carry their

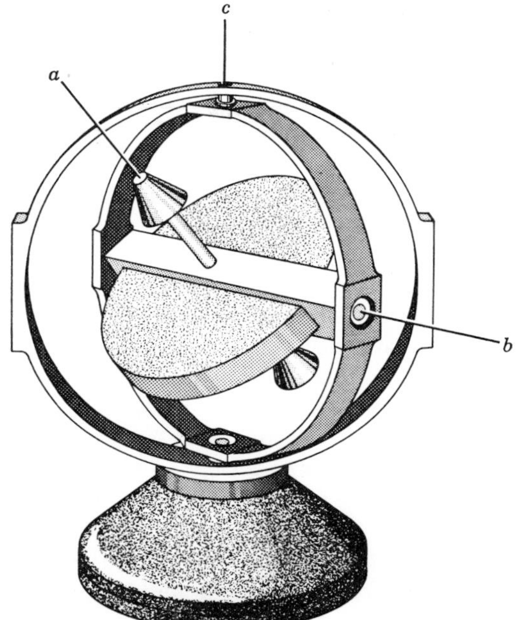

Fig. 8-17. Gimbal-mounted gyroscope.

guidance systems with them. This means that the guidance systems must experience linear accelerations. The gyroscopes contained in the guidance systems will continue to point in fixed directions under these circumstances provided that no *torques* are exerted on them. We need some sort of mounting which will not transmit a torque to the gyroscope but will transmit a linear acceleration to its center of mass. To attain this we must replace the bearings on the gyroscope axis and mount this assembly in a *gimbal mounting*. Such a mounting is shown in Fig. 8-17. The gyroscope is mounted in such a way that it is free to rotate independently about three axes of rotation, marked *a*, *b*, and *c* in the figure. As long as no two of these axes lie parallel, no rotation of the mounting will transmit a torque to the gyroscope. Linear acceleration of the mounting will not cause a torque to be applied to the gyroscope provided that all three axes of rotation *a*, *b*, and *c* pass through the center of mass of the gyroscope.

Questions

8-47 Show that the last sentence is correct.

8-48 Demonstrate that a gimbal-mounted gyro will point in a fixed direction even in a uniform gravitational field.

8-49 If you should start a very well balanced gimbal-mounted gyro rotating with its axis lying in the east-west direction on the surface of the earth, how would this axis appear to you to move with time? In what direction would you have to start the axis in order that it would not appear to you to change direction with time?

8.13 TORQUES PERPENDICULAR TO THE AXIS OF ROTATION. PRECESSION. Consider an axially symmetric rigid body rotating on bearings about its axis of symmetry. We suppose that the bearings are essentially frictionless. If all external forces are applied to the rotating body by way of the bearings (we exclude gravity for the present), these external forces cannot exert a torque about the axis of rotation. In fact, the essentially frictionless bearings will not transmit *any component* of a torque which lies parallel to the axis of rotation. As a result, the only torques which can be applied to the body by way of the bearings are torques whose directions are *perpendicular* to the axis of rotation. How will the rotating body move under the influence of these "perpendicular" torques?

The bearings of the rotating rigid body in Fig. 8-18 are acted on by two equal and opposite forces of magnitude F which are applied symmetrically but gradually to the bearings. Such a pair of equal and opposite forces is called a *couple*. Since the *net* force on the rotating body due to this couple is zero, the center of mass of the body will remain fixed. Taking moments about the lower bearing, we have $\mathbf{N}^e = \mathbf{b} \times \mathbf{F}$ which points out of the paper and thus is perpendicular to the axis of rotation.

Question

8-50 Show that the torque exerted by a couple is independent of the stationary inertial point about which this torque is calculated. Is this true of points which do not lie on the axis of rotation?

The direction of the angular momentum of the rotating axially symmetric body is upward as shown in Fig. 8-18. Because the bearings are considered frictionless, the *magnitude* of $\mathbf{L}$ must remain constant. However, Eq. (7-19) states that

$$\mathbf{N}^e = \dot{\mathbf{L}} \tag{7-19}$$

Since $\mathbf{L}$ does not change in magnitude, it must change in *direction* in order that Eq. (7-19) be satisfied. In fact, according to Eq. (7-19) $\dot{\mathbf{L}}$ must point out of the paper parallel to the torque. Because the center of mass of the rotating body remains fixed, the upper bearing of Fig. 8-18 will move *out* of the paper and the lower bearing will move *into* the paper. If the two

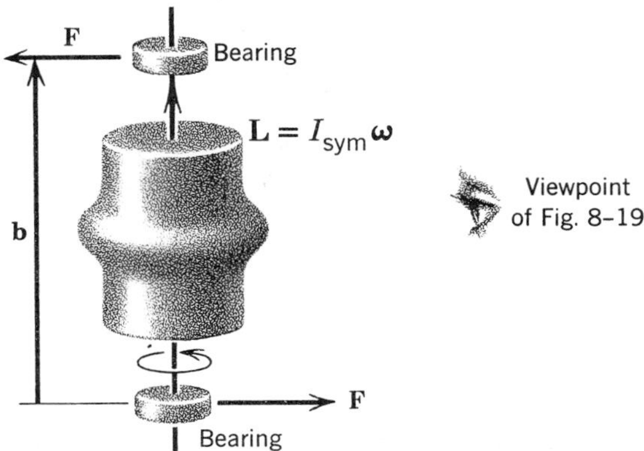

Fig. 8-18. Torque applied perpendicular to the axis of rotation of an axially symmetric rigid body.

forces of the couple continue to act perpendicular to the axis of rotation, the motion of the axis of rotation will continue and soon the reader would be looking directly down at the top of the rotating body. As long as the forces continue to act, the axis of rotation of the body will itself rotate about a horizontal axis through the center of mass in the plane of the paper.

The motion that we have been describing is called *precession*. It may be rather surprising that the rotating body does not "move" in the "direction" of the "force" which is exerted on it. An analysis of the words "move," "direction," and "force" will show that in this situation none of these words can have their usual meaning. The angular momentum does *precess* in the direction of the torque applied, as required by the laws of motion.

Now we can derive the rate of precession of the rotating body. If the angular momentum vector of Fig. 8-18 is viewed from the right-hand side, as the eyeball in that figure shows, its tip would appear to rotate in a circle as shown in Fig. 8-19. Consider the angular momentum vector $\mathbf{L}_1$ and $\mathbf{L}_2$ at two consecutive times t_1 and t_2. The angle between $\mathbf{L}_1$ and $\mathbf{L}_2$ is $d\phi$. The change $d\mathbf{L}$ during the interval $t_2 - t_1$ is shown. If $t_2 - t_1 = dt$ is infinitesimally small, $d\phi$ will be small and we can write

$$dL = L\,d\phi \tag{8-40}$$

where dL and L are the magnitudes of $d\mathbf{L}$ and $\mathbf{L}$ respectively. Divide both sides of Eq. (8-40) by dt.

$$\frac{dL}{dt} = \dot{L} = L\frac{d\phi}{dt} = L\Omega \tag{8-41}$$

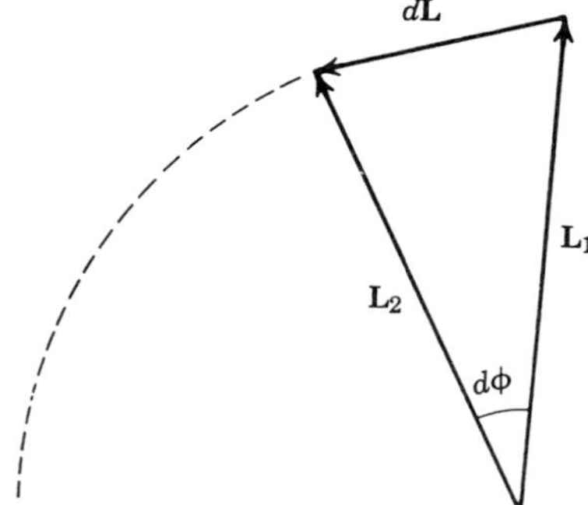

Fig. 8-19. Angular momentum vector of Fig. 8-18 viewed from the right-hand side.

where Ω (capital ω) is the angular rate of precession of the axis of the rigid body. If N^e is the magnitude of $\mathbf{N}^e$, the torque perpendicular to the axis of rotation of the rigid body, then

$$N^e = \dot{L} = L\Omega$$

or

$$\Omega = \frac{N^e}{L} \tag{8-42}$$

For the case treated above, $N^e = Fb$, so that

$$\Omega = \frac{Fb}{L} = \frac{Fb}{I_{\text{sym}}\omega} \tag{8-43}$$

It is easy to predict the direction in which the rotating body will precess: the tip of the angular momentum vector will always move in the direction of the torque.

We have assumed that the angular momentum vector $\mathbf{L}$ lies along the axis of rotation $\boldsymbol{\omega}$ of the rigid body, and when the axis of rotation is stationary this assumption is correct. However, when the body precesses there is a rotation about the axis of precession and therefore a component of angular momentum parallel to this axis also. Equations (8-42) and (8-43) for precession are valid only when this angular momentum about the axis of precession is negligible compared to the angular momentum about the axis of symmetry. It is not difficult to satisfy this condition in a practical case. However, the condition is not satisfied if $\omega \to 0$. Hence Ω will not in reality go to infinity if $\omega \to 0$ as Eq. (8-43) implies, because the angular momentum about the axis of precession cannot be neglected in this case.

We have also assumed in the preceding analysis that the forces which constitute the couple are applied symmetrically and gradually to the bearings. If these forces are applied suddenly rather than gradually, then the axis of the rotating body will not remain in a fixed plane and precess uniformly. Rather the axis will bob back and forth through this plane and the precession will proceed in a series of jerky motions. This type of bobbing motion of a precessing rotating rigid body is called *nutation*. The analysis of nutation is rather complicated and is carried out in more advanced texts.* If the forces of the couple are applied gradually enough, the nutation will be small and will die away too quickly to be noticed.

Precession can also take place in a gravitational field. Figure 8-20 shows a rotating top with one end mounted on a pivot. This top can be released in such a way that its axis will precess uniformly around the pivot. Here is the explanation of this precession: The force due to gravity can be represented as a single force $M\mathbf{g}$ acting at the center of mass of the rotating body (see Sec. 8.8). If the top is released properly, the downward gravitational force at the center of mass will be exactly balanced by an equal and opposite upward force at the pivot. These two forces then form a couple which causes precession as before.

In this analysis we have not demonstrated that the downward gravitational force on the center of mass and the upward force at the pivot are *necessarily* equal in magnitude. The reason is that they are, in fact, *not* necessarily equal in magnitude but will be so only if the top is "released properly." "Proper" release involves giving the axis of the top an initial precessional velocity equal to the angular velocity at which it will precess uniformly after release. If the top is simply released from rest, then its outer end will bob up and down as it precesses in a series of jerky motions about the pivot. This is another example of nutation.

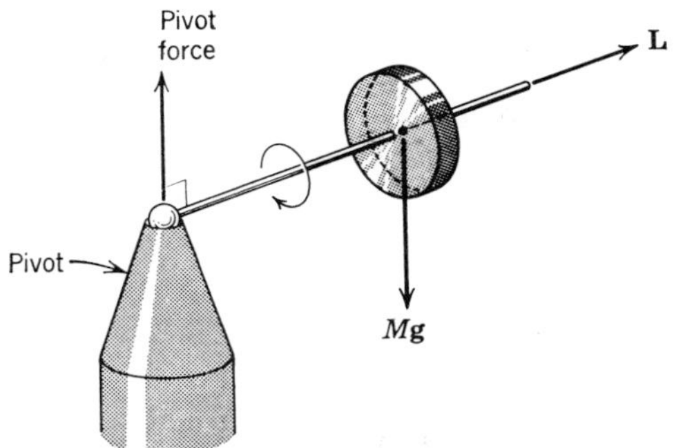

Fig. 8-20. Rotating top with one end mounted on a pivot.

* Herbert Goldstein, *Classical Mechanics*, *op. cit.*, p. 168.

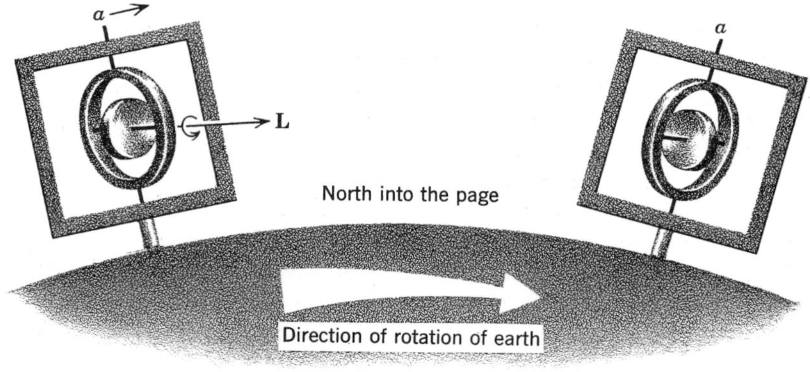

Fig. 8-21. The gyrocompass.

Question

8-51 Suppose that there is friction which tends to oppose precession in the bearing at the pivot about which precession takes place in Fig. 8-20. Show that such friction will cause the precessing top to "droop" (i.e., the outer end of the top will spiral slowly down toward the earth as time passes).

The *gyrocompass* makes use of the precession of a rotating body to indicate true north on the earth. The base of the outer frame in Fig. 8-21 is maintained in a vertical direction with respect to the surface of the earth. As the earth turns, the direction of the vertical will change with respect to an inertial reference frame. The axis a will rotate with the vertical and a torque will be exerted on the gyro. The direction of this torque will be northward. This will cause the angular momentum vector (and the axis of the gyro) to precess toward the north. This time the torque, instead of rotating as the axis of the gyro rotates, will continue to point northward as the gyro precesses. When the angular momentum vector points northward, the torque will be in the same direction as the angular momentum (or, more exactly, the "frictionless" bearings will not transmit the torque to the gyro), so the precession will stop. Thus the axis of rotation of the gyro will point toward true north.

Question

8-52 Why will a gyrocompass be undependable in vehicles which travel faster than 1000 mph?

EXERCISES

8-1 Two cylindrical disks rotate on frictionless bearings whose axes lie along the same line perpendicular to the faces, as shown in Fig. 8-22.

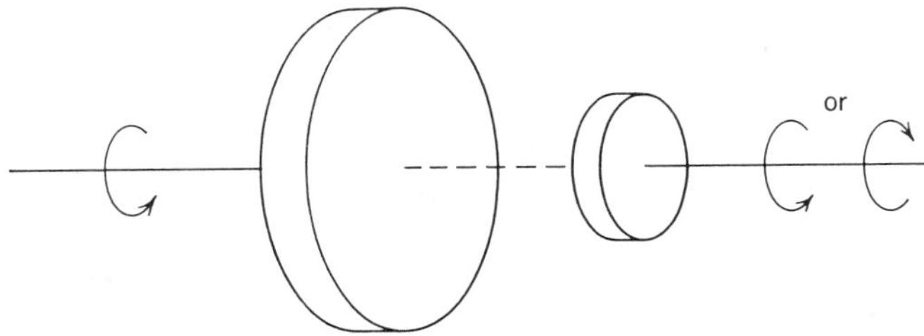

Fig. 8-22.

Initially the disks rotate with different angular velocities. The disks are now brought together so that their opposing faces come in contact, and finally they rotate together with the same angular velocity. If no external torques are applied during this process, what is the final common angular velocity of the two disks? What fraction of the initial kinetic energy of rotation is lost to friction during this process?

8-2 A string of negligible mass is wrapped around the circumference of a uniform circular disk (Fig. 8-23). The free end of the string is pulled

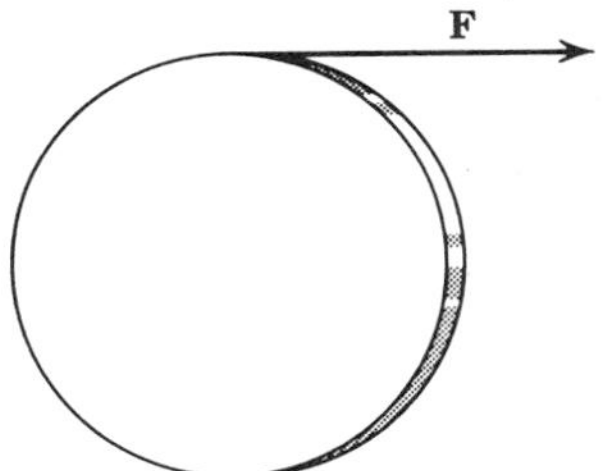

Fig. 8-23.

with a constant force in a direction tangential to the disk. Find the linear and angular acceleration of the disk.

8-3 A single blade of a DC-6 propeller is about 2 m long and has a mass of about 50 kg. Treat this propeller blade as a uniform rigid rod. If this blade is rotated about one end at 2200 rpm, what outward force does it exert on the socket that holds it to the axis of rotation?

8-4 Show that the motion of a rigid body due to any set of forces can be duplicated by replacing these forces by a properly chosen single force plus a single couple. Indicate how you would calculate the single force and the single couple equivalent to a given set of forces. Set up and solve some examples of your own.

8-5 Consider the earth to be a uniform solid sphere. If all of the mass of the earth were suddenly moved radially into a thin-walled hollow spherical shell of the same radius, how long would it take the "new earth" to rotate on its axis? What fraction of the initial kinetic energy of rotation would be lost in this process?

8-6 A space ship of cylindrical symmetry is rotating about its cylindrical axis (see Fig. 8-24). Two strings of negligible mass with

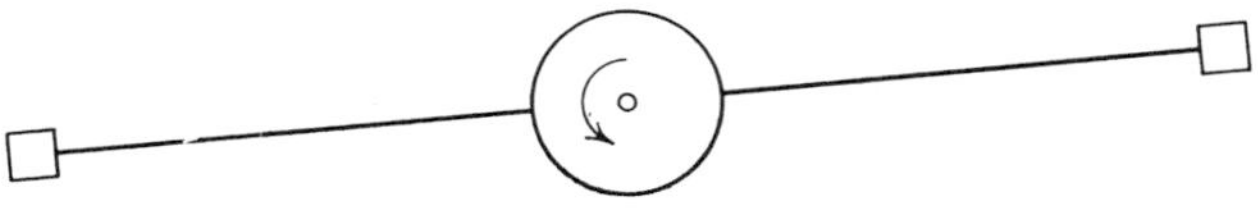

Fig. 8-24.

particles of equal mass on the ends are let out symmetrically on opposite sides of the space ship slowly enough that the particles are at all times revolving with the same angular velocity as the space ship. It is intended that the two particles shall be let out from initial radius r_1 to final radius r_2 measured from the axis of rotation. Set up a mathematical criterion which can be used to determine the maximum tension which each of the strings will have to withstand. Find explicit expressions for this maximum tension in the two limiting cases that the moment of inertia of the space ship is very large and very small.

8-7 Two identical uniform cylindrical disks are mounted on bearings at the ends of a uniform beam AC (Fig. 8-25). The beam is free to rotate

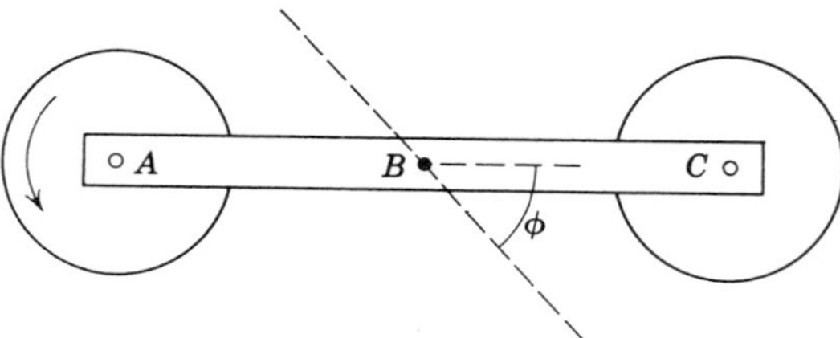

Fig. 8-25.

about a fixed bearing perpendicular to AC through its center at B. The center line of the beam makes an angle ϕ with a fixed index line. The bearing at B is frictionless, the bearing at A is not frictionless, the bearing at C is frozen so that the disk at C cannot rotate with respect to the beam. Initially the beam is not rotating, but the disk on the left is rotating. Describe qualitatively what happens as time passes if the system is left undisturbed. When the disk at A has stopped rotating with respect to AC, what is the value of the angular velocity of the beam?

8-8 The dome on an observatory situated at 42 degrees north latitude and 73 degrees west longitude can be made to rotate once in 2 minutes.

Assume that it is a thin, uniform, hemispherical shell of radius 10 m and mass 10,000 kg. In order to keep this dome rotating about an axis which remains vertical, what additional torque must be applied to the dome by the foundation because of the rotation of the earth? Give the magnitude and direction of this torque.

The following exercises deal with occurrences which take place near the surface of the earth. Assume that the surface of the earth can be used as an inertial reference frame and that the acceleration of a free particle due to the force of gravity is equal to 9.8 m/sec^2.

8-9 A particle is hung from the end of a string which is wrapped around a uniform cylindrical disk mounted on a fixed frictionless bearing

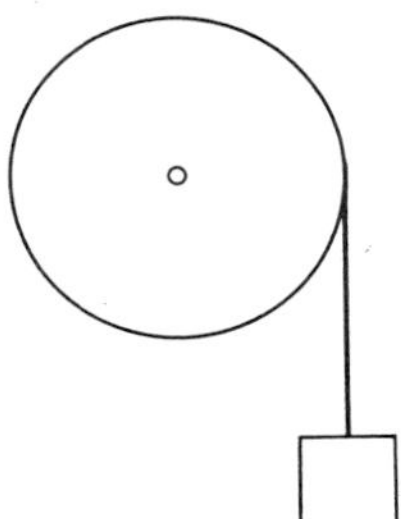

Fig. 8-26.

through its center, as in Fig. 8-26. If the particle is released and the string unwinds without slipping on the disk, what will be the acceleration of the particle? Neglect the mass and thickness of the string.

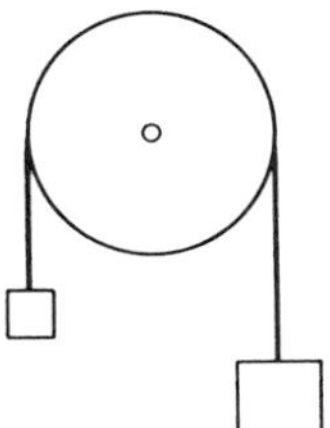

Fig. 8-27.

8-10 *Atwood's machine* consists of two particles of unequal mass connected by a string which passes over a uniform cylindrical disk mounted on a fixed bearing through its center (see Fig. 8-27). Find the acceleration of the particles in the earth's gravitational field, assuming that the string does not slip on the disk, the bearing is frictionless, and the string has negligible mass. How can this machine be used to measure the acceleration of gravity?

8-11 A yo-yo is made of two uniform disks of equal mass and radius which are joined along a common axis through their centers by a smaller disk of negligible mass (Fig. 8-28). A string is wrapped around the smaller

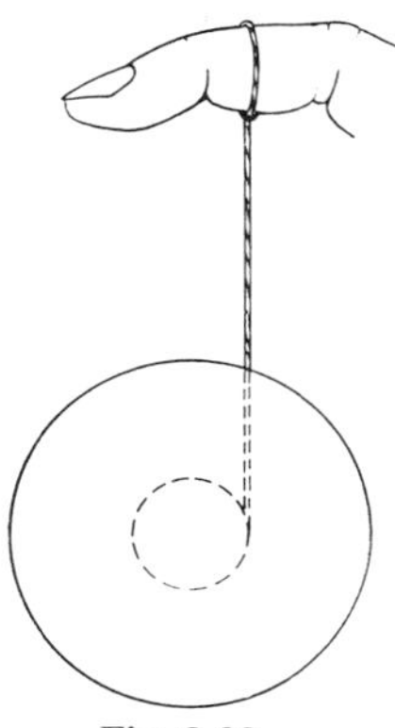

Fig. 8-28.

disk, and the other end of the string is fixed. If the yo-yo is released, what will be its linear acceleration as the string unwinds without slipping? Neglect the mass and thickness of the string.

8-12 A cylinder, a ring, and a sphere all roll without slipping down an inclined plane. If they are all released from rest at the same time and from the same height, which one will win the race?

8-13 A uniform cylinder rolls from rest down the side of a trough whose vertical dimension y is given by the equation $y = kx^2$. The cylinder does not slip from A to B, but the surface of the trough is frictionless from B on toward C. (See Fig. 8-29.) How far will the cylinder ascend toward

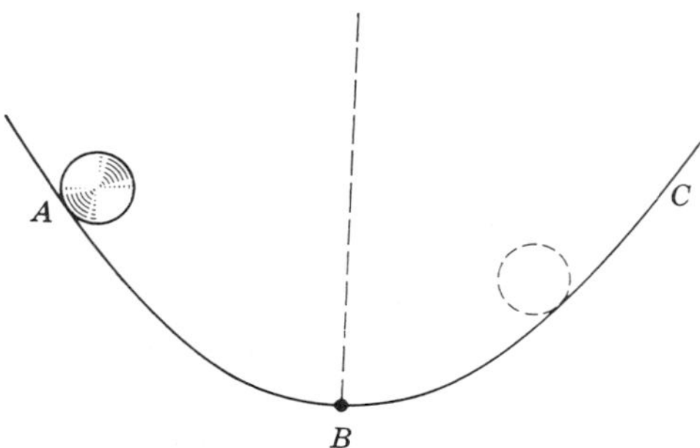

Fig. 8-29.

C? Under the same conditions, will a uniform sphere of the same radius go farther or less far toward C than the cylinder?

8-14 The bellboy picks up a suitcase and starts straight through the door. Rigidly attached inside the suitcase is the axis of a rotating wheel with its angular momentum pointing to the rear. After passing through the door, the bellboy starts to turn right. What happens next? If the bellboy is in the know, what torque will he have to apply to the suitcase in order to make a ninety-degree right turn in 5 seconds as if nothing were unusual?

8-15 A uniform spherical bowling ball is projected without initial rotation along a horizontal bowling alley. How far will the ball skid along the alley before it begins to roll without slipping? Assume that the ball does not bounce. Find a numerical solution for a ball 11 cm in radius, 6 kg mass, with an initial velocity of 5 m/sec if the coefficient of kinetic friction between ball and alley is 0.2. What is the velocity of this ball after it has stopped skidding? What fraction of the initial kinetic energy is lost to friction?

8-16 A smooth horizontal road leads to the edge of a vertical cliff. An automobile drives rapidly off this cliff. What will be the angular velocity of the car after it leaves the edge of the cliff? What approximation in your solution rests on the word "rapidly" in the statement of the problem, and under what circumstances will this approximation be invalid? What additional assumptions are required to solve the same problem for a smooth log sliding lengthwise off the cliff? You may wish to repeat the solution of Exercise 5-8 to find out whether or not the car lands on its wheels.

8-17 A *physical pendulum* consists of a rigid body which is free to rotate about a fixed horizontal axis that does not pass through the center of mass of the body. Using an analysis similar to that of the simple pendulum in the harmonic oscillator project (Project IV), show that, for small rotations from the equilibrium position, the angular frequency of the physical pendulum is given by the expression

$$\omega = \sqrt{MgD/I}$$

where M is the mass of the rigid body, I is its moment of inertia about the axis of rotation, D is the perpendicular distance between the center of mass and the axis of rotation, and g is the acceleration of gravity. Find an expression for the period of a physical pendulum. What is the period of a sphere oscillating about a horizontal axis tangent to the sphere? What are the periods of a thin circular ring and a cylindrical disk about horizontal axes perpendicular to the circular surfaces of these figures through points on their circumferences? For each of these cases, find the length of a simple pendulum with the same period.

8-18 Each of two physical pendulums consists of a uniform solid sphere of mass M and radius R to which is attached a uniform rigid rod of length R and equal mass M (see Fig. 8-30). In both cases the rod is

Fig. 8-30.

attached rigidly to the sphere, in one case radially, in the other case tangentially at one end of the rod. For both pendulums the horizontal axis of rotation passes through the other end of the rod. Find the periods of vibration for each of these pendulums for small rotations from equilibrium.

8-19 Starting from rest at the top, a particle slides off a large fixed sphere with a frictionless surface (Fig. 8-31). At what point will the particle

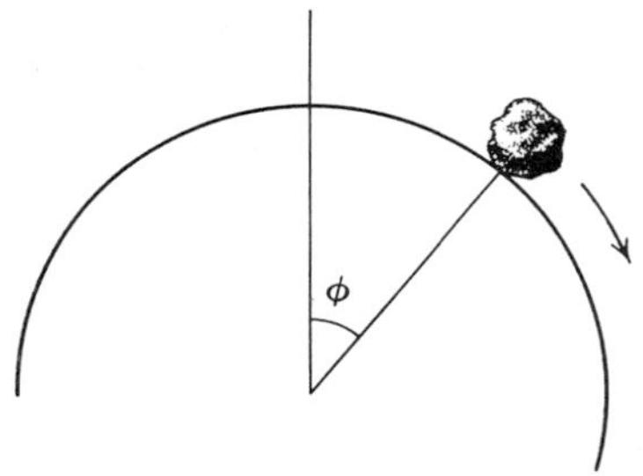

Fig. 8-31.

leave the surface of the sphere? (*Hint:* Use the law of conservation of energy.)

8-20 Starting from rest at the top, a small sphere rolls without slipping off a large fixed sphere (Fig. 8-32). At what point will the small sphere leave the surface of the big sphere?

8-21 Now repeat Exercise 8-19 for the case of a particle with a flat surface in contact with the sphere, so that the particle rotates in space as it slides along the (frictionless) surface of the sphere (Fig. 8-33). Describe the motion of the particle after it leaves the sphere.

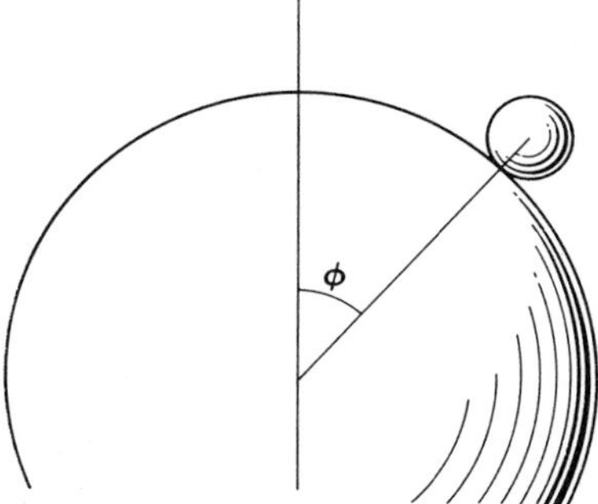

Fig. 8-32.

8-22 Develop a method for "pumping" a child's swing without touching the ground. Show in what ways your method corresponds to the methods usually seen on playgrounds and in what ways these empirical methods involve wasted effort. You may wish to test your method in the laboratory.

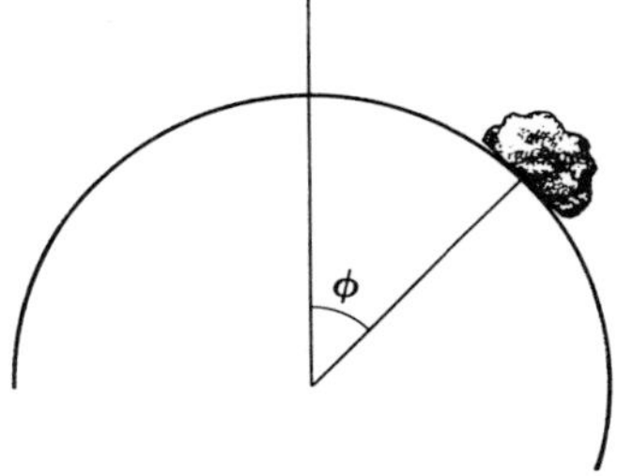

Fig. 8-33.

PROJECT VIII. STABILIZATION OF AN ORBITING ASTRONOMICAL OBSERVATORY*

INTRODUCTION. The atmosphere of the earth causes astronomers a great deal of difficulty. Even on a clear night, the same fluctuating density and temperatures of the atmosphere which make stars twinkle cause star images on photographs to be blurred. In addition, the atmosphere is opaque to electromagnetic radiation of many frequencies of interest to astronomers and physicists. For these and other reasons, space scientists have built unmanned astronomical observatories designed to be placed in orbit around the earth outside the atmosphere. In order to use telescopes in such an observatory it is necessary to be able to rotate them to point at, say, a particular star and to remain fixed on this star. In practice the telescopes are attached rigidly to the frame of the orbiting vehicle which is then rotated as a whole to the desired position. Such rotation and control is called *stabilization*. This project will be concerned with some of the mechanics involved in the stabilization of an orbiting astronomical observatory.

Stabilization is complicated by the fact that there are small but non-negligible torques acting on the satellite. These torques can be due to the magnetic field of the earth, the pressure of light from the sun, residual air resistance, and the non-uniformity of the gravitational field of the earth. They will be discussed further in what follows. In the absence of some method to counteract these torques, they may cause the observatory to rotate away from a desired direction.

In order to become acquainted with some of the techniques of stabilization, consider the following preliminary problem, which might deal with a system on the surface of the earth.

PRELIMINARY PROBLEM. A large turntable is mounted on a stationary frictionless bearing whose axis is fixed vertically and passes through the center of the turntable, as in Fig. VIII-1. A smaller wheel is mounted on a vertical axis fixed to the turntable at the center of the turntable. We shall call this smaller wheel the *reaction wheel.*

A small motor is mounted on the axis of the reaction wheel. The rotor of this motor is rigidly attached to the axis of the reaction wheel. The stator of this motor is rigidly attached to the turntable. In this way the

* For a discussion of current plans see, R. R. Ziemer, *Astronautics*, **6**, 36 (May 1961). For the more detailed analysis on which this project is based see *The Astronomical Journal*, **65**, 239 (June 1960, No. 1280).

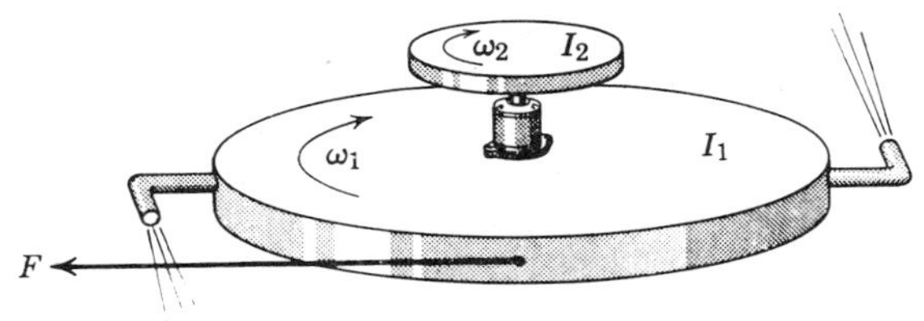

Fig. VIII-1.

motor can be used to transmit a controlled torque between the turntable and the reaction wheel. This torque can be such as either to increase or to decrease the angular velocity of the reaction wheel.

The moment of inertia of the reaction wheel is I_2. The moment of inertia of the turntable, excluding the reaction wheel, is I_1.

Now a small constant external torque N_0 is applied to the turntable about its central axis. This torque might be applied, for instance, by a tangential force F at the rim of the turntable as shown in the figure. The motor which drives the reaction wheel is turned on and adjusted so that the turntable does not rotate.

Problems

VIII-1 In terms of the symbols given above, what is the necessary rate of change of angular velocity ω_2 of the reaction wheel to keep the turntable stationary? What torque must the motor supply to the reaction wheel to cause this rate of change of angular velocity?

VIII-2 If the maximum permissible angular velocity of the reaction wheel is $\omega_{2\,\max}$, what power in watts must the motor develop in supplying the necessary torque?

VIII-3 In the absence of an external torque, how accurately must ω_2 be controlled if ω_1, the angular velocity of the turntable, is to be kept less than some small value $\omega_{1\,\max}$?

VIII-4 Analyze carefully the effects of friction in the bearing of the reaction wheel on the results you have derived above.

VIII-5 If the torque N_0 continues to act, the reaction wheel will sooner or later reach a maximum permissible angular velocity $\omega_{2\,\max}$. If the turntable is to be maintained stationary, some means must be found to "dump" the angular momentum stored in the reaction wheel. This can be done by the use of jets at the rim of the turntable as shown in Fig. VIII-1. When the jets are turned on, the motor which drives the reaction wheel may be permitted to exert a reverse torque on the wheel to slow down its rotation while the turntable remains stationary. Suppose that each jet is at a distance d from the center of the turntable, that it fires tangentially, and that the escaping gas has an exhaust velocity v_0 with respect to the jet nozzle. (Assume that these jets are fed from tanks near the center of the turntable so that I_1 is not changed appreciably by the loss of mass.) What must be the total mass flow rate from the two jets if they are to exert a total torque equal to one hundred times N_0? What is the total mass of gas which must be supplied to the jets in order to dump the maximum angular momentum from the reaction wheel one hundred times? If the turntable is to remain stationary during the dumping of angular momentum from the reaction wheel, what new specifications (similar to those calculated in Problems VIII-1 and VIII-2) will be required for the motor which drives the reaction wheel?

VIII-6 Describe qualitatively how a motor-driven reaction wheel can be used to rotate the turntable from one stationary position to another one. If no external torques are applied during this interval, what will be the relation between the angular velocity of the reaction wheel before the rotation takes place and after rotation has been accomplished? Is it theoretically possible for energy to be conserved in this process?

THE ORBITING ASTRONOMICAL OBSERVATORY. Consider now an orbiting astronomical observatory in a circular orbit around the earth. The center of mass of this observatory is accelerated toward the center of the earth at all times, but Eq. (7-47) tells us that even under these circumstances the torque about the center of mass of the observatory is equal to the rate of change of angular momentum about the center of mass. Because the satellite is in a near-vacuum, this rotation is almost perfectly frictionless. The accuracy with which the observatory must be oriented in space will be determined by the kinds of experiments to be carried out using the observatory. For instance, a reflecting optical telescope 36 in. in diameter without significant optical distortions can be used to distinguish between (the technical word is *resolve*) two stars of equal magnitude which are separated by an angular separation of about 0.075 sec of arc for light in the middle of the visible spectrum.* [One degree of arc contains sixty equal minutes of arc; one minute of arc contains sixty equal seconds of arc. You can show that one-tenth of a second of arc is equal to $\pi/(180 \times 60 \times 60 \times 10) = 4.85 \times 10^{-7}$ radian.] If a 36-in. telescope is to be used, then, in order to prevent blurring of the star image, positioning of the telescope should be accurate to better than 0.1 sec of arc during an observation. Coarse guidance is achieved by orienting the telescope with respect to predetermined target stars. What is the minimum number of target stars required? Fine guidance uses the image of the star being observed.

* In the ultraviolet region at a wavelength of 1200 Å the resolving power of a 36-in. telescope is 0.016 sec of arc.

Problems

VIII-7 As an example, consider a uniform cube of mass 1000 kg and 2 m on an edge. What constant torque N_0 must be applied to this cube to rotate it from rest through an angle of $\frac{1}{10}$ sec of arc in 1 min about an axis which passes through the center of a cube face and through the center of the cube? (*Answer:* 1.8×10^{-7} N-m.)

The sources of torque on the orbiting observatory are as follows:

(*a*) *Torque due to the magnetic field of the earth.* If there are magnetized parts in the satellite, they may experience a torque due to interaction with the magnetic field of the earth, just as a compass needle experiences a torque which tends to orient it toward the magnetic pole of the earth. Torques from this source can be reduced by using non-magnetic materials wherever possible in the satellite and by demagnetizing any magnetic materials which must be used.

(*b*) *Torques due to solar light pressure and air drag.* The light from the sun exerts a small pressure on any surface which it strikes. At the position of the earth but outside of the earth's atmosphere, this pressure is about 9×10^{-6} N/m² on a smooth perfectly reflecting surface perpendicular to the incident light (and about half this value on a surface which reflects no light). In fact, it has been proposed to use this pressure by means of a "solar sail" for interplanetary travel.*

Problems

VIII-8 If a cube 2 m on an edge has smooth perfectly reflecting faces and one of these faces is perpendicular to light from the sun, what will be the total force on this face due to solar light pressure? At what point on the surface must a single force of the same magnitude be applied to cause the same motion of the cube as the solar light pressure does? This point is called the *center of solar radiation pressure.* Orbiting observatories are designed so that for any orientation of the observatory the perpendicular distance between the center of mass and a line parallel to the incident light which passes through the center of solar radiation pressure is as small as possible. If the cube described above is not quite uniform, so that this distance is 5 cm, what torque does the solar light pressure exert on the cube? Compare this with your answer to Problem VIII-7.

VIII-9 Describe the orientation of different circular orbits 500 miles from the surface of the earth for which the observatory will be in sunlight about one-half of the time, most of the time, and all of the time.

* D. C. Hock, F. N. McMillan, and A. R. Tanguay, *Proceedings of the IRE*, **48,** 492 (April 1960).

At 500 miles above the surface of the earth there is enough residual air to exert a pressure on the side of the satellite which faces in the direction of motion of the satellite in its orbit. The magnitude of this pressure at an altitude of 500 miles is approximately equal to the solar light pressure and torques due to this pressure are reduced by the same methods used to reduce torques due to solar light pressure. If the satellite is placed in a much higher orbit, the air pressure will be much less than its magnitude at 500 miles. The light pressure will be effectively the same at any altitude above 500 miles.

(*c*) *Torque due to the non-uniformity of the gravitational field of the earth* Consider a dumbbell made up of two spheres of equal mass held together by a rigid rod of negligible mass which makes an angle ϕ with the local vertical (a line directed away from the center of the earth). (See Fig. VIII-2.) Since one sphere is slightly farther away from the center of the earth than the other one, the attraction of the earth is slightly less on it. This results in a torque about the center of mass if ϕ is not equal to zero or $\pi/2$. The magnitude of this torque is negligible at the surface of the earth compared with torques due to air currents, etc., and it becomes significant only under the essentially frictionless conditions of space.

Problems

VIII-10 Derive an approximate expression for the difference in the gravitational force on a particle of mass m at slightly different radial distances from the center of the earth. You may use differentials if you wish.

VIII-11 Derive an expression for the torque on the dumbbell in Fig. VIII-2. Show that this torque increases with the square of the distance of the spheres from the center of mass. At what angle ϕ will this torque be a maximum? If the distance between the centers of these spheres is 2 m, and if this dumbbell is in a circular orbit 500 miles from the surface of the earth (7.183×10^6 m from the center of the earth), for what equal mass of the two spheres will this maximum torque be equal to 10^{-6} N-m?

VIII-12 Consider a rigid body made up of three identical dumbbells whose connecting rods are mutually perpendicular and joined at the center of mass (see Fig. VIII-3). Without using equations, show that the gravitational torque on this rigid body will be equal to zero for any orientation of the rigid body. Extend this result to show that, if the moments of inertia of the orbiting observatory about three perpendicular axes of symmetry are made equal, there will be no net gravitational torque on the observatory. In practice these moments of inertia are made equal within one part in a thousand.

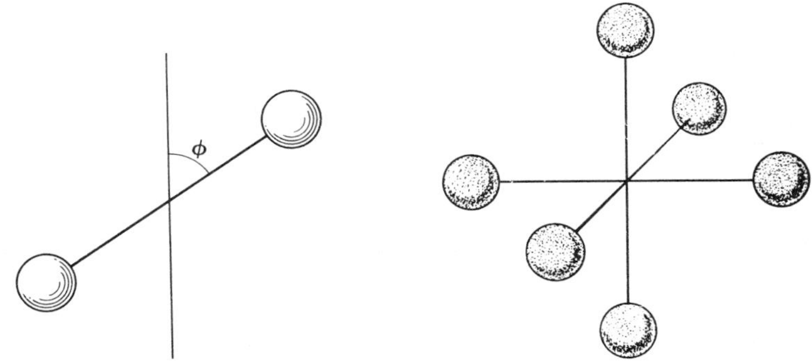

Fig. VIII-2. Fig. VIII-3.

VIII-13 Suppose that torques due to the three causes mentioned above can be kept below a total of 10^{-5} N-m, that the moment of inertia of the satellite is approximated by the cube of Problem VIII-7, and that the rotation rate of the vehicle about an axis through the centers of two parallel cube faces must be less than 0.1 sec of arc per minute. Suppose also that the maximum speed of a reaction wheel is 6000 rpm, and the speed control is accurate to $+2$ or -2 rpm. Find the dimensions of a reaction wheel made of stainless steel (density 7.7 g/cc) which could be used for this accuracy of stabilization about one axis of rotation. If the torque applied has the constant value 10^{-5} N-m, how often must angular momentum be dumped from the reaction wheel? Probably observations will not be possible during the process of dumping angular momentum. Can you design a wheel which will meet the additional requirement that a continuous observation can be made for $2\frac{1}{2}$ hours without dumping angular momentum during this time?

VIII-14 Show that the reaction wheel you have designed above cannot absorb enough angular momentum to be used to rotate the observatory as a whole from one star to another at a reasonable rate. If it is required to rotate the observatory at a rate of one half degree per second (180 degrees in 6 minutes), design a second reaction wheel for this purpose. If the speed control of this second wheel is also accurate to $+2$ or -2 rpm, show that it is not accurate enough for stabilization once the observatory is rotated into position.

VIII-15 Discuss ways of dumping angular momentum other than the gas jets described in the preliminary problem. You may consider electromagnets, solar flaps, or sliding weights to make use of any of the torques described above. Compare these among themselves and with gas jets in terms of power consumption, ease of manipulation, and long life.

VIII-16 An actual orbiting observatory must be stabilized along three axes in space, not only one as we have been discussing thus far. Consider first the use of three reaction wheels whose axes are fixed in mutually perpendicular directions with respect to the observatory. Show that, when one of these is slowed down or speeded up in order to rotate the observatory about this axis, precessional torques will be set up in the other two reaction wheels which will tend to change the direction of the axis about which rotation is desired. How can this effect be eliminated? Next suppose that a single reaction wheel is mounted in gimbals in such a way that torques can be applied to the wheel not only about the axis of rotation but also about the two axes perpendicular to the axis of rotation. Describe how such a single wheel could be used for rotation (or stabilization) about all three axes. One plan for an orbiting satellite calls for a spinning spherical metal shell to be suspended in a high frequency alternating magnetic field.* Torques could be applied to such a sphere by electromagnetic means.

* See L. Spitzer, Jr., *The Astronomical Journal*, **65**, 242 (June 1960, No. 1280).

chapter 9

Non-inertial reference frames

9.1 INTRODUCTION. Except for the sections on motion with respect to moving points and axes, every law of motion in the first eight chapters was derived for motion with respect to inertial coordinate systems. In Sec. 4.15 an inertial coordinate system was *defined* as a coordinate system in which the vector law of motion for a particle is $\mathbf{F} = m\mathbf{a}$. In this equation the force $\mathbf{F}$ is the resultant vector force exerted on the particle as described by experimental physics. This description might attribute the force to physical contact with another body, to electric or magnetic or gravitational fields, or to any combination of these or other known forces.

Some coordinate systems are clearly not inertial. The rider in an automobile which is accelerating along a straight road experiences a force that tends to pull him back in his seat. The rider does not attribute this force to electric or gravitational fields; rather he associates it with the acceleration of his reference frame (the car). Similarly, when the car turns a corner the rider associates the outward pull he feels with the motion of the car rather than with some conventional force. A frame of reference which is fixed with respect to the surface of the earth has been the frame with respect to which most of the crucial experiments in physics have been carried out. Since the earth is rotating on its axis this frame is not inertial, but it is satisfactory for most localized mechanics experiments if a simple term is added to the equation of motion to account for the gravitational force. For some mechanics experiments, however, such a simple force term is not adequate to account for the observed results. Remember that in dealing with ballistic trajectories we found it convenient to use a reference frame which did not rotate with the earth. Measurements with respect to any reference frame fixed in the earth would give different (and more complicated) mathematical expressions for these trajectories.

Our purpose in this chapter will be to work out the equations of motion in several kinds of non-inertial reference frames and to see how these results can be applied to motion with respect to the surface of the earth.

Question

9-1 Show that a non-rotating reference frame which is in uniform linear motion with respect to an inertial frame is itself inertial.

9.2 THE LAWS OF MOTION IN AN ACCELERATING BOX. Suppose that in interstellar space an observer named Mr. C is shut up in an opaque cubical box which is then made to undergo a constant acceleration **A** with respect to an inertial reference frame in which a second observer named Mr. B remains at rest. What will happen to Mr. C? (See Fig. 9-1.)

First of all, we can guess that Mr. C will find himself "falling" toward the side of the box opposite to the direction of the acceleration of the box. Call the side of the box toward which Mr. C falls the *floor*, and call the side of the box opposite the floor the *ceiling*. After Mr. C has picked himself up off the floor he will go about setting up a reference frame with respect to which he will derive his laws of motion. Suppose he chooses his reference frame to be stationary with respect to the box, with the x-axis pointing from floor to ceiling and the y-axis pointing along one edge of the box parallel to the floor as shown in Fig. 9-1. Suppose also that Mr. B in the inertial reference frame chooses his x_I axis to lie along the direction of the acceleration of the box. The subscript I means that Mr. B's reference frame is inertial. By means of a one-way mirror Mr. B

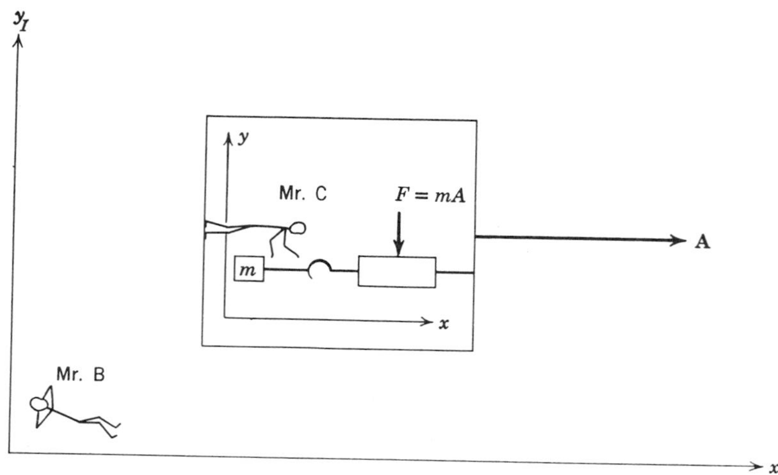

Fig. 9-1. Linear acceleration of a closed box.

can see into the box, and he chooses his y_I axis parallel to the y-axis chosen by Mr. C.

Now Mr. C has been given a set of particles of known mass, together with calibrated clocks, measuring rods, and spring balances. His job is to carry out a series of experiments in the box and to derive from the results of these experiments the laws of motion for a particle which moves with respect to his reference frame. We shall watch his experiments from the inertial reference frame of Mr. B. Since we already know the laws of motion of a particle with respect to the inertial frame of Mr. B, we shall be able to predict correctly the results of Mr. C's experiments and thus to set up the laws of motion in his frame for him.

Mr. C begins his experiments by releasing a particle from rest with respect to his frame from a point near the ceiling of the box and measuring its acceleration as it "drops" toward the floor of the box. What will be the value of the acceleration which he measures? When the particle is released, Mr. B outside the box will observe this particle to be free of forces. The laws of motion for the inertial frame of Mr. B tell us that with respect to the reference frame of Mr. B the particle will move to the right with a constant velocity equal to the instantaneous velocity of the box at the instant the particle is released. However, since Mr. B sees the box accelerating to the right with acceleration $\mathbf{A}$ he can *predict* that the floor of the box will "catch up with" the particle. In other words, *with respect to the box* the particle will appear to accelerate toward the floor with an acceleration of magnitude A. This prediction is correct. Mr. C measures the value of the acceleration of the particle toward the floor to have the value A.

Questions

9-2 Show that Mr. C will measure the same acceleration A for all particles in "free fall" in the box no matter what the masses of these particles are.

9-3 Show that the force which must be exerted externally on the box to keep it in constant acceleration $\mathbf{A}$ will be different while the particle of mass m is in free fall inside the box from what it will be before the particle is released. What is the magnitude of this change in the external force?

In his second experiment Mr. C hangs a particle of mass m from a calibrated spring balance as shown in Fig. 9-1. What force will he read on the spring balance? To Mr. B the spring balance is applying sufficient force to accelerate the particle at the same rate as the box. Hence the force exerted by the spring balance must have the value $\mathbf{F} = m\mathbf{A}$. This prediction is also correct. If Mr. C divides the reading on his spring balance by the known mass of the particle, the result will be equal to the magnitude A of the acceleration of the particle which he measured in the previous "free-fall" experiment.

With this background let us consider a more general experiment. Suppose that Mr. C applies a net force **F** to a particle of known mass m by means of one or more spring balances and observes a vector acceleration **a** of the particle with respect to his reference frame. What law of motion will he derive which relates **F** to **a** after he carries out many such experiments? We already know that in the inertial reference frame of Mr. B this equation of motion will have the form

$$\mathbf{F} = m\mathbf{a}_I \tag{9-1}$$

where $\mathbf{a}_I$ is the vector acceleration of the particle with respect to the inertial frame of Mr. B. Now **A** represents the vector acceleration of the box in the frame of Mr. B. In the present case **A** lies along the direction of the x_I axis, but the results we are about to derive will apply to linear acceleration of the box in any direction with respect to the inertial frame. Let $\mathbf{r}_I$ represent the position of the particle with respect to the origin of the inertial frame of Mr. B. Let **r** represent the position of the particle with respect to the origin of the accelerating frame of Mr. C. Let **R** represent the position of the origin of the coordinate frame of Mr. C with respect to the origin of the coordinate frame of Mr. B. These vectors are shown in Fig. 9-2.

From the figure,

$$\mathbf{r}_I = \mathbf{R} + \mathbf{r}$$

Take the second time derivative of both sides of this equation.

$$\ddot{\mathbf{r}}_I = \ddot{\mathbf{R}} + \ddot{\mathbf{r}}$$

Now $\ddot{\mathbf{R}}$ is simply the acceleration **A** of the box, while $\ddot{\mathbf{r}}_I$ is the acceleration

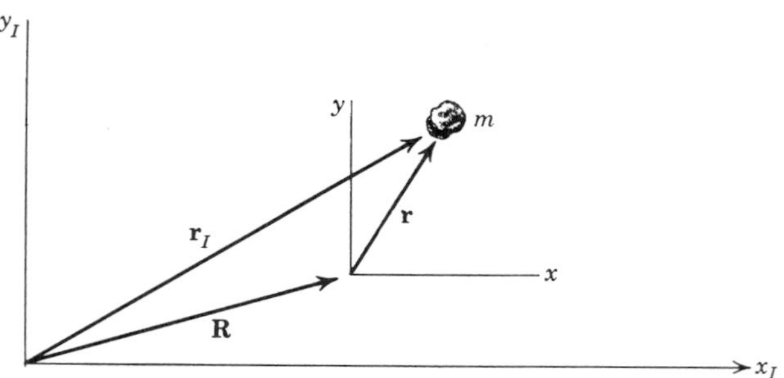

Fig. 9-2. Position of a particle in the two reference frames.

$\mathbf{a}_I$ of the particle as seen by Mr. B and $\ddot{\mathbf{r}}$ is the acceleration $\mathbf{a}$ of the particle as seen by Mr. C. With these substitutions the last equation becomes

$$\mathbf{a}_I = \mathbf{A} + \mathbf{a} \tag{9-2}$$

Substitute for $\mathbf{a}_I$ from Eq. (9-2) into Eq. (9-1).

$$\mathbf{F} = m(\mathbf{a} + \mathbf{A}) \tag{9-3}$$

This is the equation which relates the acceleration $\mathbf{a}$ of the particle as measured in the frame of Mr. C to the net force $\mathbf{F}$ applied to the particle. This equation is correct because it has been derived in the inertial reference frame of Mr. B in which the conventional laws of mechanics apply.

How will the law of motion be interpreted by Mr. C? Equation (9-3) can be rewritten to read

$$\mathbf{F} - m\mathbf{A} = m\mathbf{a} \tag{9-4}$$

The right side of this equation is in the usual form for the law of motion. The left side, on the other hand, includes not only the usual force term $\mathbf{F}$ but also an additional term $-m\mathbf{A}$. In other words, *the equation of motion derived by Mr. C will be correct only if he includes, in addition to the net force which he applies to the particle, a "force" equal in magnitude to mA and directed toward the floor of the box.* We call this "force" $-m\mathbf{A}$ a *pseudo-force* because it is not applied to the particle by any of the usual methods but is due to the acceleration of the reference frame with respect to which the results of experiments on the particle are measured. Mr. C will not be able to account for this pseudo-force in terms of forces or fields which originate in his box. Nevertheless, the prefix *pseudo* does not mean that this pseudo-force is in some way unreal. When you are pressed back against the seat of an automobile as it accelerates, the force you feel is just as measurable as the force of gravity. The prefix *pseudo* means simply that you cannot account for this force in the same way that forces are accounted for when measurements are made with respect to an inertial reference frame.

It cannot be emphasized too strongly that we are dealing with two *different* descriptions of the same event. *Either* you analyze the motion of a particle with respect to an inertial reference frame and thus do not need to postulate a pseudo-force *or* you analyze the motion of the particle with respect to an accelerated reference frame, in which case it is necessary to postulate the existence of a pseudo-force. In solving a given problem you must choose which description you wish to use and be consistent in applying the analysis relevent to that description. For instance, do *not* postulate pseudo-forces in an analysis carried out with respect to an inertial reference frame. The same remarks will apply to descriptions of motion with respect to the non-inertial reference frames which follow in later sections of this chapter.

Class Discussion Question

9-4 Discuss the meaning of the word "real" as applied to physical observables. Are pseudo-forces "real"? If not, why do non-inertial observers experience them? If so, why do different observers disagree about their presence or absence?

Consider once again observer C traveling with the accelerated box. To this observer the pseudo-force which attracts particles toward the floor will act very much like the force due to a gravitational field. For him all particles in free fall experience the same acceleration. For him all particles have a weight equal to their mass times this acceleration of free fall. In fact, it might be difficult for observer C to distinguish between the results of a constant acceleration of his box in field-free space and the presence of a uniform gravitational field in which the box is stationary or moving with uniform velocity. Such a constant acceleration has been proposed to replace the force of gravity on long, manned interstellar space flights.

This result is a special case of a more general *principle of equivalence* which states that *there is no physical experiment which can be carried out in a sufficiently small closed box in order to distinguish whether the box is at rest in a uniform gravitational field or is being linearly accelerated in a field-free region of space.* We have not proved the principle of equivalence in the foregoing experiment but rather have given one example of it. The application of the principle of equivalence is very much wider than to the laws of classical mechanics alone. The principle implies that the laws of electricity and magnetism and every other law of physics will be the same with respect to a reference frame which is at rest in a uniform gravitational field as they will be with respect to a box which is being linearly accelerated in a field-free region of space.

Notice carefully that the principle of equivalence holds only for a "sufficiently small" closed box. The reason is that it is not possible to find a gravitational field which is uniform over an arbitrarily large region of space. On the earth, for instance, it is possible to detect the decrease of the gravitational force with altitude. Thus it would be possible for you to distinguish between the laws of physics in a very large box at rest on the surface of the earth and the laws in the same box in uniform acceleration in interstellar space. Whether or not a given box is "sufficiently small" for the principle of equivalence to apply will depend on the nature and accuracy of the experiments which are to be carried out in the box. The limitation of the principle of equivalence is that it applies only to small regions of space. At the end of Chapter 13 we shall discuss briefly the analysis of experiments which cannot be localized in this way.*

Class Discussion Questions

9-5 Suppose that Mr. C shines a narrow beam of light across his box perpendicular to the direction of acceleration of the box. Demonstrate qualitatively that Mr. C will observe this beam of light to be bent downward toward the floor. Use the principle of equivalence to demonstrate that light is bent when it passes across a gravitational field. How far would you expect a beam of light to be deviated from a straight line while traveling a distance of 1000 km perpendicular to a uniform gravitational field of magnitude g?

9-6 Is there any operational method by which Mr. C can determine whether the agency which pulls particles toward the floor of his box is a *pseudo-force* resulting from acceleration of the box or a gravitational *force* due to masses outside the box? Should Mr. C label this agency a *force* or a *pseudo-force*? Is the force of gravity on earth a force or a pseudo-force?

The remainder of this chapter will deal with the pseudo-forces experienced in several different non-inertial reference frames. The method used in each case will follow very closely the method employed above. The steps in this method are as follows.

I. By geometrical or other arguments find the relation between the acceleration $\mathbf{a}$ of a particle measured in the non-inertial system and the acceleration $\mathbf{a}_I$ measured in an inertial system.

II. Set up the equation of motion $\mathbf{F} = m\mathbf{a}_I$ in the inertial system which we know to be correct. $\mathbf{F}$ represents the applied forces. Then substitute for $\mathbf{a}_I$ from the results of the first step.

III. Rewrite the new equation with only the term $m\mathbf{a}$ on one side. Terms on the other side, other than $\mathbf{F}$, will be pseudo-forces experienced in the non-inertial frame because of its acceleration.

Both in the previous example and in the remainder of the cases to be treated in this chapter it is not necessary to carry out any actual experiments to derive the results, since these results follow from geometry and from the equations of motion already derived for inertial reference frames. Nevertheless, the results so derived have been checked by many experiments without being disproved.

9.3 THE LAWS OF MOTION ON A PHONOGRAPH TURNTABLE.

Many of the "rides" in an amusement park depend for their unexpected effects on the pseudo-forces which are experienced in rotating noninertial

* See V. Fock *The Theory of Space Time and Gravitation*, Pergamon Press, New York 1959, Sec. 61.

reference frames. These pseudo-forces are the centrifugal pseudo-force and the Coriolis pseudo-force. In the next section these two forces will be derived mathematically in a three-dimensional rotating frame. In this section we shall discuss these forces in two dimensions on a rotating phonograph turntable. Our purpose in discussing these pseudo-forces first on a phonograph turntable will be not only to increase your appreciation of rides in an amusement park but also to explain the physical origins of these pseudo-forces more explicitly than is possible in the more rigorous mathematical analysis of the next section.

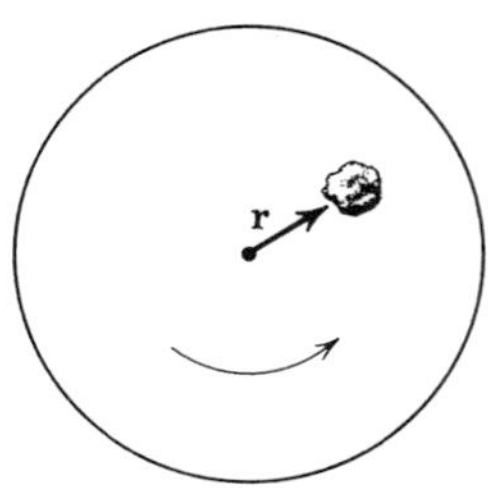

Fig. 9-3. Position of a particle on a rotating turntable.

The centrifugal pseudo-force. Suppose that we have a large flat turn-table similar to a phonograph turntable which, by means of a motor, is made to rotate at a constant angular velocity of ω radians per second (see Fig. 9-3). This time the reference frame of the non-inertial observer, Mr. C, will be fixed with respect to the turntable with its origin at the center of the turntable. The reference frame of the inertial observer, Mr. B, also has its origin at the center of the turntable, but this inertial frame (by definition) does not rotate. Let $\mathbf{r}$ be a vector with its tail at the center of the turntable and its head at the position of a test particle on the plane. This vector will represent the position of the test particle. Since the origins of the two coordinate systems coincide, we can use the single vector $\mathbf{r}$ to represent the position of the test particle with respect to both systems.

Question

9-7 How can Mr. B and Mr. C agree to use the same vector $\mathbf{r}$ to represent the position of the test particle even though they do not measure the same Cartesian components of the vector $\mathbf{r}$ in their respective reference frames?

What pseudo-forces will Mr. C observe in the motion of particles with respect to his rotating coordinate system? Taking the simplest case first, suppose that a test particle of mass m is held at rest with respect to the turntable at a position given by the position vector $\mathbf{r}$. From the results of Sec. 6.3 we know that Mr. B will calculate that the particle is experiencing a radial acceleration $-\omega^2\mathbf{r}$ which keeps it on its circular path. This is called the *centripetal acceleration.* If the particle does not move with respect to the turntable, then both the velocity and the acceleration of this particle are zero in the rotating reference frame of Mr. C. For this case the only acceleration of the particle with respect to the inertial reference frame of Mr. B is $-\omega^2\mathbf{r}$. Thus the equation of motion for Mr. B is

$$\mathbf{F} = m\mathbf{a}_I = -m\omega^2\mathbf{r}$$

Transposing the term $-m\omega^2\mathbf{r}$, we have, for observer C,

$$\mathbf{F} + m\omega^2\mathbf{r} = 0 \qquad \text{particle at rest in the rotating frame} \qquad (9\text{-}5)$$

In the rotating frame, then, a particle which is at rest has on it a pseudo-force $m\omega^2\mathbf{r}$ tending to move it in a positive radial direction. This pseudo-force is called the *centrifugal pseudo-force* (*centrifugal* means "flying from the center"). If the particle is to remain at rest in this reference frame, a force $\mathbf{F}$ equal in magnitude and opposite in direction to the centrifugal pseudo-force must be applied to the particle to keep it from moving. Equation (9-5) has been demonstrated only for the case in which the particle is at rest with respect to the rotating reference frame. Problems in which this condition exists will be *statics* problems in the rotating frame. Notice that the magnitude of the radial pseudo-force which will have to be balanced by an applied force $\mathbf{F}$ will be different at different radial distances of the particle from the origin of the rotating system.

Questions

9-8 Using the law of action and reaction, show that the centrifugal pseudo-force is simply the reaction to the centripetal force.

9-9 A rod is fixed on the turntable in a radial direction from the origin. A rider on the turntable starts at the center and climbs slowly outward along the rod. If the rider can hold onto the rod with a force equal to his own weight on earth, how far out along the rod can he move before he loses his grip?

9-10 Show that, if the turntable is accelerating with an angular acceleration $\dot{\omega}$ radians per second squared, the particle at rest with respect to the turntable will experience an additional pseudo-force given by the expression $-mr\dot{\omega}\hat{\theta}$, where $\hat{\theta}$ is a unit vector lying in the plane of the turntable and pointing perpendicular to $\mathbf{r}$ in the direction of increasing θ.

The Coriolis pseudo-force. Now suppose that, instead of remaining at rest with respect to the turntable, the particle moves with a constant vector velocity $\mathbf{v}$ as measured with respect to the turntable. The fact that the particle is moving with respect to the rotating frame will cause it to experience two additional accelerations with respect to the inertial frame. These two accelerations have the same magnitude and act in the same direction. The first of these accelerations arises from the fact that the velocity which appears constant in the rotating frame is actually changing

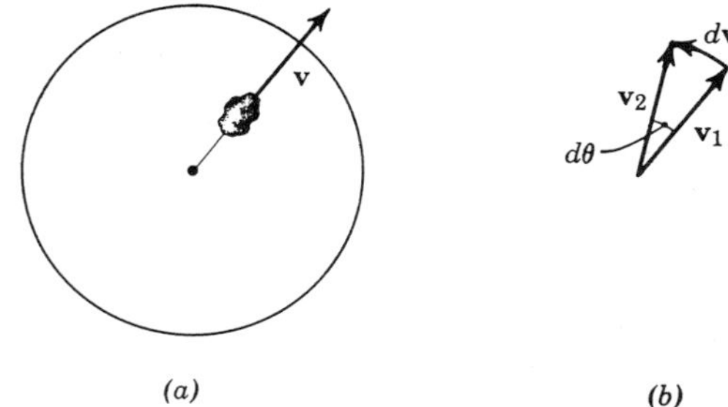

Fig. 9-4. (*a*) Particle moving outward along a radius. (*b*) Change in direction of radial velocity with respect to inertial frame.

direction with respect to the inertial frame. An acceleration results from this change of direction. The second of these accelerations arises from the fact that different points on the turntable have different tangential velocities with respect to the inertial frame. As a particle moves from point to point on the turntable it changes the direction or magnitude of its tangential velocity with respect to the inertial frame, and this change in tangential velocity results in an acceleration with respect to the inertial frame. These two accelerations always occur together and can be separated only conceptually for purposes of analysis. The two accelerations will now be explained in more detail for two specific cases and then for the general case.

Case I. Particle moving outward along a radius with constant velocity with respect to the turntable.

Consider a particle which is forced to move outward along a radius with constant velocity $\mathbf{v}$ as measured with respect to the turntable (Fig. 9-4*a*). For instance, the particle could be a toy cog-railway engine with a motor which turns the cog-wheel at a constant rate. Even though this radial velocity is constant in the rotating frame, it is changing direction with respect to the inertial frame (see Fig. 9-4*b*). If the turntable rotates counterclockwise, then in a time interval dt the velocity vector will have rotated through an angle $d\theta = \omega\, dt$ with respect to the inertial frame. The magnitude dv of the change of this velocity is given by

$$dv = v\, d\theta = v\omega\, dt$$

where v is the magnitude of the velocity $\mathbf{v}$. If both sides of this equation are divided by dt, the acceleration associated with this change of direction is found to be

$$\frac{dv}{dt} = \omega v \tag{9-6}$$

As can be seen in Fig. 9-4*b*, the particle experiences this acceleration in a direction perpendicular to its direction of motion and to the left of this direction.

A second acceleration results from the fact that, as the particle moves out along a radius, there is an increase in its tangential speed with respect to the inertial coordinate system (see Fig. 9-5). The tangential speed v_T of the particle at any radius r is given by the expression

$$v_T = \omega r$$

If the particle moves radially a distance dr the tangential speed increases by

$$dv_T = \omega\, dr$$

The acceleration associated with this change in speed is found by dividing both sides of this equation by dt.

$$\frac{dv_T}{dt} = \omega \frac{dr}{dt}$$

Here dr/dt is equal to the radial speed v. Hence the acceleration becomes

$$\frac{dv_T}{dt} = \omega v \qquad (9\text{-}7)$$

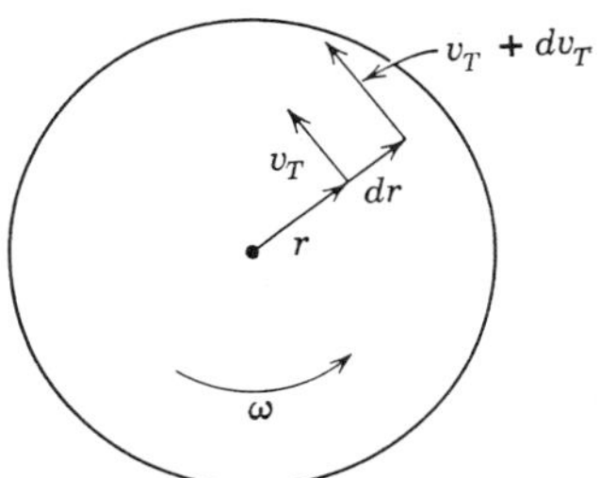

Fig. 9-5. Increase in tangential speed with increased radius.

If the turntable rotates counterclockwise, the direction of this acceleration is perpendicular to the direction of motion and to the left of this direction.

We have shown that there are two accelerations associated with the motion of the particle in an outward radial direction. One of these is due to the *change in direction* of the radial velocity vector with respect to the inertial coordinate system. The other is due to the *increase in the tangential speed* of the particle with respect to the inertial coordinate system as the particle moves outward along the radius. Both of these accelerations are in a direction perpendicular to **v** and to the left of this direction. Hence the sum of these two accelerations will have a magnitude equal to $2\omega v$ and a direction perpendicular to **v** and to the left of this direction on the turntable. This total acceleration associated with the velocity of the particle is called the *Coriolis acceleration* after G. G. Coriolis (1792–1893), who first discussed it.

In addition to the Coriolis acceleration, the particle will experience the centripetal acceleration associated with the position r with respect to the center of the turntable. Altogether in this case the particle will experience two accelerations as it moves outward along the radius with constant velocity with respect to the turntable.

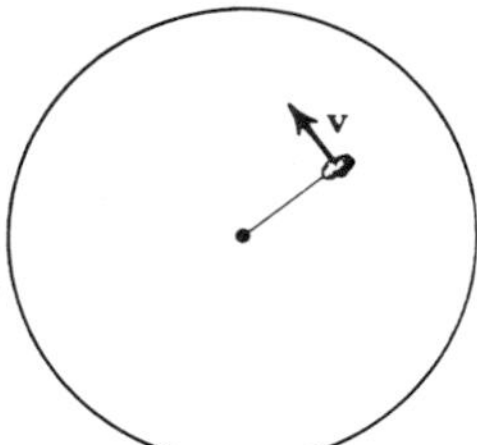

Fig. 9-6. Particle moving in a tangential direction with respect to the turntable.

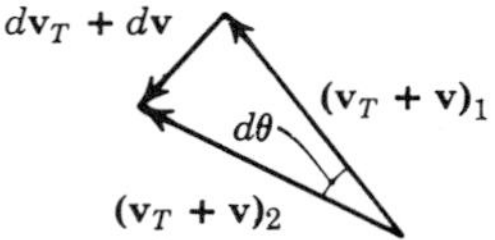

Fig. 9-7. Change in direction of tangential velocity with respect to inertial frame.

(1) a centripetal acceleration of magnitude $\omega^2 r$ in a direction toward the center of the turntable, and

(2) a Coriolis acceleration of magnitude $2\omega v$ in a direction perpendicular to $\mathbf{v}$ and to the left of this direction on the turntable.

Questions

9-11 Suppose that $\omega = 10$ radians/sec, $v = 2$ m/sec, $r = 10$ m, and $m = 1$ kg. Calculate the radial and tangential accelerations of the particle under the conditions of Case I.

9-12 Show that, if the particle moves *inward* along a radius with constant velocity $\mathbf{v}$ as measured with respect to the turntable, the Coriolis acceleration will point in a direction perpendicular to $\mathbf{v}$ and to the left of this direction (i.e., in the direction opposite that of Case I). Draw a diagram showing the relative directions of $\mathbf{v}$ and the Coriolis acceleration.

Case II. Particle moving in a tangential direction at a constant velocity with respect to the turntable.

Suppose that the particle again moves with constant velocity with respect to the turntable but this time the observations are made at an instant when this velocity points tangentially in the direction of increasing θ (see Fig. 9-6). With respect to the inertial observer Mr. B, the total tangential velocity of the particle is equal to $\mathbf{v}$ plus the tangential velocity of the turntable at the position of the particle, $\mathbf{v}_T$ (Fig. 9-7). After a time interval dt this total velocity vector will have rotated through an angle $d\theta = \omega\, dt$. The change in velocity of the particle in the reference frame of Mr. B will have a magnitude

$$dv_T + dv = (v_T + v)\, d\theta = (v_T + v)\omega\, dt$$

If we divide both sides of this equation by dt, we have the acceleration of the particle due to this change of direction.

$$\frac{dv_T}{dt} + \frac{dv}{dt} = v_T\omega + v\omega \tag{9-8}$$

The first term on both sides of this equation represents the centripetal acceleration. The second term represents the acceleration in the inertial frame due to the change in the direction of the velocity vector $\mathbf{v}$. The magnitude of the second term is ωv, and, from Fig. 9-7, its direction is perpendicular to the velocity vector $\mathbf{v}$ and to the left of this vector.

A second acceleration results from the fact that the tangential velocity of the turntable at the point occupied by the particle will change direction as the point occupied by the particle changes. Consider Fig. 9-8*a*, which is a picture taken with respect to the turntable. Suppose that in an interval of time dt the particle moves a distance ds on the turntable along the dotted line from point 1 to point 2 in the figure. The vectors $\mathbf{r}_1$ and $\mathbf{r}_2$ from the origin to points 1 and 2 include an angle $d\phi$ measured with respect to the turntable. From the figure we have the relation

$$ds = r\,d\phi \tag{9-9}$$

Now point 1 on the turntable is moving with a tangential velocity $\mathbf{v}_{T1}$ with respect to the inertial frame, and point 2 on the turntable is moving with a tangential velocity $\mathbf{v}_{T2}$ with respect to the inertial frame. As shown in Fig. 9-8*b*, the angle between $\mathbf{v}_{T1}$ and $\mathbf{v}_{T2}$ is also $d\phi$. Hence the magnitude of the change in tangential velocity dv_T which the particle experiences in moving from point 1 to point 2 is given by the expression

$$dv_T = v_T\,d\phi$$

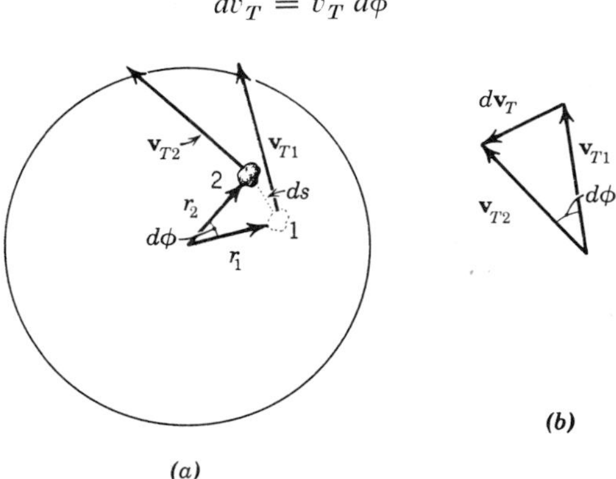

Fig. 9-8. (*a*) Displacement ds of the particle with respect to the turntable. (*b*) Tangential velocity of points 1 and 2 of the turntable.

but from Eq. (9-9) $d\phi = ds/r$, so that

$$dv_T = \frac{v_T}{r}\,ds$$

Divide both sides of this equation by dt.

$$\frac{dv_T}{dt} = \frac{v_T}{r}\frac{ds}{dt}$$

The left side of this equation is simply the acceleration which the particle experiences in changing position on the turntable. On the right side of the equation v_T/r is equal to ω and ds/dt is equal to the speed v of the particle with respect to the turntable. Hence

$$\frac{dv_T}{dt} = \omega v \tag{9-10}$$

From Fig. 9-8*b*, the direction of this acceleration is perpendicular and to the left of vector **v**.

Both of the accelerations we have just discussed are in a direction perpendicular to the direction of **v** and to the left of this direction. Hence the sum of these two accelerations will have a magnitude equal to $2\omega v$. When the centripetal acceleration is also taken into account, the particle will experience two accelerations as it moves in a tangential direction with respect to the turntable:

(1) a centripetal acceleration of magnitude $\omega^2 r$ in a direction toward the center of the turntable, and

(2) a Coriolis acceleration of magnitude $2\omega v$ in a direction perpendicular to **v** and to the left of this direction on the turntable.

Notice that, if the velocity **v** points in the direction of *increasing* θ, both the centripetal and Coriolis accelerations act in the same direction.

Question

9-13 Show that, if the velocity **v** of the particle is in a tangential direction but in the direction of *decreasing* θ, the Coriolis acceleration will point in a direction perpendicular to **v** and to the left of this direction (i.e., in the direction opposite that of Case II). Draw a diagram showing the relative direction of **v** and the Coriolis acceleration.

Case III. Particle moving in any direction in the plane of the turntable with constant velocity **v** with respect to the turntable.

We can analyze the case of a particle moving in any direction in the plane of the turntable by resolving **v** into radial and tangential components

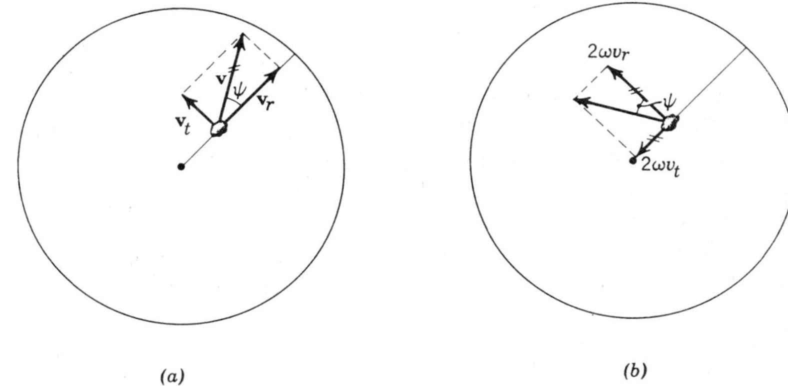

Fig. 9-9. (*a*) A resolution of velocity **v** into radial and tangential components with respect to the turntable. (*b*) Coriolis accelerations associated with the radial and tangential components of velocity in (*a*).

v_r and v_t as shown in Fig. 9-9*a*. Notice that the velocity **v** is measured *with respect to the turntable.* Apply the results of Cases I and II to these separate components. The radial component v_r will be associated with a Coriolis acceleration of magnitude $2\omega v_r$ which points in the direction of increasing θ as in Fig. 9-9*b*. The tangential component v_t (assumed positive in the direction of increasing θ) will be associated with a Coriolis acceleration of magnitude $2\omega v_t$ which points in the direction toward the center of the turntable as in Fig. 9-9*b*. The magnitude of the resultant Coriolis acceleration of the particle is given by the square root of the sum of the squares of these components.

$$\sqrt{4\omega^2 v_r^{\,2} + 4\omega^2 v_t^{\,2}} = 2\omega\sqrt{v_r^{\,2} + v_t^{\,2}} = 2\omega v$$

From Fig. 9-9*a*, the tangent of the angle ψ which the velocity **v** makes with the radius vector is $\tan \psi = v_t/v_r$. From Fig. 9-9*b*, the tangent of the angle ψ which the resultant acceleration makes with a line perpendicular to the radius vector is also

$$\tan \psi = \frac{2\omega v_t}{2\omega v_r} = \frac{v_t}{v_r}$$

Because these angles are in the same counterclockwise sense, it follows that the Coriolis acceleration is perpendicular to, and to the left of, the velocity vector **v** as in the first two cases.

In summary, a particle moving with constant velocity **v** with respect to a turntable rotating counterclockwise will experience, in addition to the centripetal acceleration, a Coriolis acceleration whose magnitude is $2\omega v$ and whose direction is perpendicular to the direction of **v** and to the left of this direction with respect to the turntable.

Questions

9-14 Show that if the turntable rotates clockwise then the Coriolis acceleration will be in a direction perpendicular to the direction of $\mathbf{v}$ and to the *right* of this direction with respect to the turntable.

9-15 State carefully what you *mean* by saying that a turntable rotates clockwise or counterclockwise. Will not a turntable which rotates counterclockwise when viewed from the "top" appear to rotate clockwise when viewed from the "bottom"? Show that the rules for the direction of the Coriolis acceleration derived above and expanded in the last question will be valid if the turntable is viewed from either side.

There is a concise way to indicate the direction of the Coriolis acceleration which will be correct for all directions of the velocity $\mathbf{v}$ in the plane of the turntable and for both senses of rotation of the turntable on its axis. Remember, from Sec. 8.11, that the vector angular velocity $\boldsymbol{\omega}$ of the turntable can be defined as a vector of magnitude ω with a direction along the axis of rotation of the turntable pointing the way a right-handed screw would advance along the axis if rotated in the same sense as the turntable. The direction of the Coriolis acceleration will then be the same as the direction of the vector cross product $\boldsymbol{\omega} \times \mathbf{v}$.

Question

9-16 Demonstrate that the direction of the Coriolis acceleration will be the same as the direction of the vector $\boldsymbol{\omega} \times \mathbf{v}$ for all directions of $\mathbf{v}$ in the plane of the turntable and for both senses of rotation of the turntable on its axis.

Both the *magnitude* and the *direction* of the Coriolis acceleration can be represented by the vector $2\boldsymbol{\omega} \times \mathbf{v}$. The Coriolis acceleration depends on the velocity $\mathbf{v}$ of the particle. In deriving the equations for the Coriolis acceleration we assumed that this velocity $\mathbf{v}$ is constant when measured with respect to the turntable. However, these derivations used only *increments* of time dt. Since the change in velocity of even an accelerating particle is vanishingly small during an incremental time interval, these equations will give the Coriolis acceleration for any particle if $\mathbf{v}$ is the *instantaneous* velocity of the particle with respect to the turntable.

All the theory presented about the Coriolis acceleration in this section can be summarized by saying that the Coriolis acceleration with respect to the inertial frame of a particle moving with an instantaneous velocity $\mathbf{v}$ with respect to the turntable will have the vector value $2\boldsymbol{\omega} \times \mathbf{v}$.

Suppose now that in addition to the Coriolis and centripetal accelerations due to the rotation of the turntable there is also an acceleration $\mathbf{a}$ of the particle in the plane of the turntable measured by Mr. C with respect to the turntable. Then the resultant or total acceleration $\mathbf{a}_I$ of the particle with respect to the inertial frame is given by the equation

$$\mathbf{a}_I = \mathbf{a} - \omega^2\mathbf{r} + 2\boldsymbol{\omega} \times \mathbf{v} \qquad (9\text{-}11)$$

Hence the equation of motion in the inertial frame (which we know to be correct in this frame) is

$$\mathbf{F} = m\mathbf{a}_I = m\mathbf{a} - m\omega^2\mathbf{r} + 2m\boldsymbol{\omega} \times \mathbf{v} \qquad (9\text{-}12)$$

If all the terms except $m\mathbf{a}$ are transposed to the left side of this equation, we shall have the equation of motion of the particle with respect to the rotating frame.

$$\mathbf{F} + m\omega^2\mathbf{r} - 2m\boldsymbol{\omega} \times \mathbf{v} = m\mathbf{a} \qquad (9\text{-}13)$$

In addition to the force $\mathbf{F}$ which he applies to the particle, the rotating observer, Mr. C, will have to postulate two pseudo-forces in order to account for the observed acceleration of the particle. These pseudo-forces are, first, the *centrifugal pseudo-force* and, second, the *Coriolis pseudo-force*. The centrifugal pseudo-force acts on the particle whether it is at rest or in motion with respect to the turntable (except when $r = 0$) in a direction *outward along the radius* from the center of the turntable. The Coriolis pseudo-force acts on the particle only if it is in motion with respect to the turntable, and then in a direction perpendicular to the direction of the vector $\mathbf{v}$ and *to the right of this direction* if the turntable is turning counterclockwise. This analysis assumes that all motion takes place in the plane of the turntable.

Questions

9-17 From Eq. (9-13) verify the directions of the centrifugal and Coriolis pseudo-forces.

9-18 Can you define a Coriolis force in such a way that the Coriolis pseudo-force is the reaction to it?

9-19 Where $\mathbf{v}$ is a constant, as assumed in Cases I, II, and III, show that the rotating observer, Mr. C, will have to apply a force to the particle in each case in order to keep it moving with constant speed in a straight line in his frame. Show what the magnitude and direction of this force will have to be in each case.

9-20 An orbiting space station has the shape of a hollow doughnut (Fig. 9-10). The outer radius R is very much greater than the height of a man. The space station rotates with constant angular velocity ω about an axis through its center perpendicular to the plane of the paper in the diagram. Describe the magnitude and direction of the pseudo-forces experienced by a man inside the space station near the outer radius if he is

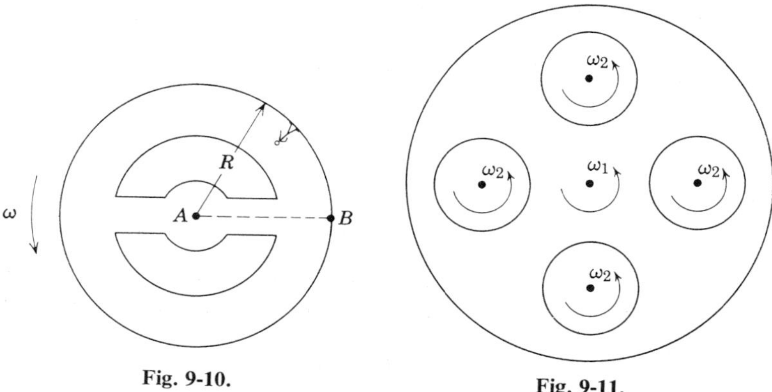

Fig. 9-10.

Fig. 9-11.

standing still with respect to the space station. What is the angular velocity ω of the space station for which the man will experience a pseudo-gravitational acceleration of magnitude g under these circumstances?

9-21 If the occupant of the space station in the previous question runs around inside the outer circumference of the space station, how will the value of the pseudo-gravity which he experiences be changed? For what speed and direction of running will this pseudo-gravity disappear? In this case what is the velocity of the occupant with respect to the inertial frame?

9-22 Suppose that a spaceman enters the space station at point A in Fig. 9-10 and "descends" toward point B along the dotted line. Describe the magnitude and direction of the pseudo-forces experienced by this spaceman.

9-23 An amusement park device consists of a large turntable which rotates with constant angular velocity ω_1 on which are mounted smaller turntables which themselves rotate with constant angular velocity ω_2 with respect to the large turntable. Describe the pseudo-forces experienced by riders on the smaller turntables at various points in their rotation. (See Fig. 9-11.)

9.4 THE LAWS OF MOTION IN A THREE-DIMENSIONAL ROTATING REFERENCE FRAME. In this section we shall derive the laws of motion for a particle viewed from a three-dimensional non-inertial reference frame which is rotating about an axis fixed with respect to an inertial reference frame. This derivation will be mathematically more rigorous than the derivations in the last section and will lead to the same results for motion in a plane perpendicular to the axis of rotation (as on a turntable). In Sec. 9.6 we shall apply these results to the equation of motion for a particle with respect to the surface of the earth.

To begin with, consider the two coordinate systems shown in Fig. 9-12. They have a common origin and a common z-axis, but the x_I, y_I, z_I reference frame is inertial, whereas the x, y, z frame rotates about the z-axis with angular velocity ω with respect to the inertial reference frame. By the convention of Sec. 8.11 the vector $\boldsymbol{\omega}$ points in the direction of the positive z-axis in the figure.

Now consider a particle which is at rest with respect to the rotating frame (Fig. 9-13). Let the position vector of this particle in this frame be given by $\mathbf{r}$. If ρ is the perpendicular distance from the z-axis to the particle, then the magnitude of the velocity of the particle with respect to the *inertial* frame x_I, y_I, z_I is given by the expression

$$\frac{dr_I}{dt} = \rho\omega = (r \sin \phi)\omega \qquad \text{particle at rest in rotating frame}$$

Now the expression $\omega r \sin \phi$ is reminiscent of the cross product of two vectors. In fact, both the *magnitude* and the *direction* of the velocity of the particle with respect to the inertial frame will be given by the expression

$$\frac{d\mathbf{r}_I}{dt} = \boldsymbol{\omega} \times \mathbf{r} \qquad \text{particle at rest in rotating frame}$$

Questions

9-24 Demonstrate that the direction of the velocity vector given by the preceding equation points in the correct direction for all locations of

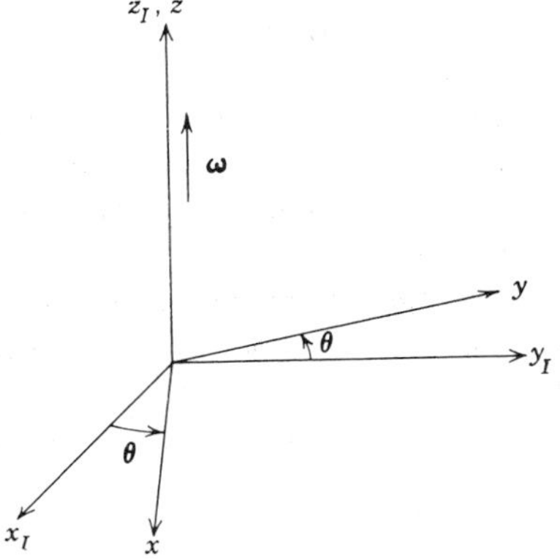

Fig. 9-12. Inertial frame x_I, y_I, z_I and rotating frame x, y, z.

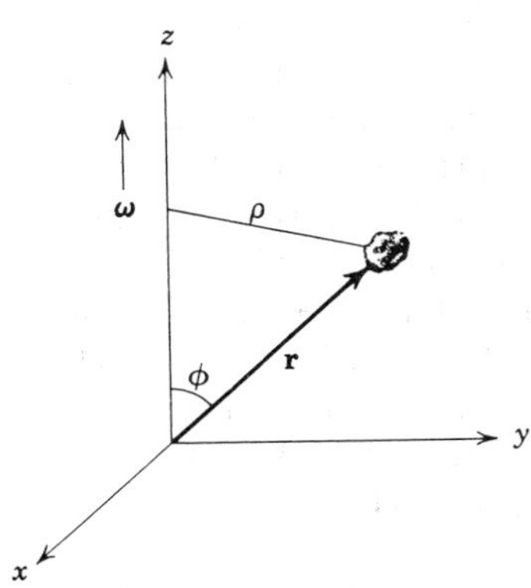

Fig. 9-13. Particle at rest in rotating frame x, y, z.

the particle in the rotating frame and for both directions of rotation of this frame about the z-axis. Show that this velocity is equal to zero if the particle is on the axis of rotation.

9-25 Show that the Cartesian components of **r** will, in general, be different with respect to the inertial frame from what they are with respect to the rotating frame. How can observers at rest with respect to the two frames agree on the vector **r** if they do not agree on its components?

Next suppose that the particle is moving with respect to the rotating frame and has a velocity vector $d\mathbf{r}/dt$ with respect to the rotating frame. An observer in the inertial system will see the velocity of this particle equal to the *vector sum* of the velocity of the particle with respect to the rotating frame *plus* the velocity which the particle would have if it were at rest at the same position in the rotating frame. In other words, the observer in the *inertial* frame can predict correctly the velocity of the particle $d\mathbf{r}_I/dt$ which he will measure in his frame if he adds the velocity vector $d\mathbf{r}/dt$ with respect to the rotating coordinate system to the vector $\boldsymbol{\omega} \times \mathbf{r}$, which expresses the velocity of the rotating frame with respect to the inertial frame at the position of the particle. In the form of an equation we may write

$$\frac{d\mathbf{r}_I}{dt} = \frac{d\mathbf{r}}{dt} + \boldsymbol{\omega} \times \mathbf{r} \tag{9-14}$$

This equation relates the time derivative of position of the particle with respect to the rotating reference frame to the time derivative of position of the particle with respect to the inertial reference frame. The first term on the right of Eq. (9-14) results from the change of **r** with respect to the rotating frame. The second term results from the rotation itself and is a function of only the *position* **r** of the particle if $\boldsymbol{\omega}$ is constant.

Now, if you look carefully at the derivation of Eq. (9-14), you will see that the result can be made more general than it is in this equation. Instead of the position vector, any other vector which describes the motion of a particle could have been used and the result would have been the same. For instance, since a vector does not change by being moved about parallel to itself, any vector **Q** which is constant with respect to the rotating frame can be placed with its tail at the origin of this frame. The result would look like Fig. 9-13 with **r** replaced by **Q**. In this case the rate of change of **Q** with respect to the inertial frame is given by

$$\frac{d\mathbf{Q}_I}{dt} = \boldsymbol{\omega} \times \mathbf{Q} \qquad \mathbf{Q} \text{ constant in rotating frame}$$

Question

9-26 Carry out the analysis which leads to this equation, using the same procedure as for $d\mathbf{r}_I/dt$.

The analysis for a **Q** which is not constant with respect to the rotating frame would proceed formally exactly as before with $d\mathbf{Q}/dt$ replacing $d\mathbf{r}/dt$. In general, if some vector **Q** has the time derivative $d\mathbf{Q}/dt$ with respect to the rotating frame, then the time derivative $d\mathbf{Q}_I/dt$ with respect to the inertial frame will be given by

$$\frac{d\mathbf{Q}_I}{dt} = \frac{d\mathbf{Q}}{dt} + \boldsymbol{\omega} \times \mathbf{Q} \tag{9-15}$$

Question

9-27 Carry out the analysis which leads to Eq. (9-15), using the same procedure as in the derivation of Eq. (9-14).

Q can be any vector. In particular, it can be a velocity vector $d\mathbf{r}/dt$ or an angular velocity vector $\boldsymbol{\omega}$ or a combination of these.

Let us use Eqs. (9-14) and (9-15) to find the relation between the acceleration of a particle in the rotating frame and its acceleration in the inertial frame. If we let **Q** be equal to $d\mathbf{r}/dt + \boldsymbol{\omega} \times \mathbf{r}$ and let $d\mathbf{Q}_I/dt$ be $d^2\mathbf{r}_I/dt^2$, then Eq. (9-15) becomes

$$\frac{d^2\mathbf{r}_I}{dt^2} = \frac{d}{dt}\left(\frac{d\mathbf{r}}{dt} + \boldsymbol{\omega} \times \mathbf{r}\right) + \boldsymbol{\omega} \times \left(\frac{d\mathbf{r}}{dt} + \boldsymbol{\omega} \times \mathbf{r}\right) \tag{9-16}$$

The left side of this equation is simply the acceleration of the particle with respect to the inertial coordinate system. Let us consider the right side of the equation in some detail. Consider the second term first. The second term, $\boldsymbol{\omega} \times (d\mathbf{r}/dt + \boldsymbol{\omega} \times \mathbf{r})$, represents the accelerations of the particle due to the *change in direction* of any vector because of the rotation of the rotating system. If we expand this parenthesis, the first term, $\boldsymbol{\omega} \times d\mathbf{r}/dt = \boldsymbol{\omega} \times \mathbf{v}$, corresponds to the acceleration due to the rotation of the velocity vector **v** of the particle with respect to the inertial frame. This is the first contribution to the Coriolis acceleration. The expression $\boldsymbol{\omega} \times \mathbf{r}$ is equal to the tangential velocity of the rotating frame at the position of the particle, so that the expression $\boldsymbol{\omega} \times (\boldsymbol{\omega} \times \mathbf{r})$ corresponds to the acceleration of the particle due to the change in direction of the tangential velocity of the turntable at the position of the particle. This is the centripetal acceleration.

Now consider the first term on the right side of Eq. (9-16). The first term, $(d/dt)(d\mathbf{r}/dt + \boldsymbol{\omega} \times \mathbf{r})$, represents the accelerations of the particle due to the *change in position* of the particle with respect to the rotating frame. If we expand this parenthesis, the first term, $d^2\mathbf{r}/dt^2$, is simply the acceleration of the particle with respect to the rotating frame. If the angular velocity $\boldsymbol{\omega}$ is constant, then the second term, $(d/dt)(\boldsymbol{\omega} \times \mathbf{r}) = \boldsymbol{\omega} \times d\mathbf{r}/dt = \boldsymbol{\omega} \times \mathbf{v}$, is simply the change in the tangential velocity of the particle due to the change in position of the particle on the turntable. This is the second contribution to the Coriolis acceleration.

Questions

9-28 Show that the direction of the centripetal acceleration $\boldsymbol{\omega} \times (\boldsymbol{\omega} \times \mathbf{r})$ is toward the z-axis and perpendicular to this axis. Show that this acceleration is equal to zero if the particle lies anywhere on the z-axis.

9-29 Carry out the expansion of Eq. (9-16) under each of the following assumptions. Predict the direction of each of the acceleration terms. Identify each acceleration in the case of motion on a turntable (Sec. 9.3).

a. The angular velocity of the rotating frame is equal to zero.

b. The particle remains at rest with respect to the rotating frame, and the angular velocity of the rotating frame is constant.

c. The particle remains at rest with respect to the rotating frame, but the angular velocity of the rotating frame is not constant.

d. The particle moves with constant velocity with respect to the rotating frame, and the angular velocity of the rotating frame is constant.

e. The particle moves with a non-constant velocity with respect to the rotating frame, and the angular velocity of the rotating frame is constant.

Now proceed with the expansion of Eq. (9-16).

$$\frac{d^2\mathbf{r}_I}{dt^2} = \frac{d^2\mathbf{r}}{dt^2} + \left(\frac{d\boldsymbol{\omega}}{dt}\right) \times \mathbf{r} + \boldsymbol{\omega} \times \frac{d\mathbf{r}}{dt} + \boldsymbol{\omega} \times \frac{d\mathbf{r}}{dt} + \boldsymbol{\omega} \times (\boldsymbol{\omega} \times \mathbf{r}) \quad (9\text{-}17)$$

In what follows we shall assume that the angular velocity $\boldsymbol{\omega}$ of the rotating frame is constant in magnitude and direction, so that $d\boldsymbol{\omega}/dt = 0$. If we collect terms and use explicit symbols for the velocity and accelerations of the particle, Eq. (9-17) becomes

$$\ddot{\mathbf{r}}_I = \ddot{\mathbf{r}} + 2\boldsymbol{\omega} \times \dot{\mathbf{r}} + \boldsymbol{\omega} \times (\boldsymbol{\omega} \times \mathbf{r})$$

or

$$\mathbf{a}_I = \mathbf{a} + 2\boldsymbol{\omega} \times \mathbf{v} + \boldsymbol{\omega} \times (\boldsymbol{\omega} \times \mathbf{r}) \quad (9\text{-}18)$$

The left side of Eq. (9-18) gives the acceleration of the particle with respect to the inertial reference frame. The right side of the equation expresses this acceleration in terms of the position, velocity, and acceleration of the particle with respect to the rotating reference frame. This equation can be compared with Eq. (9-11) for the special case of motion of a particle on a turntable. The Coriolis acceleration, $2\boldsymbol{\omega} \times \mathbf{v}$, has the same form in both equations. The centripetal acceleration, $\boldsymbol{\omega} \times (\boldsymbol{\omega} \times \mathbf{r})$ of Eq. (9-18) has a form different from that of the term $-\omega^2\mathbf{r}$ in Eq. (9-11). However, if $\mathbf{r}$ is perpendicular to $\boldsymbol{\omega}$, as on a turntable, both expressions will be identical in magnitude and direction. The expression in Eq. (9-18) deals with the more general case.

Question

9-30 A particle moves with speed v outward along a radius fixed in the rotating frame which makes an angle λ with the x-y plane. Find the magnitudes of the Coriolis and centripetal accelerations in terms of the angle λ. What are the directions of these accelerations?

Now let us consider the equation of motion in the rotating frame to see what pseudo-forces are present. In the *inertial* frame the equation of motion is $\mathbf{F} = m\mathbf{a}_I$. Using Eq. (9-18), this becomes

$$\mathbf{F} = m\mathbf{a}_I = m\mathbf{a} + 2m\boldsymbol{\omega} \times \mathbf{v} + m\boldsymbol{\omega} \times (\boldsymbol{\omega} \times \mathbf{r}) \tag{9-19}$$

If all the terms except $m\mathbf{a}$ are transposed to the left side of this equation, we shall have the equation of motion of the particle with respect to the rotating frame.

$$\mathbf{F} - 2m\boldsymbol{\omega} \times \mathbf{v} - m\boldsymbol{\omega} \times (\boldsymbol{\omega} \times \mathbf{r}) = m\mathbf{a} \tag{9-20}$$

In addition to the force $\mathbf{F}$ which he applies to the particle, the rotating observer will have to postulate two pseudo-forces in order to account for the observed acceleration of the particle. These pseudo-forces are the *centrifugal pseudo-force* and the *Coriolis pseudo-force*. The centrifugal pseudo-force, $-m\boldsymbol{\omega} \times (\boldsymbol{\omega} \times \mathbf{r})$, acts on the particle whether it is at rest or in motion with respect to the rotating frame (except when the particle is on the axis of rotation) in a direction perpendicularly *away* from the axis of rotation. The Coriolis pseudo-force acts on the particle only if it is in motion with respect to the rotating frame, and then in the direction of $-\boldsymbol{\omega} \times \mathbf{v}$, perpendicular to both $\mathbf{v}$ and $\boldsymbol{\omega}$.

Questions

9-31 A particle moves with speed $\mathbf{v}$ outward along a radius fixed in the rotating frame which makes an angle λ with the x-y plane. Find the magnitudes of the Coriolis and centrifugal pseudo-forces in terms of the angle λ. What are the directions of these pseudo-forces?

9-32 If the angular velocity of the rotating coordinate system is changing at the vector rate $\dot{\boldsymbol{\omega}}$, show from Eq. (9-17) that a pseudo-force of vector value $-m\dot{\boldsymbol{\omega}} \times \mathbf{r}$ will have to be added to the left side of Eq. (9-20).

What is the direction of this pseudo-force if $\boldsymbol{\omega}$ is increasing in magnitude and the axis of rotation remains along the z_I-axis? What is the direction of this pseudo-force if $\boldsymbol{\omega}$ is constant in magnitude but is changing direction with respect to the inertial reference frame?

9.5 THE LAWS OF MOTION IN THE GENERAL NON-INERTIAL REFERENCE FRAME. We have now dealt with non-inertial reference frames which are accelerating and rotating with respect to an inertial reference frame. What is the most general motion of a non-inertial reference frame? The rigorous solution to this question involves considerable mathematical analysis.* The answer, which seems reasonable intuitively, is that any arbitrary continuous motion of a non-inertial coordinate system can be analyzed as a linear acceleration plus a rotation about an axis. In the most general case both the direction of the axis of rotation and the magnitude of the angular velocity of rotation may be changing with time. In other words, the vector $\dot{\boldsymbol{\omega}}$ is not equal to zero. The axis about which the coordinate system is rotating at any instant is called the *instantanteous axis of rotation.*

Let us define the z-axis of the non-inertial coordinate system to lie along the instantaneous axis of rotation. Then the most general motion of this coordinate system (with respect to an inertial coordinate system) can be characterized by a linear acceleration $\mathbf{A}$ of the origin of the non-inertial frame plus an instantaneous angular velocity $\boldsymbol{\omega}$ about the z-axis plus a rate of change $\dot{\boldsymbol{\omega}}$ of this angular velocity in magnitude or direction or both.

If the parameters $\mathbf{A}$, $\boldsymbol{\omega}$, and $\dot{\boldsymbol{\omega}}$ which characterize the non-inertial coordinate system are known, together with the mass m, position $\mathbf{r}$, and the velocity $\mathbf{v}$ of a particle with respect to this coordinate system, we can set up the equation of motion of the particle in this non-inertial reference frame. By adding the linear acceleration $\mathbf{A}$ to Eq. (9-17) we can calculate the total acceleration $\mathbf{a}_I$ of the particle with respect to an inertial reference frame.

$$\mathbf{a}_I = \mathbf{a} + \mathbf{A} + \dot{\boldsymbol{\omega}} \times \mathbf{r} + 2\boldsymbol{\omega} \times \mathbf{v} + \boldsymbol{\omega} \times (\boldsymbol{\omega} \times \mathbf{r}) \qquad (9\text{-}21)$$

The equation of motion of the particle in the inertial frame is

$$\mathbf{F} = m\mathbf{a}_I = m\mathbf{a} + m\mathbf{A} + m\dot{\boldsymbol{\omega}} \times \mathbf{r} + 2m\boldsymbol{\omega} \times \mathbf{v} + m\boldsymbol{\omega} \times (\boldsymbol{\omega} \times \mathbf{r}) \quad (9\text{-}22)$$

If all terms except $m\mathbf{a}$ are transposed to the left side of this equation, then we shall have the equation of motion of the particle with respect to the rotating frame.

$$\mathbf{F} - m\mathbf{A} - m\dot{\boldsymbol{\omega}} \times \mathbf{r} - 2m\boldsymbol{\omega} \times \mathbf{v} - m\boldsymbol{\omega} \times (\boldsymbol{\omega} \times \mathbf{r}) = m\mathbf{a} \quad (9\text{-}23)$$

* See H. Goldstein, *Classical Mechanics*, Addison-Wesley Publishing Co., Cambridge, Mass., 1953, Sec. 4-6.

In addition to the force **F** which he applies to the particle, an observer moving with this accelerating and rotating frame will have to postulate four pseudo-forces in order to account for the observed acceleration of the particle. The pseudo-forces are, first, a pseudo-force $-m\mathbf{A}$ due to the linear acceleration of the reference frame; second, a pseudo-force $-m\dot{\boldsymbol{\omega}} \times \mathbf{r}$ due to the change in the rotation of the reference frame; third, the Coriolis pseudo-force $-2m\boldsymbol{\omega} \times \mathbf{v}$; and, fourth, the centrifugal pseudo-force $-m\boldsymbol{\omega} \times (\boldsymbol{\omega} \times \mathbf{r})$.

Equation (9-23) summarizes a vast amount of knowledge. The classical laws of motion of a particle in *any* reference frame can be considered a special case of Eq. (9-23).

Question

9-33 The Hammer, a ride in an amusement park, is a device (pictured in Fig. 9-14) which rotates in a vertical plane with constant angular velocity ω_1. The "hammer head" consists of a hollow capsule which rotates on its axis with angular velocity ω_2 which is constant in magnitude. Riders are strapped to seats inside the circumference of this capsule. List expressions for the directions and magnitudes of all forces and pseudo-forces which act on a rider, including that due to gravity and those applied by the seatbelts. Treat the rider as a particle. Using reasonable values for the parameters, find numerical values for these forces and pseudo-forces. If the rider releases a coin, predict the initial direction of acceleration of the coin as observed by the rider.

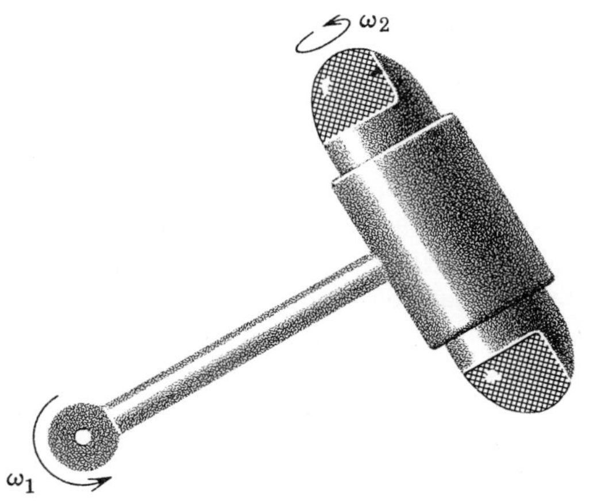

Fig. 9-14.

9.6 THE LAWS OF MOTION NEAR THE SURFACE OF THE ROTATING EARTH. Consider a spherical planet which rotates with constant angular velocity $\boldsymbol{\omega}$ about a diameter. We shall define the *north pole* of the planet as the point on the axis of rotation which intersects the surface of the planet in the same direction from the center of the planet as the angular velocity vector points. (See Fig. 9-15.) Consider a plane perpendicular to the axis of rotation such that the center of the planet lies in the plane. We call this the *equatorial plane.* The circle formed by the intersection of the equatorial plane with the surface of the sphere is called the *equator* of the planet. The *northern hemisphere* is that part of the planet on the same side of the equatorial plane as the north pole. The *southern hemisphere* is that part of the planet on the opposite side of the equatorial plane from the north pole. Consider a point on the surface of the planet. The *east direction* at that point is defined as that tangential direction in which the surface of the planet at that point is moving with respect to a non-rotating reference frame in which the center of the planet is at rest.

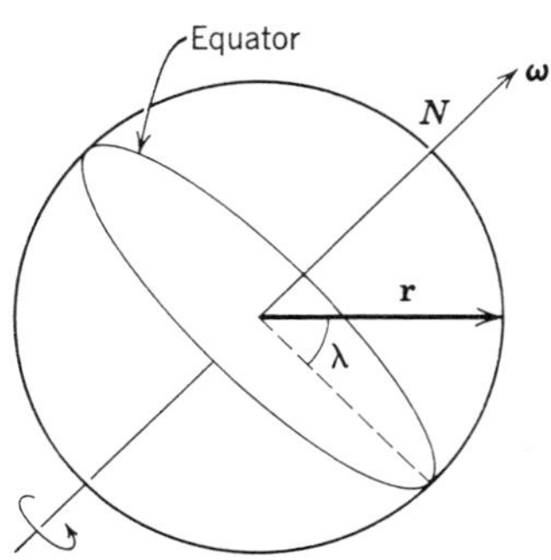

Fig. 9-15. Definitions for a spherical planet.

Question

9-34 Define the south pole of the planet. Define the north, south, and west directions at any point on the surface of the planet.

Let the vector $\mathbf{r}$ be the position vector of some particle near the surface of the planet. The *latitude* λ of the particle is defined as the angle which the vector $\mathbf{r}$ makes with the equatorial plane. (See Fig. 9-15.) The latitude is considered positive in the northern hemisphere and negative in the southern hemisphere. The *radial vertical* at any point on the surface of the planet is defined as the direction of the position vector $\mathbf{r}$ from the center of the planet to that point on the surface.

Using these definitions, let us apply the results of the last sections to the motion of a particle near the surface of the earth. The shape of the earth is almost spherical but it is slightly flattened at the poles, so that it is more precisely described as an *oblate spheroid.* The polar radius is 6.357×10^6 m, while the equatorial radius is 6.378×10^6 m. We shall assume that the earth is spherical with radius 6.371×10^6 m, which is the radius of a sphere having the same volume as the earth.

The earth turns once on its axis with respect to an inertial reference frame in 23 h, 56 min, and 4 sec, or in 86,164 sec. Thus its angular velocity $\boldsymbol{\omega}$ has a magnitude of 0.729×10^{-4} radian/sec. The magnitude of the angular velocity is decreasing very slowly with time, and the direction of $\boldsymbol{\omega}$ with respect to the fixed stars changes over long periods of time. Both these changes in $\boldsymbol{\omega}$ have negligible effect on most mechanics experiments carried out near the surface of the earth, and we shall neglect $\dot{\boldsymbol{\omega}}$. This means that the acceleration $\dot{\boldsymbol{\omega}} \times \mathbf{r}$ in Eq. (9-21) will be neglected.

The acceleration $\mathbf{g}$ due to gravity at the surface of the earth varies from place to place according to the altitude and nearby geological structures. These variations can be measured easily, but in no case do they exceed 1 percent. For instance, a height of about 30,000 m must be achieved before the magnitude of $\mathbf{g}$ decreases by 1 percent, whereas Mount Everest has a height of slightly less than 9000 m. We shall assume that $\mathbf{g}$ has the magnitude 9.80 m/sec^2 everywhere near the surface of the earth and that this vector points toward the center of the earth (that is, in the direction opposite to the radial vertical). If the precise local magnitude and direction of $\mathbf{g}$ are known, they may be substituted for this approximate value.

Question

9-35 Show that the direction of the vector $\mathbf{g}$ changes by one degree in a distance of about 110 km over the surface of the earth.

The earth revolves about the sun in a path that is approximately circular, of radius 1.495×10^8 m, taking one year (approximately 31.56×10^6 sec) for one revolution. The average acceleration of the center of mass of the earth is thus equal to 0.59×10^{-5} m/sec^2, or less than one-millionth of the acceleration due to gravity at the surface of the earth. The acceleration of the center of the earth about the sun corresponds to the term $\mathbf{A}$ in Eq. (9-21). We shall neglect this acceleration and assume that the center of the earth is at rest with respect to an inertial reference frame.

Let us consider the pseudo-forces experienced by a particle of mass m near the surface of the earth. With the elimination of the terms $-m\mathbf{A}$ and $-m\dot{\boldsymbol{\omega}} \times \mathbf{r}$, Eq. (9-23) becomes identical with Eq. (9-20). Define a force $\mathbf{F}'$ equal to all the forces applied to the particle except the force of gravity, $m\mathbf{g}$. Then

$$\mathbf{F} = \mathbf{F}' + m\mathbf{g} \qquad \text{definition of } F'$$

With this substitution Eq. (9-20) becomes

$$\mathbf{F}' + m\mathbf{g} - 2m\boldsymbol{\omega} \times \mathbf{v} - m\boldsymbol{\omega} \times (\boldsymbol{\omega} \times \mathbf{r}) = m\mathbf{a} \qquad (9\text{-}24)$$

The pseudo-forces experienced by the particle are the centrifugal pseudo-force and the Coriolis pseudo-force. Let us consider these in turn.

Centrifugal pseudo-force. The centrifugal pseudo-force on the particle has the vector value $-m\boldsymbol{\omega} \times (\boldsymbol{\omega} \times \mathbf{r})$. This vector points perpendicularly away from the axis of rotation. Its magnitude is equal to $mr\omega^2 \cos \lambda$, where λ is the latitude of the particle.

Questions

9-36 Verify the last sentence.

9-37 Suppose that your mass is 75 kg. Calculate the magnitude of the centrifugal pseudo-force which you are experiencing. Express this result as a fraction of your weight mg.

The presence of the centrifugal pseudo-force will cause a plumb line to hang in a direction other than the radial vertical at some places on the surface of the earth. A *plumb line* is a piece of string attached to a particle called the *plumb bob*. The plumb line is used by attaching one end of the line to a fixed point near the surface of the earth, hanging the bob from the other end and noting the direction taken by the plumb line when the bob comes to rest hanging free. We define the *plumb line vertical* at a point on the surface of the earth as the direction away from the surface along a line determined by a plumb line. It is the usual practice in surveying to define the "vertical direction" to coincide with the plumb line vertical, because the plumb line is used in practice to determine this direction. At

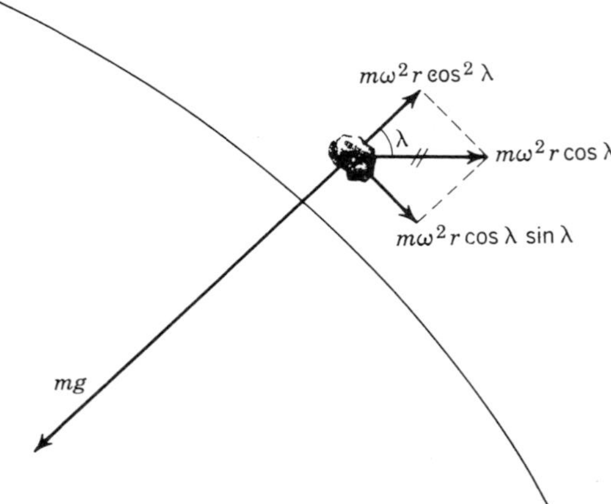

Fig. 9-16. Calculation of the plumb line vertical (relative magnitude of centrifugal pseudo-force greatly exaggerated).

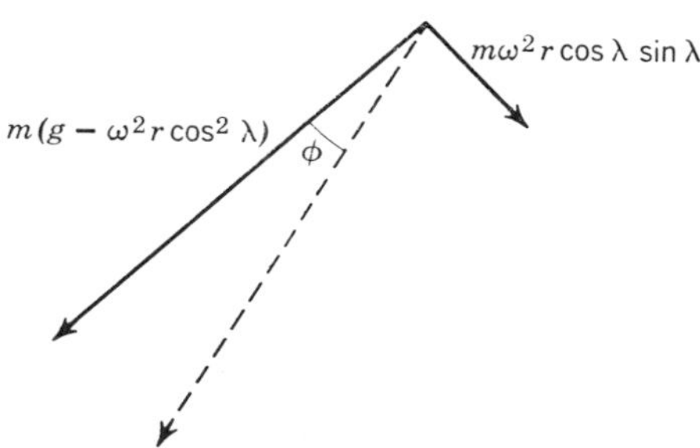

Fig. 9-17. Calculation of the plumb line vertical.

some places on the surface of the earth the plumb line vertical will be inclined at a small angle with respect to the radial vertical defined above. Since the motion of a particle on the surface of the earth will be described by using the radial vertical, it is important to know the angle between the plumb line vertical (which is easy to measure) and the radial vertical (which is more convenient for analyzing the motion of particles). The calculation of this angle follows.

Figure 9-16 shows the force of gravity and the centrifugal pseudo-force acting on a particle which is at rest near the surface of the earth at the northern latitude λ. We assume that **g** points toward the center of the earth along the radial vertical. The centrifugal pseudo-force is resolved along the radial vertical and a direction perpendicular to the radial vertical. The resulting force components are shown in Fig. 9-17. The angle ϕ is the angle between the local radial vertical and the direction of the net force on the particle. A plumb line will hang in the direction of this net force, and a stone released from rest will fall initially in the direction of this net force.

Questions

9-38 Develop an expression for the *magnitude* of g', the resulting initial acceleration of a particle released near the surface of the earth at a latitude λ. Approximately how much will this value differ from g at your latitude? Geologists can measure differences in the magnitude of g' with an error of approximately $\pm 10^{-6}$ m/sec². Is the difference between the magnitudes g and g' at your latitude significant in terms of this accuracy?

9-39 Show that if $\mathbf{g}'$ is defined as

$$\mathbf{g}' = \mathbf{g} - \boldsymbol{\omega} \times (\boldsymbol{\omega} \times \mathbf{r}) \qquad \text{definition} \qquad (9\text{-}25)$$

then Eq. (9-24) becomes

$$\mathbf{F}' + m\mathbf{g}' - 2m\boldsymbol{\omega} \times \mathbf{v} = m\mathbf{a} \qquad (9\text{-}26)$$

Now from Fig. 9-17 the tangent of the angle ϕ is given by the expression

$$\tan \phi = \frac{\omega^2 r \cos \lambda \sin \lambda}{g - \omega^2 r \cos^2 \lambda} \tag{9-27}$$

For the earth, $\omega^2 r$ is approximately equal to 3×10^{-2} m/sec^2. This means that ϕ will be small so that we can make the approximation $\tan \phi \approx \phi$. Also, the second term in the denominator of Eq. (9-27) will be very much less than g. Hence Eq. (9-27) becomes approximately

$$\phi \approx \frac{\omega^2 r}{g} \cos \lambda \sin \lambda \tag{9-28}$$

For a latitude of 45 degrees this angle will be about 1.7×10^{-3} radians, or about one tenth of a degree. The angle ϕ will be less than this for all other latitudes. The result is that, when mechanics experiments are carried out in which directions are to be determined more accurately than about one tenth of a degree, the plumb line is not a sufficiently accurate instrument for determining the direction of the radial vertical. This difference is important for some astronomical observations.

Questions

9-40 Will a plumb bob hang to the north, south, east, or west of the point it would occupy if the earth were not rotating? Is your answer different for the northern and the southern hemispheres?

9-41 What will determine the orientation of the plane formed by the surface of a still lake? How would you define the word *horizontal* at any point on the surface of the earth? Could this word have more than one definition? Is the direction determined by a surveyor's *spirit level* perpendicular to the plumb line vertical or the radial vertical?

9-42 The planet Jupiter rotates on its axis once in 9 h and 51 min, it has a radius of approximately 70,000 km, and the acceleration due to gravity at the surface is approximately 26.5 m/sec^2. What will be the maximum deviation of the plumb line vertical from the radial vertical on the surface of Jupiter?

Coriolis pseudo-force. Suppose that a particle of mass m located at a northern latitude λ moves due south with velocity $\mathbf{v}$. The Coriolis pseudo-force on the particle will be $-2m\boldsymbol{\omega} \times \mathbf{v}$. The angle between $\boldsymbol{\omega}$ and $\mathbf{v}$ is $\pi - \lambda$. Thus the magnitude of the Coriolis pseudo-force will be

$$2m\omega v \sin (\pi - \lambda) = 2m\omega v \sin \lambda$$

The pseudo-force will point due west. Verify these statements for yourself.

Now suppose that the same particle moves due east. In this case the angle between $\boldsymbol{\omega}$ and $\mathbf{v}$ is $\pi/2$, so that the magnitude of the Coriolis force is $2m\omega v$. The *direction* of the Coriolis force will be perpendicularly away from the axis of rotation of the earth. This means that the component of this pseudo-force due south is equal to $2m\omega v \sin \lambda$ and the component of this pseudo-force along the radial vertical is $2m\omega v \cos \lambda$. Verify these statements for yourself.

Now suppose that the same particle moves outward in the radial vertical direction. In this case the angle between $\boldsymbol{\omega}$ and $\mathbf{v}$ is $\pi/2 - \lambda$, so that the magnitude of the Coriolis pseudo-force is $2m\omega v \sin(\pi/2 - \lambda) = 2m\omega v \cos \lambda$. The direction of the Coriolis pseudo-force will be toward the west. Verify these statements for yourself.

Now consider a particle of mass m moving with an arbitrary vector velocity $\mathbf{v}$ with respect to the surface of the earth at a northern latitude λ. This velocity can be resolved into components in the south, east, and radial vertical directions. Let v_S, v_E, and v_V respectively represent these velocity components. Then, from the last three paragraphs, the three components of the Coriolis pseudo-force, f_S, f_E, and f_V, in the south, east, and radial vertical directions respectively will be given by the equations

$$\begin{aligned} f_S &= 2m\omega v_E \sin \lambda \\ f_E &= -2m\omega v_S \sin \lambda - 2m\omega v_V \cos \lambda \qquad (9\text{-}29) \\ f_V &= 2m\omega v_E \cos \lambda \end{aligned}$$

The minus signs in the equation for f_E mean that the Coriolis pseudo-forces associated with the southward and vertical components of velocity point due west. Verify these equations for yourself.

Questions

9-43 You are flying due east in a jet plane at 450 m/sec (about 1000 mph). If your mass is 75 kg, what will be the components of the Coriolis pseudo-force on you? If the plane should turn around and fly at the same speed due west, could you detect your apparent change of weight on a bathroom scale?

9-44 Demonstrate that Eqs. (9-29) will be correct for the southern hemisphere provided the latitude λ is considered to be negative in the southern hemisphere.

9.7 EXAMPLES OF MOTION NEAR THE SURFACE OF THE EARTH. We shall use the results of the last section to illustrate the motion of a particle near the surface of the earth under several different circumstances. We shall use approximations which simplify these solutions considerably. The approximations are usually justified because the pseudo-forces are themselves small; but be sure that you understand the nature of the approximations and the error introduced by them in each case.

Example 1. Centrifugal loss of weight. How much less does a 75 kg man weigh at the equator than at the north pole, assuming that the earth is spherical?

Solution. The weight of the man at the north pole is mg or about 735 N. From Fig. 9-16 this weight is reduced at the equator ($\lambda = 0$) by an amount $m\omega^2 r$. If m is 75 kg, this reduction in weight is equal to $75 \times (0.729 \times 10^{-4})^2 \times 6.371 \times 10^6$ N or about 2.5 N. This is a change in weight of about 0.3 percent. A sensitive spring balance might detect this difference.

Question

9-45 Show that this difference could not be detected by using an equal-arm balance.

Example 2. Particle dropped from a great height. A particle is dropped from rest at a height h equal to 1000 m above the surface of the earth at $\lambda = 25$ degrees north latitude. Predict its point of impact.

Solution. We shall assume that the acceleration of gravity $\mathbf{g}$ is constant up to this height h and that the radial distance r of the particle from the center of the earth is nearly the same from top to bottom of the particle's path, so that the centrifugal pseudo-force is constant along the path. This means that $\mathbf{g}'$, the effective acceleration due to gravity, is constant along the path. If it were not for the presence of the Coriolis pseudo-force, the point of impact could be predicted by hanging a plumb line toward the earth from the point at which the particle is released. Our subsequent calculations will deal with the displacement of the point of impact due to the Coriolis pseudo-force from the point predicted by using the plumb line.

In the absence of the Coriolis pseudo-force the particle would have a speed toward the earth given by $v = g't$ if $t = 0$ at the instant of release. From Eqs. (9-29) the Coriolis pseudo-force on this particle would be toward the east (since v_V is negative) and would have the magnitude $2m\omega v \cos \lambda = 2m\omega g't \cos \lambda$. The acceleration a_E of the particle toward the east due to this force is given by

$$ma_E = 2m\omega g't \cos \lambda$$

or

$$a_E = 2\omega g't \cos \lambda$$

The eastward component of velocity, v_E, resulting from this acceleration can be found by integrating this equation with respect to time and setting the initial eastward component of velocity equal to zero.

$$v_E = \omega g' t^2 \cos \lambda \tag{9-30}$$

Finally the net eastward displacement y_E resulting from this acceleration can be found by integrating the equation for v_E with respect to time and setting the initial eastward displacement equal to zero.

$$y_E = \tfrac{1}{3}\, \omega g' t^3 \cos \lambda \tag{9-31}$$

Now the particle will strike the ground after a time of fall t_f given by the expression

$$h = \tfrac{1}{2} g' t_f^2$$

or, solving for t_f,

$$t_f = \sqrt{\frac{2h}{g'}}$$

Substitute this into Eq. (9-31) to obtain the total eastward displacement y_{Ef} of the particle when it strikes the ground.

$$y_{Ef} = \tfrac{1}{3}\omega g' \left(\frac{2h}{g'}\right)^{3/2} \cos \lambda$$

$$= \tfrac{1}{3}\omega \sqrt{\frac{8h^3}{g'}} \cos \lambda \tag{9-32}$$

Setting $g' \approx g = 9.8$ m/sec², $h = 1000$ m, $\lambda = 25$ degrees, $\omega = 0.73 \times 10^{-4}$ radians/sec, the result is $y_{Ef} \approx 0.60$ m, or 60 cm.

Questions

9-46 In the preceding analysis the Coriolis pseudo-force due to the eastward velocity of the particle was neglected. Using Eqs. (9-29), find the ratio of the Coriolis pseudo-force component in, say, the southward direction to the Coriolis pseudo-force component in the eastward direction at the instant before impact.

9-47 Repeat the problem above for the case in which the particle has an initial velocity v_1 of 500 m/sec vertically downward.

Example 3. Long-range ballistic projectile. A ballistic projectile is launched with an initial speed v_1 equal to 700 m/sec southward at an angle θ of sixty degrees from the horizontal from a point at $\lambda = 40$ degrees north latitude. Predict the point of impact. Neglect air resistance.

Solution. Once again we shall assume that the effective acceleration g' due to the gravitational force and the centrifugal pseudo-force have been measured and are the same for every point on the path of the projectile. The range R of this projectile, according to the equation in Project I, is equal to

$$R = \frac{v_1^2 \sin 2\theta}{g'}$$

If $g' \approx g = 9.80$ m/sec^2, the range is equal to 43.3 km. We assume that the curvature of the earth can be neglected in this distance.

If it were not for the Coriolis pseudo-forces the answer would be 43.3 km south of the point of launch. According to Eqs. (9-29) there will be Coriolis pseudo-force components due to both the vertical and the southward components of velocity. We can find the deviation from the previously predicted point of impact due to each of these pseudo-forces separately and then add these deviations to find the resultant deviation due to both of these pseudo-forces acting together. Let us analyze first the deflection corresponding to the vertical component of velocity v_V.

The vertical component of velocity as a function of time after launch will be given by the equation

$$v_V = v_1 \sin \theta - g't \tag{9-33}$$

From Eqs. (9-29) the Coriolis pseudo-force due to this component of velocity will point due west during the ascent of the projectile and will have a magnitude $2m\omega v_V \cos \lambda = 2m\omega(v_1 \sin \theta - g't) \cos \lambda$. The westward acceleration a_{W1} due to this force will be given by

$$a_{W1} = 2\omega(v_1 \sin \theta - g't) \cos \lambda$$

Question

9-48 Show that this westward acceleration is negative (i.e., eastward) during the descent of the projectile from its maximum altitude.

The westward component of velocity v_{W1} resulting from this acceleration can be found by integrating this equation with respect to time and setting the initial westward velocity equal to zero.

$$v_{W1} = 2\omega v_1 \sin \theta (\cos \lambda)t - \omega g'(\cos \lambda)t^2$$

The westward displacement y_{W1} of the particle resulting from this component of velocity can be found by integrating this equation with respect to time and setting the initial westward displacement equal to zero.

$$y_{W1} = \omega v_1 \sin \theta (\cos \lambda)t^2 - \tfrac{1}{3}\omega g' (\cos \lambda)t^3 \tag{9-34}$$

Now we need to know the time of flight t_f. The projectile will reach its maximum altitude when $v_V = 0$. This will occur at a time equal to one-half the time of flight. According to Eq. (9-33) this will occur when

$$0 = v_1 \sin\theta - g' \frac{t_f}{2}$$

or

$$t_f = \frac{2v_1 \sin\theta}{g'} \tag{9-35}$$

Substitute this expression for t_f into Eq. (9-34)

$$y_{W1} = \frac{4\omega v_1^3 \sin^3\theta \cos\lambda}{g'^2} - \frac{8}{3}\frac{\omega v_1^3 \sin^3\theta \cos\lambda}{g'^2}$$

$$y_{W1} = \frac{4}{3}\frac{\omega v_1^3 \sin^3\theta \cos\lambda}{g'^2} \tag{9-36}$$

This is the westward deflection of the projectile due to the Coriolis pseudo-force corresponding to the vertical component of velocity.

Question

9-49 It may be argued that there should be no net displacement of the projectile due to its vertical component of velocity because the westward acceleration due to the vertical component of velocity of the projectile at any altitude on the way up will be equal in magnitude to the eastward acceleration due to the vertical component of velocity of the projectile at the same altitude on the way down. Show the error in reasoning which leads to this incorrect conclusion. Plot an approximate graph of v_{W1} vs time during the flight.

The westward Coriolis pseudo-force on the projectile corresponding to the *southward* component of velocity v_S can be found from Eqs. (9-29). It has the value $2m\omega v_S \sin\lambda$. Since $v_S = v_1 \cos\theta$ remains constant during the flight, the westward acceleration a_{W2} due to this pseudo-force will be constant.

$$a_{W2} = 2\omega v_1 \cos\theta \sin\lambda$$

The westward displacement y_{W2} to this acceleration during the time of flight will be given by

$$y_{W2} = \tfrac{1}{2} a_{W2} t_f^2$$

From Eq. (9-35) this becomes

$$y_{W2} = \tfrac{1}{2}(2\omega v_1 \cos\theta \sin\lambda)\left(\frac{4v_1^2 \sin^2\theta}{g'^2}\right)$$

$$= \frac{4\omega v_1^3 \sin^2\theta}{g'^2} \cos\theta \sin\lambda \tag{9-37}$$

The total westward displacement of the projectile during its flight will be found by adding the right sides of Eqs. (9-36) and (9-37).

$$y_W = y_{W1} + y_{W2} = \frac{4\omega v_1^3 \sin^2\theta}{g'^2}\left(\frac{\sin\theta\cos\lambda}{3} + \cos\theta\sin\lambda\right) \quad (9\text{-}38)$$

Substituting the values $\omega = 0.73 \times 10^{-4}$ radian/sec, $v_1 = 700$ m/sec, $g' \approx g = 9.80$ m/sec², $\theta = 60$ degrees, and $\lambda = 40$ degrees, we obtain an answer of about 424 m for the total westward displacement. This could be a significant error in point of impact.

The complete answer to this example is that the projectile will land about 43.3 km due south of the point of launch and about 424 m to the west.

Questions

9-50 List all the approximations used in this solution, both those expressed and those implied. Can you justify all of them quantitatively?

9-51 Suppose that the same projectile is shot toward the east at the same elevation and initial velocity. Predict the point of impact for this projectile.

Example 4. The direction of rotation of cyclones. The forces which drive large air masses over the surface of the earth arise in large part from thermal effects and from pseudo-forces due to the rotation of the earth. These pseudo-forces can be important because the motion of air masses can take place over great distances and extended periods of time and thus the displacement due to these pseudo-forces is cumulative.

The viscosity of air and thermal and pressure gradients play so large a part in the motion of air masses that quantitative calculations of these motions are very difficult. However, it is sometimes possible to provide a qualitative description. We shall describe here the pseudo-forces which determine the direction of rotation of cyclones.

In general, air will tend to flow from a region of higher pressure toward a region of lower pressure. Suppose that several masses of air are traveling radially toward a low pressure region in the northern hemisphere, as in Fig. 9-18*a*. As these masses move they will experience a Coriolis pseudo-force which deflects them to the right, as in the figure. After each mass of air has been deflected, it will tend to follow an approximately circular path. Here is the explanation of this rotation. Since the radius of this circular path can be many miles and the air velocities are low, a negligible centripetal force is required to keep an air mass on the circular path. Instead, each mass of air is more or less in equilibrium, with the pressure gradient tending to pull it to the left and the Coriolis pseudo-force tending

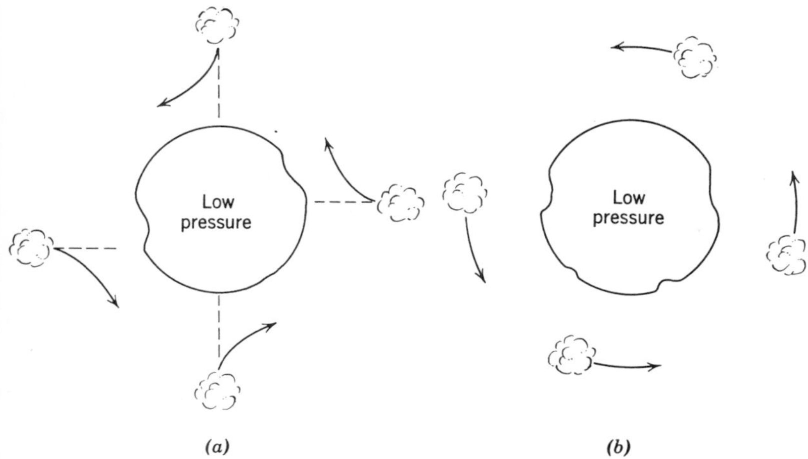

Fig. 9-18. (*a*) Establishment of a cyclone in the northern hemisphere. (*b*) Rotation of a cyclone in the northern hemisphere.

to pull it to the right. Such a circulating configuration of air is called a *cyclone*. As can be seen, in the northern hemisphere cyclones rotate counterclockwise when viewed from above. The same effect can sometimes be seen in the rotation of water about the drain of a washbasin or bathtub when the plug is drawn out, although any initial angular momentum of the water will mask this effect.

Question

9-52 Show that in the southern hemisphere cyclones rotate clockwise when viewed from above.

Example 5. The Foucault pendulum. The Foucault pendulum is a classic example of the effect of the rotation of the earth on a simple mechanical system. The Foucault pendulum is a long pendulum with a very massive bob (to reduce the effects of air currents) which is hung from a support designed to allow the pendulum to swing freely in any direction. When the pendulum is set into oscillation, the plane in which the pendulum oscillates is observed to rotate slowly with time. The angle ϕ in Fig. 9-19 between the line along which the pendulum oscillates and a reference polar axis will change slowly with time. The effect is particularly striking because, unlike some of our previous examples, the motion takes place in a small region of space, and the velocity of the pendulum is never very great.

Jean B. Foucault (1819–1868), who first demonstrated this effect, showed that the rate of rotation $\dot{\phi}$ of the direction of swing of the bob is

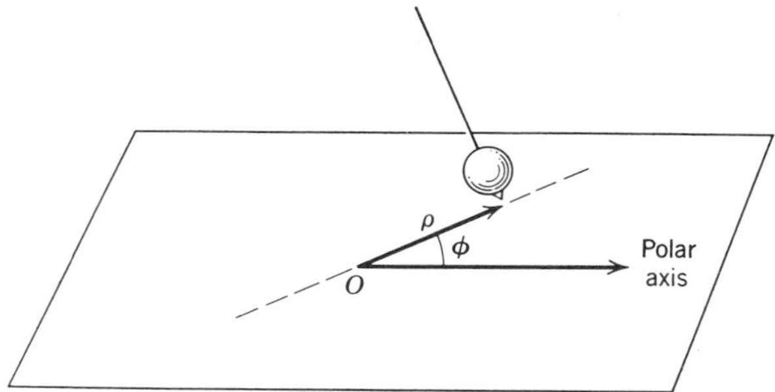

Fig. 9-19. Nomenclature for the Foucault pendulum. Point O is the position of equilibrium.

related to the latitude λ of the pendulum on the earth and the angular velocity ω of the earth by the expression

$$\dot{\phi} = \omega \sin \lambda \tag{9-39}$$

This formula can be derived as follows.

In Project IV on the harmonic oscillator you showed that, if the string which supports the bob of a simple pendulum makes a small angle θ with the plumb bob vertical, this angle will vary as a function of time according to the equation

$$\theta = D \cos bt \tag{9-40}$$

if the bob is released from rest at an initial angle D at $t = 0$. Here $b = \sqrt{g'/L}$ is used instead of ω in order to avoid confusion with the angular velocity of the earth. L is the length of the pendulum. If we multiply both sides of Eq. (9-40) by L we have

$$L\theta = LD \cos bt \tag{9-41}$$

From Fig. 9-20 it can be seen that, if the angle θ is small, the distance $L\theta$ is approximately equal to the horizontal displacement of the bob at any instant from its equilibrium position and LD is the maximum displacement of the bob, or the amplitude of swing. Let ρ be equal to the horizontal displacement of the bob from equilibrium as in Fig. 9-19 and A be equal to the amplitude of swing. Then Eq. (9-41) becomes

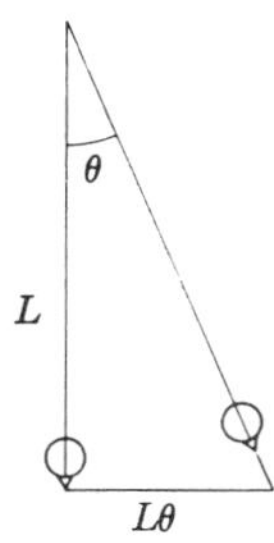

Fig. 9-20. Horizontal displacement of a simple pendulum.

$$\rho = A \cos bt \tag{9-42}$$

Now, if the pendulum were started swinging along the polar axis in Fig. 9-19, it would continue swinging back and forth along this same line if there were no additional forces on it. However, in the northern hemisphere of the rotating earth there will be both lateral and vertical components of the Coriolis pseudo-force due to the horizontal velocity of the bob. See Eqs. (9-29). The lateral components concern us here. The magnitude of the lateral Coriolis pseudo-force is given by $2m\omega \sin \lambda\sqrt{v_E^2 + v_S^2} = 2m\omega\dot{\rho} \sin \lambda$, where $\dot{\rho}$ is the horizontal velocity of the bob. In the northern hemisphere the direction of this lateral pseudo-force is always perpendicular to and to the right of the velocity vector. Since the bob is deflected to the right for both directions of its swing, the plane of oscillation will rotate clockwise when viewed from above in the northern hemisphere.

Question

9-53 Show that the plane of oscillation of a Foucault pendulum will rotate counterclockwise when viewed from above in the southern hemisphere.

Now we shall find the rate $\dot{\phi}$ at which this plane of oscillation rotates. Consider the vertical or z-component n_z of the torque on the bob with respect to the equilibrium point O in Fig. 9-19 due to the lateral Coriolis pseudo-force. This component of torque is equal in magnitude to ρ times the lateral Coriolis pseudo-force. Since the pseudo-force is to the right of the direction of motion in the northern hemisphere, the direction of this torque will be in the negative z-direction. Using the expression above for the horizontal component of the Coriolis pseudo-force, we have for n_z

$$n_z = -\rho 2m\omega\dot{\rho} \sin \lambda = -2m\omega\rho\dot{\rho} \sin \lambda \tag{9-43}$$

This torque must result in a rate of change of the z-component of angular momentum l_z of the bob about point O. The vertical component of the angular momentum is given by the displacement ρ of the particle times the component $m\rho\dot{\phi}$ of its linear momentum perpendicular to this displacement.

$$l_z = \rho m\rho\dot{\phi} = m\rho^2\dot{\phi}$$

The time derivative of this component of angular momentum is given by

$$\dot{l}_z = 2m\rho\dot{\rho}\dot{\phi} + m\rho^2\ddot{\phi} \tag{9-44}$$

Equate the left sides of Eqs. (9-43) and (9-44).

$$n_z = \dot{l}_z$$

$$-2m\omega\rho\dot{\rho} \sin \lambda = 2m\rho\dot{\rho}\dot{\phi} + m\rho^2\ddot{\phi} \tag{9-45}$$

Let $q = \dot{\phi}$. Then, after some cancellation and rearrangement, Eq. (9-45) becomes

$$\dot{q} + 2\frac{\dot{\rho}}{\rho}q = -2\frac{\dot{\rho}}{\rho}\omega \sin \lambda \tag{9-46}$$

Substitute, from Eq. (9-42),

$$\rho = A \cos bt$$

$$\dot{\rho} = -Ab \sin bt$$

to obtain

$$\dot{q} - 2b(\tan bt)q = 2b(\tan bt)\omega \sin \lambda$$

This equation can be integrated if it is multiplied through by $\cos^2 bt$.

$$\dot{q} \cos^2 bt - 2b(\sin bt \cos bt)q = 2b(\sin bt \cos bt)\omega \sin \lambda$$

This can be written

$$\frac{d}{dt}[q \cos^2 bt] = \omega \sin \lambda \frac{d}{dt}[\cos^2 bt]$$

Multiply through by dt and integrate from $t = 0$ to t.

$$\int_0^t \frac{d}{dt}[q \cos^2 bt]\, dt = \omega \sin \lambda \int_0^t \frac{d}{dt}[\cos^2 bt]\, dt$$

$$q \cos^2 bt \Big|_0^t = \omega \sin \lambda \cos^2 bt \Big|_0^t$$

or

$$q(\cos^2 bt - 1) = \omega \sin \lambda(\cos^2 bt - 1)$$

or

$$q = \omega \sin \lambda$$

but, since $q = \dot{\phi}$,

$$\dot{\phi} = \omega \sin \lambda \tag{9-47}$$

which is the formula derived by Foucault. The plane of oscillation of a Foucault pendulum will rotate at a rate given by Eq. (9-47), clockwise when viewed from above in the northern hemisphere and counterclockwise when viewed from above in the southern hemisphere.

Questions

9-54 At what point or points on the surface of the earth will the plane of oscillation of a Foucault pendulum rotate once a day? Where will this plane not rotate at all? Explain the rate of rotation of this plane at the north pole from simple arguments which do not require the mathematical proof above.

9-55 The plane of oscillation of a certain Foucault pendulum is observed to rotate 360 degrees counterclockwise when viewed from above in an elapsed time of 2 days. In what hemisphere and at what latitude did this experiment take place?

EXERCISES

9-1 Describe carefully and quantitatively the conditions under which the various pseudo-forces on an object near the surface of the earth are less than one thousandth of the weight of the object.

9-2 On a railroad train you sit next to a window with a double pane. Water has been trapped between the two panes of the window up to eye level. As the train starts, the water level tilts upward toward the rear of the train. Using arbitrary units, you measure that the vertical height of the water level is one unit higher for every fifty units of horizontal length. If the train is moving on a horizontal track, what is the acceleration of the train with respect to the ground?

9-3 During the spin cycle the drum in an automatic washing machine rotates at 600 rpm. The diameter of the drum is about 50 cm. The clothes at the perimeter of the drum will experience a centrifugal pseudo-force how many times their weight? The drums of some *extractors*, which are spin-dry machines used in commercial laundries, have about the same diameter but spin three times as fast. What centrifugal pseudo-force will clothes experience in such a commercial extractor?

9-4 A ballistic missile is shot from 45 degrees north latitude and lands at 45 degrees south latitude. Its initial velocity has only vertical and southward components with respect to the rotating earth. Describe *qualitatively* the east-west components of acceleration, velocity, and displacement during its flight. Will the impact point be at the same longitude as the launch point?

9-5 A wedge of wood rests on a horizontal surface, as in Fig. 9-21. A uniform sphere is placed on the upper surface of the wedge. The wedge is accelerated along the horizontal surface with a constant acceleration. What must the acceleration of the wedge be in order that the sphere will remain at rest with respect to the wedge?

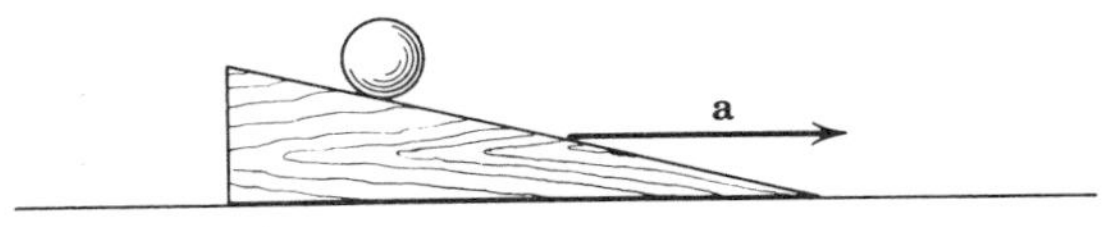

Fig. 9-21.

9-6 A uniform cube of wood rests on a horizontal turntable with its inner edge in a tangential direction. The turntable is rotated from rest with a very small angular acceleration. What must be the conditions on the coefficient of static friction between the block and the turntable so that the block will slide rather than tip over? Under these conditions, at what angular velocity of the turntable will the block of wood begin to slide?

9-7 A long uniform rod rotates about a fixed axis perpendicular to the rod through one end. A motor drives the rod at a constant angular velocity. A particle slides along the rod without friction. If the particle is released without initial radial velocity from some point on the rod, what will be its radial velocity when it reaches the end of the rod? What is the instantaneous power which must be developed by the motor to keep the rod in uniform rotation as the particle slides along it? *Hint:* Let

$$v = \frac{dr}{dt}$$

Then

$$\frac{dv}{dt} = \frac{dv}{dr}\frac{dr}{dt} = v\frac{dv}{dr}$$

9-8 Suppose that in the previous exercise the rod rotates on a frictionless bearing and the driving motor is removed. If now the sliding particle is released without initial radial velocity, with what radial velocity will it reach the end of the rod? Do not neglect the moment of inertia of the rod.

9-9 A foolish fly rides on the arm of a windshield wiper a distance r from the pivot. The arm of the windshield wiper executes simple harmonic motion about its center position so that the angle it makes with this center position is given by the expression

$$\theta = \theta_0 \sin bt$$

If the fly maintains its footing at the same position on the arm, derive a vector expression for the force exerted by the arm on the fly. What additional forces does the arm exert on the fly if the fly crawls with constant speed along the arm toward the pivot? Neglect forces due to gravity, wind, and the motion of the car.

9-10 Consider the procedure for comparing masses outlined in Sec. 3.10. Suppose that this procedure is carried out on two particles by measuring their accelerations with respect to a reference frame which is itself moving with constant linear acceleration. Show that this comparison of masses will yield the same result as one carried out in an inertial reference frame in interstellar space only if the masses are equal and if the force is applied to the particles in the same direction in each case. Modify the procedure of Sec. 3.10 for measuring mass with respect to a reference frame in constant linear acceleration.

PROJECT IX. STATICS

The theory of statics is based on the result of mechanics which says that a rigid body which remains at rest in an inertial coordinate system must be subject to no net force and no net torque about any point. If these conditions are satisfied, the rigid body is said to be in *equilibrium*. If these conditions are not satisfied, the center of mass of the rigid body will accelerate in the direction of the net force and the rigid body will change its angular momentum with respect to the point about which there is a net torque. Note that the net torque must be zero about *every* point for a rigid body which remains at rest (even about points which do not fall inside the rigid body). An important technique in solving statics problems is to choose the point about which torques are calculated in such a way that some of the forces whose magnitudes or directions are unknown exert no torque about the point chosen. Torques and forces on a rigid body due to its weight in a uniform gravitational field are calculated on the assumption that this weight acts as a single force exerted at the center of mass of the rigid body, as derived in Sec. 8.8. Quite often it is useful to analyze forces in terms of their components in convenient directions.

Example. A crane lifts a load of 10^4 kg mass as shown in Fig. IX-1. The boom of the crane is uniform, has a mass of 1000 kg, and a length of 10 m. Calculate the tension in the upper cable and the magnitude and direction of the force exerted on the boom by the lower pivot.

Solution. Isolate the boom analytically and indicate all forces on it as in the right-hand portion of the figure, where **T** is the tension in the upper cable, **F** is the force exerted on the boom by the lower pivot, m is the mass of the boom, and M is the mass of the load being lifted by the crane. The magnitude of **T** is unknown and both the magnitude and direction of

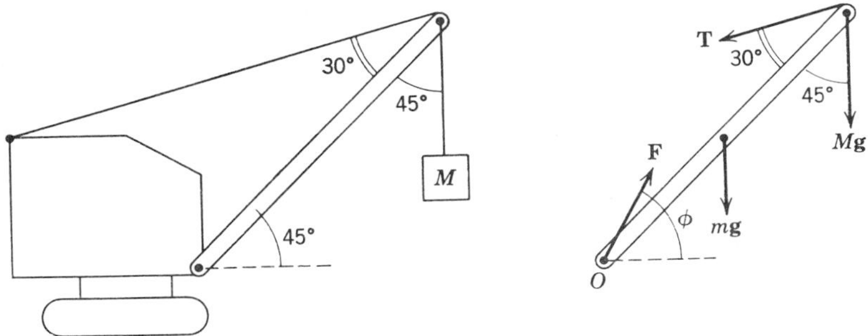

Fig. IX-1.

F are unknown. Set the net torque about point O equal to zero. If the length of the boom is S, this net torque is given by the equation

$$\frac{S}{2} mg \sin 45^\circ + SMg \sin 45^\circ - ST \sin 30^\circ = 0$$

or

$$\frac{g(m/2 + M) \sin 45^\circ}{\sin 30^\circ} = T$$

Substitute the values given above.

$$T = \frac{9.8(500 + 10{,}000)(1/\sqrt{2})}{\frac{1}{2}} = 1.46 \times 10^5 \text{ N}$$

We can find F_x and F_y, the x- and y-components of **F** respectively, by requiring that both the x- and y-components of the net force on the boom be equal to zero.

$$F_x - T \cos 15^\circ = 0$$

$$F_y - T \sin 15^\circ - mg - Mg = 0$$

whence

$$F_x = 1.41 \times 10^5 \text{ N}$$

$$F_y = 1.46 \times 10^5 \text{ N}$$

so that the magnitude of **F** is

$$F = \sqrt{F_x^2 + F_y^2} = 2.03 \times 10^5 \text{ N}$$

and the angle ϕ which F makes with the horizontal is given by

$$\tan \phi = \frac{F_y}{F_x} = \frac{1.46}{1.41} = 1.035$$

so that

$$\phi = 46^\circ$$

Problems

IX-1 Why was point O chosen as the point about which to calculate torques on the boom?

IX-2 Explain the physical reason why the upper cable must make a non-zero angle with the boom.

Another classic set of problems in statics has to do with ladders. For these problems it is usually necessary to use some of the results of Project II on sliding friction.

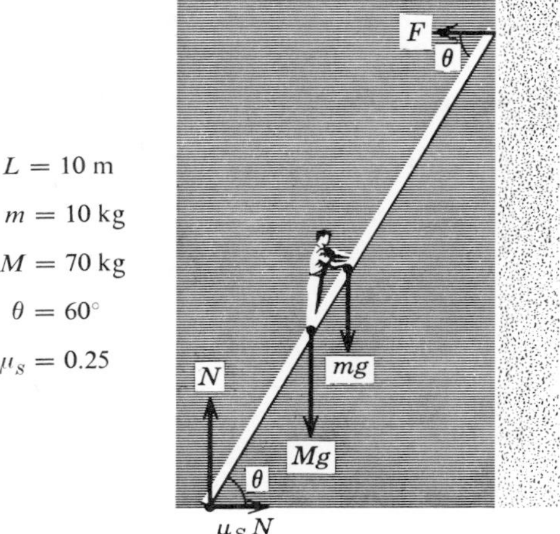

Fig. IX-2.

Example. A ladder of length 10 m and mass 10 kg leans against a frictionless vertical wall at an angle of 60 degrees from the horizontal. The coefficient of static friction between the horizontal floor and the foot of the ladder is $0.25 = \mu_S$. A man of mass 70 kg starts up a ladder. How far along the ladder does he get before the ladder begins to slide down the wall? (See Fig. IX-2.)

Solution. The forces on the ladder are shown. The horizontal force on the foot of the ladder is equal to $\mu_S N$ only at the instant before the ladder begins to slide. We wish to find the position of the man at this instant. Because the vertical wall is frictionless, it can exert a force on the ladder only perpendicular to itself as shown.

Since the net force on the ladder is zero, we find, taking vertical components,

$$N - 10g - 70g = 0$$

and, from horizontal components,

$$\mu_S N - F = 0$$

Let x be the distance of the man along the ladder from the foot at the instant the ladder begins to slide. Equate the torque about the foot of the ladder to zero.

$$\frac{L}{2} \cdot mg \cos\theta + xMg \cos\theta - FL \sin\theta = 0$$

From the first equation above,

$$N = 80 \text{ g newtons}$$

From this and the second equation,

$$F = 0.25 \cdot 80g = 20 \text{ g newtons}$$

From this and the third equation,

$$\tfrac{1}{2}mLg \cos \theta + xMg \cos \theta - 20gL \sin \theta = 0$$

$$x = \frac{20\not{g}L \sin \theta - \frac{1}{2} mL\not{g} \cos \theta}{M\not{g} \cos \theta}$$

$$= \frac{200 \times 0.866 - \frac{1}{2} \times 10 \times 10 \times \frac{1}{2}}{70 \times \frac{1}{2}} = 4.2 \text{ meters}$$

Problems

IX-3 Why is the horizontal force on the foot of the ladder equal to $\mu_S N$ only at the instant before the ladder slips? How does horizontal force before the man reaches 4.6 m compare with the horizontal force when he reaches this point?

IX-4 Why does the answer not depend on g, the acceleration of gravity?

IX-5 The same man climbs the same ladder again. This time the vertical wall also has a coefficient of static friction $\mu_S = 0.25$ with the top of the ladder. What is the smallest angle θ that the ladder can make with the floor and still allow the man to reach the top of the ladder without the ladder sliding down the wall?

Bridge structures are studied using statics. This study is usually begun by neglecting the weight of the structural members except for the roadbed itself and assuming that all members are hinged together (as they sometimes are in large structures) so that each member experiences only tension or compression. Then the conditions of statics are applied to one structural member at a time until the compression or tension in each member has been calculated.

Problem

IX-6 Show that, if a straight rigid rod remains at rest, has negligible weight, and has forces applied to it only at the ends through frictionless hinges, the rod experiences only tension or compression.

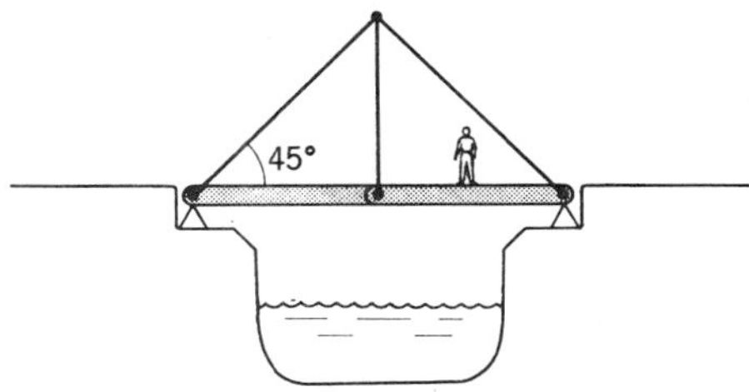

Fig. IX-3.

Example. The bridge in Fig. IX-3 consists of trusses as shown on both sides of the bridge. The roadbed is 5 m long, has a mass of 200 kg, and is hinged in the center. A 70-kg man stands one-quarter of the way across the bridge and in the center laterally. Find the compression or tension in each member of the superstructure. Neglect the weight of these members.

Solution. Since the roadbed is hinged in the middle, half of the weight of each hinged section will rest on the central support. Because all loads are laterally symmetrical, the trusses on either side of the bridge each carry half the load. If M is the mass of the roadbed and m is the mass of the man, the forces on the set of trusses at one side of the road will look as shown in Fig. IX-4. Half the weight of the man falls on the central struts. Hence the total tension in each central strut is $Mg/4 + mg/4$. Consider the forces on one of the central struts C in the figure. Since members A and B are in compression or tension, the force which each of them exerts on C (F_{CA} and F_{CB} respectively) will be in a direction parallel

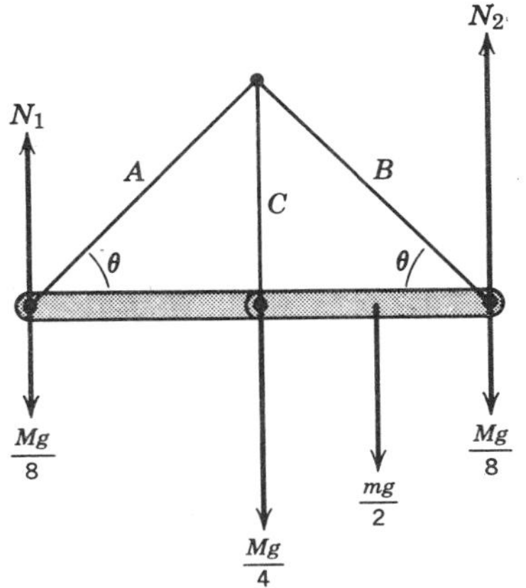

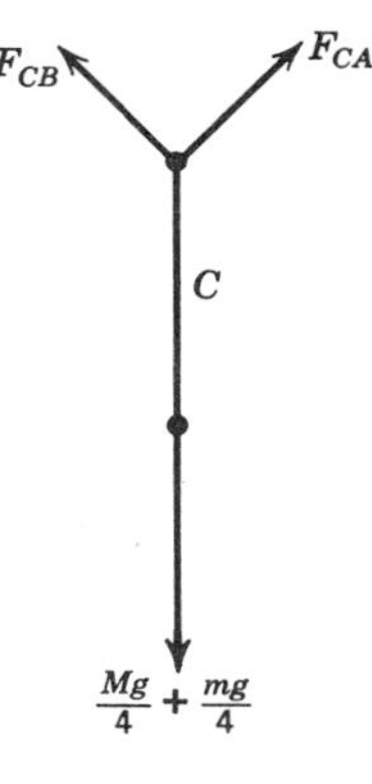

Fig. IX-4.

to the member which exerts the force. Take horizontal and vertical components of the forces in the figure.

$$F_{CA}\cos\theta - F_{CB}\cos\theta = 0$$

$$F_{CA}\sin\theta + F_{CB}\sin\theta - \frac{Mg}{4} - \frac{mg}{4} = 0$$

whence

$$F_{CA} = F_{CB} = \frac{(M+m)g}{8\sin\theta}$$

Problems

IX-7 Show that $F_{CA} = F_{CB}$ is equal to the compression in trusses A and B. Complete the numerical solution of the problem.

IX-8 Find N_1 and N_2, the forces on the bridge which hold it up at the ends.

Statics problems deal with rigid bodies in *equilibrium*. A pencil balanced on its point is in equilibrium. So is a pendulum bob hung from a string. If the pencil is tilted slightly from the vertical it will fall over. On the other hand, if the pendulum bob is displaced from equilibrium it will tend to return toward this equilibrium position (or to oscillate about it). The pencil standing on its point is an example of *unstable equilibrium*. The pendulum bob is an example of *stable equilibrium*. In general, a rigid body is said to be in stable equilibrium if an arbitrary small displacement from the equilibrium position results in a small bounded motion about the position of equilibrium. If this motion is not small, the equilibrium is *unstable*. Whether a rigid body is in stable or unstable equilibrium can be determined by considering a slight displacement from equilibrium and showing whether or not torques or forces will result which tend to return it toward the equilibrium position. If a slight displacement from equilibrium causes neither bounded motion about the equilibrium position or large motion, the equilibrium is called *neutral equilibrium* (sometimes called *labile* or *indifferent* equilibrium). A sphere resting on a flat horizontal table is in neutral equilibrium.

Problems

IX-9 Suppose that a pencil is balanced on a *flat* point. Is this equilibrium stable or unstable?

IX-10 Suppose that a pencil is balanced on a round point but stands against a vertical wall on one side. Is this equilibrium stable or unstable?

Some dynamics problems can be reduced to statics problems by treating them in accelerated reference frames. This means that pseudo-forces must be added to other forces of the problem. In fact, it is possible to reduce *all* dynamics problems involving a single rigid body to problems in statics in which various pseudo-forces appear which are due to the non-inertial nature of the coordinate system.

Example. A railroad car rounds a circular turn of radius R on unbanked rails. The radius of the turn is very much greater than the dimensions of the railroad car. The horizontal thrust necessary to keep the car moving in a circle is supplied to the flanges of the inner wheels. Find the forces exerted on the car by the rails. (See Fig. IX-5.)

Solution. Since the radius of the curve is very much greater than the dimensions of the railroad car, the problem is equivalent to one in which the car is accelerated to the left in Fig. IX-5 with an acceleration v^2/R. Consider the car in a frame in which the car is at rest. In this accelerating frame a pseudo-force equal to Mv^2/R acts on the center of mass of the car to the right in the figure, where v is the speed of the car around the curve. Isolate the railroad car analytically as on the right. Using the symbols in the figure, equate the horizontal and vertical components of the forces to zero.

$$N_1 + N_2 - Mg = 0$$

$$F - \frac{Mv^2}{R} = 0$$

Take the torque about the outer rail.

$$DN_1 + h\frac{Mv^2}{R} - \frac{D}{2}Mg = 0$$

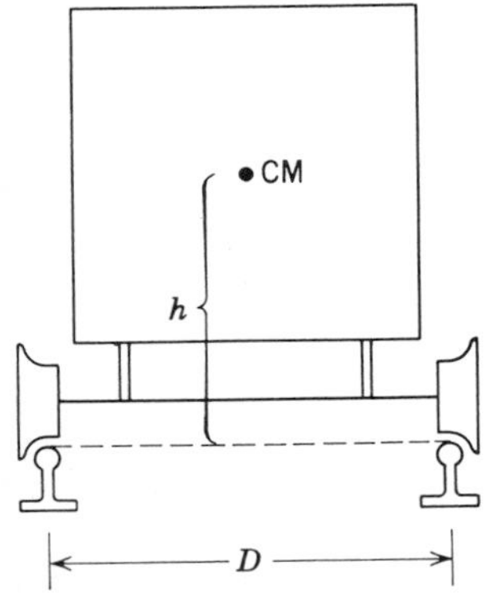

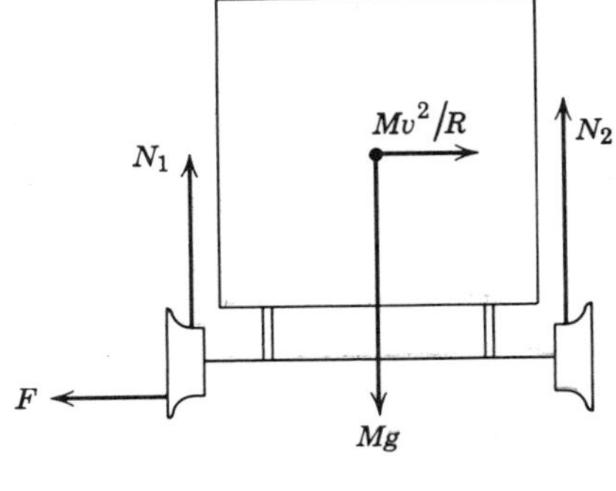

Fig. IX-5.

From the last equation,

$$N_1 = M\left(\frac{g}{2} - \frac{hv^2}{DR}\right)$$

From this and the first equation,

$$N_2 = M\left(\frac{g}{2} + \frac{hv^2}{DR}\right)$$

From the second equation,

$$F = \frac{Mv^2}{R}$$

N_1, N_2, and F represent the sum of the force components applied to the railroad car by *all* the wheels on their respective sides.

Problems

IX-11 What is the greatest speed with which the railway car can round this turn without overturning?

IX-12 At what angle from the horizontal should the tracks be banked in order that the rails will exert forces only normal to the line between them when a car rounds the curve with speed v?

Now answer the following problems. You will find that much of the technique in solving statics problems is concerned with choosing the part of the system to be isolated for analysis. For instance, in Problem IX-13 it is best to isolate for analysis the intersection of the three strings, even though there is no distinguishable particle at this intersection. All the following problems concern systems in a uniform gravitational field of acceleration g.

Problems

IX-13 Find the tension in all three cords in Fig. IX-6.

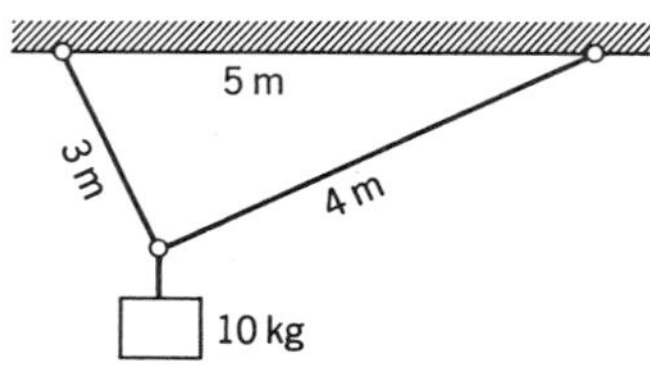

Fig. IX-6.

IX-14 Two men lift a body of mass 20 kg hung from a pole as shown in Fig. IX-7. The pole is uniform and of mass 4 kg. What vertical force must each man exert on the pole? What can you say about the horizontal force which each man exerts on the pole?

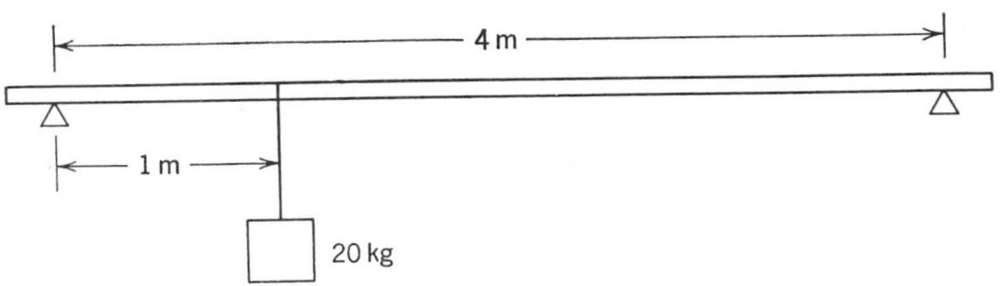

Fig. IX-7.

IX-15 The two men now carry a deer on the same pole. The mass of the deer is 20 kg, and its center of mass is located as shown in Fig. IX-8. Find the vertical force exerted by each man on the pole.

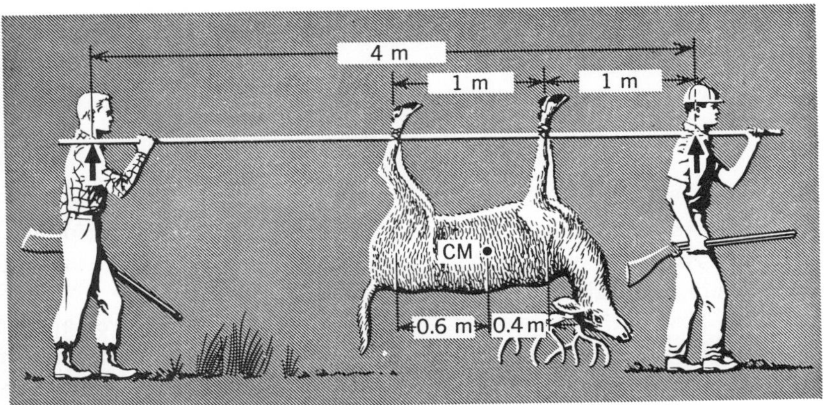

Fig. IX-8.

IX-16 The horizontal strut in Fig. IX-9 is hinged at the wall. Its mass is 100 kg. Find the tension in the upper cable and the magnitude and direction of the force exerted on the strut by the hinge.

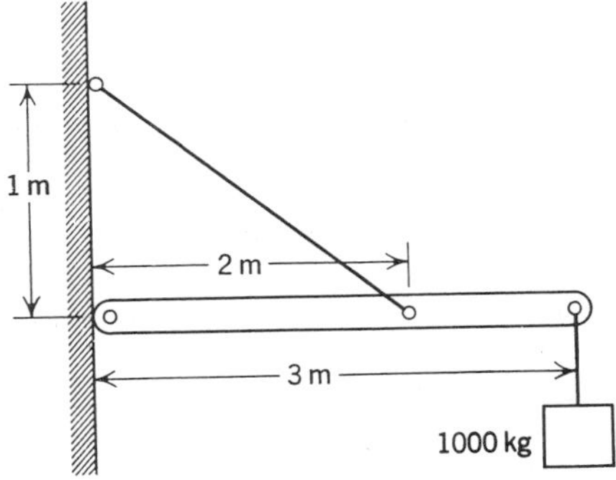

Fig. IX-9.

IX-17 Design a simple crane to lift 1000 kg to a height of 30 m. The highest point available to which to attach the cable which supports the boom is 5 m above the ground. Your design should include the maximum tension in the cables to be used and the maximum compression and bending torque which the boom must sustain.

IX-18 Find the tension or compression in every structural member of the bridge shown in Fig. IX-10. The struts form equilateral triangles. State carefully the assumptions under which your solution is carried out.

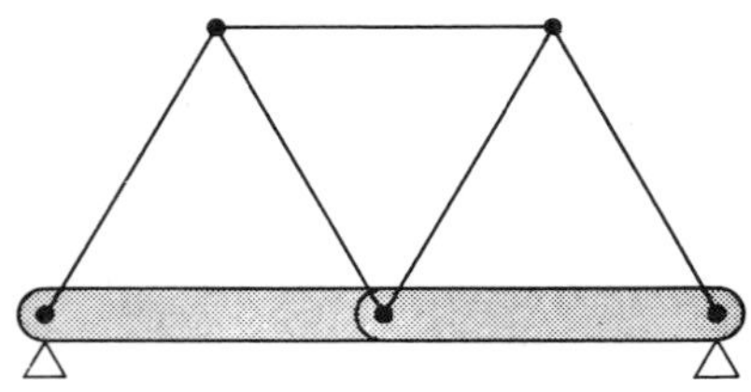

Fig. IX-10.

IX-19 An automobile rounds a curve. Will it skid? Will it tip over?

IX-20 An automobile rounds a curve on two wheels. Show that this equilibrium is unstable.

IX-21 A wedge rests on a horizontal table. A horizontal force is applied to the wedge as shown in Fig. IX-11 at the same instant that a uniform cube is placed at rest on the upper surface of the wedge. Will the cube remain at rest on the wedge, slide up or down the wedge, or tip over? Do not neglect sliding friction.

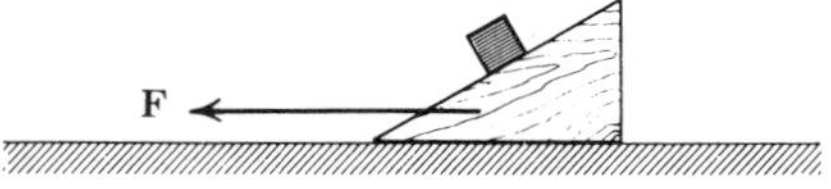

Fig. IX-11.

IX-22 Explain the physical basis for the following rhyme:

> And hence no force, however great,
> Can draw a cord, however fine,
> Into a horizontal line
> Which shall be absolutely straight.*

Do you believe this statement?

* Quoted by L. Perrine, in *Sound and Sense*, Harcourt, Brace and Company, New York, 1956, p. 10.

IX-23 A rope is wrapped around a fixed cylinder, as shown in Fig. IX-12. The force exerted on one end of the rope is enough greater than the force exerted on the other end that the rope is just about to slip. By considering the forces on a small element of rope, show that the formula which relates the forces on the ends of the rope is

$$\frac{F_2}{F_1} = e^{\mu_S \theta}$$

where μ_S is the coefficient of static friction between the rope and the cylinder. Using this formula, explain why a few turns of a rope around a tree will allow one man to withstand the pull of many men.

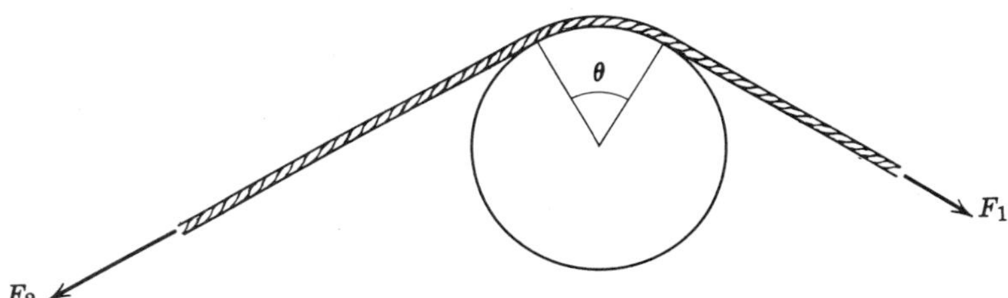

Fig. IX-12.

IX-24 A rigid body with at least one flat surface rests with this surface against a flat horizontal table. Only the force of gravity and forces due to the table act on the rigid body. Show that, if a vertical line drawn from the center of mass of the body intersects the tabletop inside of the boundary of the flat surface of the body against the table, the body is in *stable* equilibrium. Under what circumstances will the body be in unstable equilibrium? not in equilibrium at all? Extend these results to rigid bodies which touch the table at only a few points. Under what circumstances will a rigid body be in neutral equilibrium on a table top? Apply your results to a rocking horse. Extend your results to uneven and non-horizontal supporting surfaces.

IX-25 A small boy on a tricycle rounds a corner. Under what circumstances will he tip over?

chapter 10

Some difficulties with the laws of classical mechanics

10.1 INTRODUCTION. The laws of classical mechanics can be used to describe in an accurate and self-consistent manner the motions of most of the objects we encounter in our everyday experience. In fact, these laws can be used to describe many motions which most of us observe rarely or about which our information must come second hand, such as the motions of the planets or galaxies, the phenomenon of weightlessness in earth satellites, the motions of a Foucault pendulum or of large air masses. Indeed, in this larger sense the term "everyday experience" has been expanded to include reports and pictures from the other side of the moon, from the world of microbiology, and from many laboratories of physics. In each of these places the classical laws of motion have been useful, and in each of them these laws are continually tested under an ever-wider range of experimental conditions. Perhaps it is not surprising that some of these experimental conditions violate one or more of the limiting assumptions under which our analysis of motion was carried out. For instance, consider limiting assumption f in Sec. 3.12: "Only those experiments will be considered in which no particle involved in the experiment attains a speed with respect to the reference particle greater than one-tenth of the speed of light." What happens to the laws of motion if this limiting assumption is violated, i.e., if we consider experiments in which particles move faster than one-tenth the speed of light? Now a flash of light travels at a speed of nearly three hundred million meters per second. One-tenth of this speed is thirty million meters per second. It is difficult to accelerate objects large enough to be visible to the unaided human eye to this speed within the confines of an earthbound laboratory. However, it is not unusual (an "everyday experience" for some people) to encounter experiments in which elementary particles such as electrons or protons are made to travel in the laboratory at speeds approaching that of light. Almost every major university in the world has one or more large devices in which these high speeds are reached. The primary purpose of most of these devices is to study elementary particles and the structure of the atomic nucleus. In order to design these devices it is important to know whether or not the laws of classical mechanics can be used to describe the motion of elementary particles moving at great speed.

"Elementary particles" are not *particles* in the way we have defined the term, because they are not "material bodies visible to the unaided human eye." (See Sec. 3.12.) In fact, they are not "visible" in the ordinary sense to any extension of the human eye such as the microscope. Rather specialized equipment such as Geiger counters and fluorescent screens is required to detect the presence of individual elementary particles. This means that if we do an experiment in classical mechanics with a particular kind of elementary particle we shall have to be wary of applying the result to visible particles until more evidence accumulates. Nevertheless elementary particles are the only objects currently available to us which we can make to move as fast as we would like in order to test the laws of classical mechanics at high speeds. In the next section we shall describe such an experiment using electrons.

10.2 VIOLATION OF THE LAWS OF CLASSICAL MECHANICS BY FAST ELECTRONS.* The electron was identified as an elementary particle at the turn of the century and was shown to be one constituent of all ordinary matter.† Later study has shown that every atom is made up of a central nucleus surrounded by a "cloud" of one or more electrons. Electrons can be released from atoms by high voltages, light, or electric discharge. Such free electrons will quickly recombine with atoms in the air, but in a laboratory vacuum they will move unhindered. Their paths can be traced by means of the fluorescence they cause when they strike glass and some other materials. By studying the motions of electrons in electric and magnetic fields,‡ it was found that *if electrons are considered to be particles* then they must each be assigned a mass m_e and an electric charge e with the following values.

$$\begin{aligned} m_e &= 9.11 \times 10^{-31}\ \text{kg} \\ e &= 1.60 \times 10^{-19}\ \text{coulomb} \end{aligned} \tag{10-1}$$

* The idea for this section was taken from the mimeographed report, *Relativity in College Physics*, a report of the Cornell Meeting, 30-31 January 1961, available from the Commission on College Physics, Bryn Mawr College, Bryn Mawr, Pennsylvania.

† J. J. Thomson, *Philosophical Magazine*, Series 5, **44**, 293 (1897).

‡ See Thomson, *ibid.;* and R. A. Millikan, *Physical Review*, Series 1, **32,** 349 (1911).

Electrons can easily be accelerated to high kinetic energies using electric fields. It is found experimentally that, if electrons of high kinetic energy fall on metal targets, high frequency light waves called X-rays are given off from the targets. These X-rays can be detected using Geiger counters.

With this background let us consider the following experiment, pictured in Fig. 10-1. An electron accelerator accelerates electrons to a high known kinetic energy. Because this acceleration takes place in pulses, electrons are produced in bunches, represented by the two clouds of dots in the figure. After leaving the accelerator, these bunches of electrons enter a long vacuum chamber. In the chamber are two X-ray targets a distance D apart. These targets are situated slightly to one side of the path of the center of the bunches of electrons, so that only a few of the electrons at the edge of each bunch hit the targets, causing X-rays to be given off. These X-rays are detected by two Geiger counters outside the vacuum chamber. When Geiger counter 1 in the figure detects an X-ray, it sends an electrical signal along wire AB which starts a clock. When Geiger counter 2 in the figure detects an X-ray, it sends an electrical signal along the wire EF which stops the clock. In this way the velocity of the electron bunch can be measured by dividing the distance D by the time interval measured on the clock. For reasonable values of D, say a few tens of meters, the time interval will be very short. For this reason the "clock" will not be a mechanical one but may involve, for instance, the deflection of a fluorescent spot sweeping rapidly at a known speed across the face of an oscilloscope. Perhaps the signal from Geiger counter 1 might start the horizontal sweep and the signal from Geiger counter 2 might cause a vertical deflection in this sweep as shown in Fig. 10-1. A camera could record this single sweep for later study.

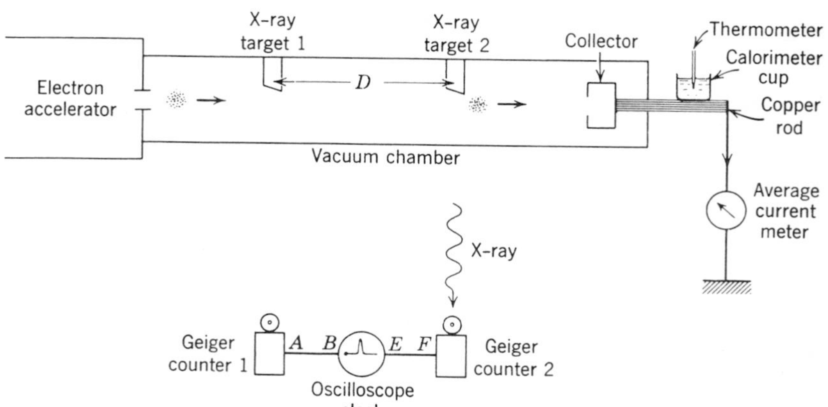

Fig. 10-1. Schematic diagram of apparatus for measuring $\frac{1}{2}m_e v^2$ vs kinetic energy of electrons.

Questions

10-1 Suppose D is 30 m and the velocity of the electron bunches is one-tenth the velocity of light. What will be the time interval recorded by the clock? Express your result in microseconds.

10-2 Suppose that the fluorescent spot on the face of the oscilloscope clock moves at a uniform speed such that it covers 1 cm in 0.2 μsec. At what distance from the start of the sweep will the deflection be caused by the signal arriving from Geiger counter 2 under the conditions stated in the preceding question?

For such short time intervals it cannot be assumed that the X-ray travels instantaneously from target 1 to Geiger counter 1 or that the resulting electrical signal travels instantaneously from A to B. However, the only assumption we need to make is that the interval of time between the production of the X-ray at target 1 and the arrival of the resulting electrical signal at the clock from Geiger counter 1 is the *same* as the interval of time between the production of the later X-ray at target 2 and the arrival of the resulting electrical signal at the clock from Geiger counter 2. If this condition is satisfied, the clock will read the correct time of flight of the bunch of electrons between target 1 and target 2.

Question

10-3 How can you test experimentally whether or not this assumption is satisfied for any two given Geiger counters and electrical lines?

The purpose of this experiment is to determine whether or not the kinetic energy of the electrons is equal to $\frac{1}{2}m_e v^2$ for high velocities. The expression $\frac{1}{2}m_e v^2$ can be calculated since we know the value of m_e from Eq. (10-1) and we can measure the value of v using the procedure outlined above. If we wish, we can take the word of the technician who runs the electron accelerator as to the kinetic energy of the electrons which he is supplying us at any given setting of his dials. Alternatively, we can measure the average kinetic energy of the electrons by the following method.

After passing target 2 the bunches of electrons enter a *collector* and are absorbed by it. The excess charge built up by the electrons is allowed to leak away through a meter which measures average current in coulombs per second. Knowing the average current and the charge on the electron (Eq. 10-1), we can calculate the number of electrons which are caught by the collector each second.

Question

10-4 If the average current meter reads 2×10^{-6} coulomb/sec, how many electrons are caught by the collector each second?

Now, the electrons which collide with the collector are brought to rest by this impact. All their kinetic energy is converted to heat energy. This heat energy raises the temperature of the collector. The amount of heat energy released per second at the collector can be determined experimentally. For instance, in Fig. 10-1 a copper rod is used to conduct this heat to a cup (called a *calorimeter*) containing water. By knowing how much heat is required to raise the temperature of the water, calorimeter cup, rod, and collector by a given amount and also the rate at which the temperature rises during the experiment, the total heat released per second at the collector can be calculated. In practice the rod and calorimeter would be carefully insulated to reduce loss of heat to the surroundings. From the average current leaving the collector, the number of electrons arriving at the collector per second can be calculated. From the results of these two observations the energy released *per electron* can be calculated. This must be equal to the average kinetic energy per electron before impact. Using this value for kinetic energy, we can compare it to the value of the expression $\frac{1}{2}m_ev^2$ calculated from the measured value of v and the mass m_e taken from Eq. (10-1).

Question

10-5 A preliminary experiment shows that 400 joules of heat energy are required to raise the temperature of the water, calorimeter cup, copper rod, and collector by one degree Centigrade. In the experiment with electrons from the accelerator, the average current from the collector is measured to be 2×10^{-6} coulomb/sec and the thermometer indicates a rise of 5 degrees Centigrade in 100 sec. What is the average kinetic energy of the electrons before impact with the collector?

If this procedure is carried out for a wide range of different kinetic energies, a graph of the resulting values of $\frac{1}{2}m_ev^2$ as a function of the kinetic energy per electron will look like Fig. 10-2.

Notice first that for low energies between points O and G on the curve the result is approximately a straight line which makes an angle of 45 degrees with each axis. This means that for low energies the kinetic energy T is equal to $\frac{1}{2}m_ev^2$ as derived in classical mechanics.

$$T = \tfrac{1}{2}m_ev^2 \qquad \text{non-relativistic velocities} \qquad (10\text{-}2)$$

This reassures us that at low speeds the electron behaves like a visible particle in at least some ways. We call the region from O to G the classical or non-relativistic region and say that Eq. (10-2) is valid for *non-relativistic velocities.*

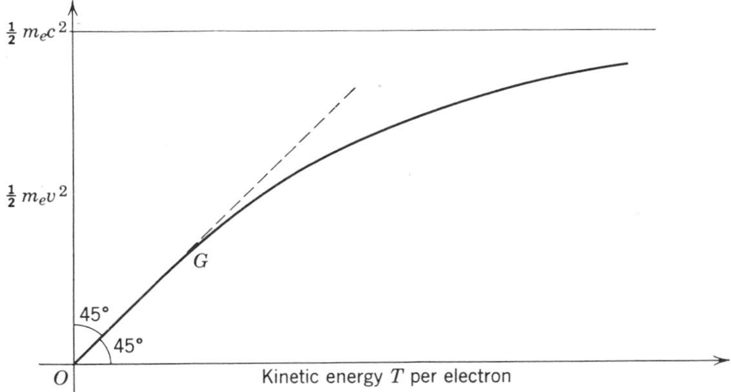

Fig. 10-2. Graph of $\frac{1}{2}m_ev^2$ vs kinetic energy per electron derived by using the equipment of Fig. 10-1. The symbol c represents the speed of light.

Question

10-6 Can you say that Eq. (10-2) is *exactly* correct to the left of G? What determines the position of point G on the curve?

Now, if the equation $T = \frac{1}{2}m_ev^2$ were true for all energies, the experimental curve should continue to follow this straight line as indicated by the dashed line in Fig. 10-2. In fact, however, the experimental curve bends downward to the right. This means that except for small energies the kinetic energy of the electron is greater than $\frac{1}{2}m_ev^2$. We call the region to the right of G on the curve the non-classical or relativistic region, and the velocities of particles corresponding to this region *relativistic velocities.*

$$T > \tfrac{1}{2}m_ev^2 \qquad \text{relativistic velocities} \tag{10-3}$$

Notice the horizontal line drawn in Fig. 10-2 at a value $\frac{1}{2}m_ec^2$, where c is the speed of light in a vacuum. The experimental curve approaches this line in the figure but does not cross it. This corresponds to the experimental result that the observed speed of the electrons remains less than the speed of light. This is one source of experimental observation 7 in Sec. 3.12, i.e., that no particle has been observed to travel at a speed greater than the speed of light in a vacuum.

This experiment shows that, although electrons can be given arbitrarily large kinetic energies, the classical expression $T = \frac{1}{2}m_ev^2$ is not valid at these very high kinetic energies, and the velocity of the electrons cannot be made to exceed the velocity of light in a vacuum. This leads us to be suspicious of the other basic laws of classical mechanics when they are applied to particles with high velocities. These suspicions find added support in the fact that similar (though not identical) results are obtained for other elementary particles such as the proton and the neutron. We shall find in what follows not only that these suspicions are confirmed but also that in order to set up the laws of motion for particles traveling at these higher velocities a new conceptual foundation will have to be put under the science of mechanics.

10.3 CONCEPTUAL DIFFICULTIES WITH THE CLASSICAL LAWS OF PHYSICS. At the turn of the twentieth century when the theory of special relativity was formulated, the experiment described in the last section had not been performed. The formulation of special relativity took place because of some conceptual difficulties with classical mechanics and classical electromagnetic theory. A few of these conceptual difficulties are presented below.

The paradox of magnetic forces. In Sec. 5.3 it was stated that magnetic forces can exist between two unmagnetized electrically charged particles only when *both* of them are moving with respect to an inertial coordinate system. This statement can lead to a paradox. Suppose we have two charged particles in motion in such a way that a magnetic force is predicted to act on each of them. Now suppose we observe the same motion from another inertial coordinate system which is in motion relative to the first and in which at least one of the particles is at rest instantaneously. Since at least one of the charged particles is at rest in this coordinate system, no magnetic forces are predicted to exist between the two charged particles in this system. In one inertial coordinate system, magnetic forces are predicted; in another inertial coordinate system, no magnetic forces are predicted. A specific example of such a paradox was considered in Question 5-19 in Chapter 5.

Question

10-7 Show that according to the laws of classical mechanics any acceleration of the charged particles will be measured to have the same value in the two inertial coordinate systems in relative motion. Show that the paradox above extends to the motion predicted for the two particles as a result of the magnetic forces acting on them.

In addition to magnetic forces acting between moving charged particles there will also be electrical forces acting between these particles. Perhaps a clue to the paradox of magnetic forces can be found in the fact that the magnitude of the magnetic forces acting between charged particles becomes comparable to the magnitude of the electrical forces acting between these particles only when the speeds of the charged particles are significant fractions of the speed of light. Hence we return again, as in the last section, to the central importance of the speed of light.

The paradox of the speed of light. The paradox of magnetic forces is not the only conceptual difficulty with the classical laws of electricity and magnetism. Light itself is an electromagnetic wave (see Sec. 11.2) whose speed c can be predicted from the classical laws of electricity and magnetism. This predicted speed has been verified experimentally many times.* The problem arises: With respect to which inertial reference frame does light have the predicted speed c? It seems reasonable to suppose that, if two inertial reference frames are in relative motion with uniform relative velocity $\mathbf{v}$ and if a flash of light is emitted in the same direction as $\mathbf{v}$, the speed of this flash of light when measured in the two frames should differ by the relative speed v. Yet is not the prediction that the speed of light is equal to c in both frames by the classical laws of electricity and magnetism valid in both reference frames? Here is another paradox: Does the measured speed of light differ in two inertial reference frames in uniform relative motion, or is this speed the same in both of these inertial reference frames?

Class Discussion Question

10-8 Show that, if the speed of light should differ in the two inertial frames in uniform relative motion, it might be possible to establish a unique inertial frame experimentally distinguishable from other inertial frames. In this case would there be only one such frame? We could then *define* this unique inertial frame (or frames) to be *absolutely at rest.*

One of the alternatives in this paradox was eliminated in a series of brilliant experiments carried out after 1880 by Michelson and Morley. They chose one reference frame to be the earth moving in one direction around the sun in, say, January and the other reference frame to be the earth moving in the *opposite* direction (with respect to the fixed stars) in, say, July. Since the speed of the earth in its orbit is about 30 km/sec, the difference in speed between these two reference frames is about 60 km/sec. Using sensitive optical equipment, they were able to show that the speed of light was the same in both of these reference frames with an experimental uncertainty of less than one-sixth of the speed of the earth in its orbit.†

* C. L. Andrews, *Optics of the Electromagnetic Spectrum*, Prentice-Hall Inc., Englewood Cliffs, New Jersey, 1960, Chapter 4.

† C. W. Sherwin, *Basic Concepts of Physics*, Holt, Reinhart, and Winston, New York, 1961, Chapter 4; A. A. Michelson and E. W. Morley, *American Journal of Science*, **34,** 333 (1887).

A series of later experiments using light from the sun and from stars showed that this result was independent of the state of motion of the light source.*

In one sense this result was reassuring, because it meant that the speed of light could not be used to distinguish one inertial reference frame from another. In another sense it was disturbing because it meant that *two velocities cannot be added as vectors if either one is comparable in magnitude to the speed of light.* This is directly contradictory to the assumptions used for small velocities in classical mechanics.

Einstein assumed that the results of these experiments were generally true and postulated that *the speed of light is the same in all inertial reference frames and is independent of the motion of the light source.* This will be one of our basic assumptions in the next chapter.

The paradox of simultaneity. The concept of simultaneity is central to our description of motion. The statement, "The particle was six meters away at ten o'clock," means, in terms of the observations actually carried out, "The reading of ten o'clock on my clock and the position of the particle six meters away occurred simultaneously." Without a clear meaning for the word *simultaneous* we would not be able to describe the motion of particles, much less set up the laws which govern this motion. In classical mechanics the meaning of the word *simultaneous* is clear because we have assumed that information can be transferred from place to place instantaneously. In fact, however, our fastest messenger is a flash of light.

Question

10-9 Show that the word *simultaneous* can be interpreted unambiguously even if events take place so far apart that communication by means of light cannot be assumed to be instantaneous, as long as only one inertial reference frame is used. Devise an experiment in principle to verify the following statement: "Satellite Y21 landed on the surface of Mars at 10:34 this morning Greenwich mean time."

The fact that the speed of light has the same value in two inertial reference frames in uniform relative motion means that when light is used as a messenger it may lead to disagreements about the simultaneity of events between observers moving with these two reference frames. Einstein was able to show this in an elegant manner using the following simple thought experiment.†

* R. Tomaschek, *Annalen der Physik*, **73,** 105 (1924). See discussion in W. Pauli, *Theory of Relativity*, Pergamon Press, New York, 1958, pp. 8 and 207.

† A. Einstein, *Relativity*, Hartsdale House, New York, 1947. Einstein was his own best popular writer.

Consider an observer A riding in the center of a long train which moves with constant velocity. Label the ends of the train B and C. Suppose that two bolts of lightning strike B and C, leaving marks on the ends of the train and also on the tracks. Label the positions of these marks on the tracks E and F. Now suppose that a second observer D is standing on the ground halfway between points E and F. The situation is pictured in Fig. 10-3*a*.

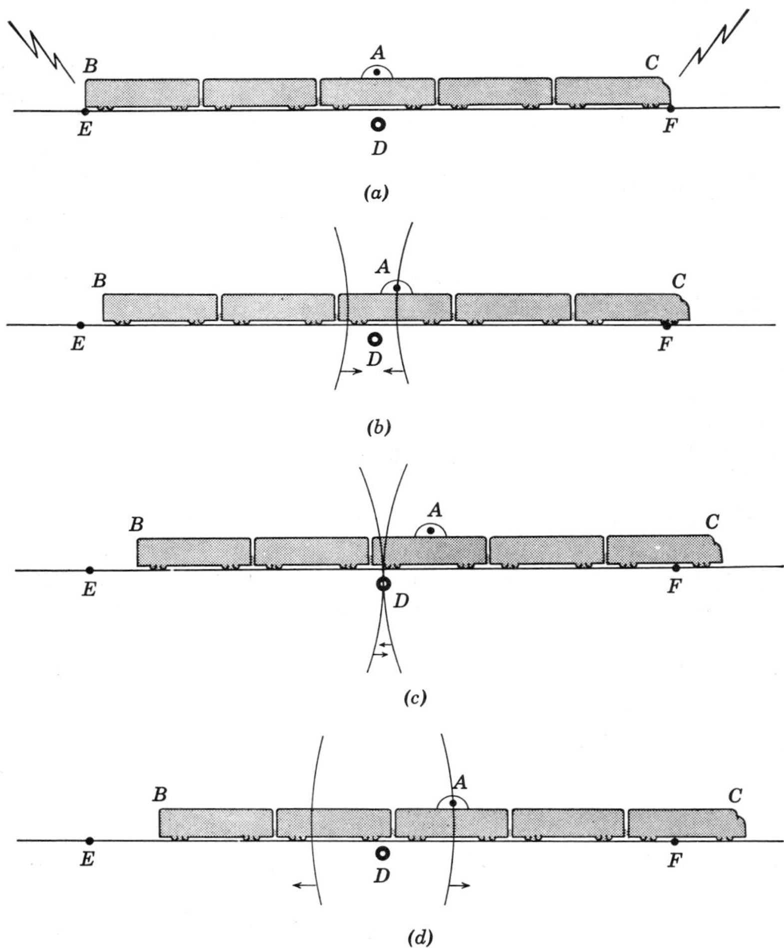

Fig. 10-3. Einstein's illustration of the paradox of simultaneity using a moving train both ends of which are struck by lightning. (*a*) Lightning bolts strike both ends of the train. (*b*) Flash from front end passes observer A. (*c*) Flashes from both ends reach observer D. (*d*) Flash from rear end passes observer A.

Flashes of light from the lightning strokes spread out in all directions. Suppose that the flashes of light from both ends of the train reach observer D at the same time, as shown in Fig. 10-3*c*. Since observer D can verify by measurement that the distance from his position is the same to each mark on the track made by the lightning, he will conclude that the two strokes of lightning occurred *simultaneously*. Will observer A also observe that the two strokes of lightning occurred simultaneously? In Figs. 10-3*b* and 10-3*d* we see that the flash from the front end of the train reaches observer A before the flash from the rear end of the train. He can measure that the distance from his position is the same to the marks on each end of the train. Since the train also constitutes an inertial reference frame, the speed of light is the same for observer A as for an observer in any other inertial reference frame. Observer A concludes, therefore, that one lightning bolt struck the front end of the train before the other bolt struck the rear end of the train. Hence observers A and D cannot agree on the simultaneity of the two lightning strokes. The inability of two observers in relative motion to agree on the simultaneity of some events is referred to as the *relativity of simultaneity*.

Questions

10-10 Show that there is no disagreement if the train is at rest with respect to the track.

10-11 Show that there would be no disagreement if light traveled instantaneously from one place to another.

10-12 Be sure you understand the exact nature of the disagreement between observers A and D. Will observer D agree that the two flashes of light from the two ends of the train arrived at observer A at different times? Will observer A agree that the two flashes reached observer D at the same time?

10-13 If the train is traveling at a speed of 45 m/sec (about 100 mph) and is 1000 m long, what will be the elapsed time between the reception of the two flashes by observer A? Express your answer in nanoseconds. Why was the relativity of simultaneity not discovered experimentally as soon as trains were invented?

10-14 Show that the above thought experiment is symmetrical: If the flashes of light should arrive at observer A at the same time, observer D would not observe the lightning strokes to occur simultaneously. In this case which stroke would observer D observe to occur first?

The paradox of the presence or absence of magnetic forces, the paradox of the speed of light, and the paradox of simultaneity are all grave conceptual difficulties which cannot be resolved by the laws of classical physics. None of these difficulties is significant under circumstances in which particle velocities are low. The fact that these difficulties are experimentally significant at high particle velocities and are not just matters of language is shown by the Michelson-Morley experiments and by the experiment on the kinetic energy of electrons described in the last section. The fact that the simultaneity of two events depends on the relative velocity of the observer means that whatever solution we find to these difficulties will have to be both basic and radical because the concept of simultaneity lies at the foundation not only of our description of motion in classical mechanics but also of our common sense attitude toward the physical world.

In the next chapter we shall begin once again from the beginning with a statement of rules which will govern our new approach to mechanics. Actually the same rules have governed our approach to mechanics from the beginning of this book, but now we shall have to make the rules explicit and apply them more rigorously so that they will lead us without error or misconceptions into the world of relativity.

chapter 11

The observation of rapidly moving objects by a single observer

11.1 THE OPERATIONAL PRINCIPLE. *Scientific statements about a physical system are limited to those statements which can be verified, at least in principle, by means of physically realizable experiments.* We shall call this the *operational principle.* The word "operational" is used because the principle refers to statements which are based on experiments, or *operations.* The *statements* referred to in the operational principle can be *descriptions* of the physical state of a system, such as the velocity or energy of a particle, or *predictions* about the results of experiments to be carried out, or *data* resulting from experiments already carried out.

Behind the descriptions, predictions, and data about a physical system must lie *definitions* of the terms used in these statements. We shall demand that these definitions also be based directly or indirectly on physically realizable experiments. For instance, the definition of the length of an object is based on the choice of a device (such as a matchstick) to be the unit length and a set of instructions concerning the operations to be used to compare the unit length to the object whose length is to be measured. A definition of a concept which involves one or more *devices* and also *instructions* for manipulating these devices is called an *operational definition.* Length, time, force, and mass were all defined earlier in the book by means of operational definitions which will have to be re-examined in this and the next two chapters. Not all definitions are operational. For instance, the definitions of kinetic energy and momentum involve the mathematical combination of the quantities mass and velocity. Nevertheless, since the concepts of kinetic energy and momentum are based indirectly on measurements of length, time, and force, they have operational foundation.

Questions

11-1 Can you remember the operational definitions of length, time, force, and mass? How does each of these definitions utilize a device and instructions for manipulating this device? Check yourself by looking back.

11-2 Can *velocity* be defined operationally, or is this concept a derived one like those of kinetic energy and momentum?

11-3 Is every statement involving a device and instructions for manipulating this device an operational definition? Is either of the following statements an operational definition?

To use can opener, engage top of can in slot A and press button B until can top pops up.

Stars are what you see when you hit your head.

Returning now to the operational principle, you will see that it is really a *definition* of the term *scientific statement* as applied to physical systems. There is not much use in asking whether or not the operational principle is "true" or "valid" since it is simply a definition. Notice that the operational principle does not exclude the possibility that some scientific statements may apply validly to things other than physical systems. For instance, some mathematical symbols might properly be called "scientific" symbols.

Example 1. "The speed of that particle with respect to this coordinate system is ten meters per second." Because this statement deals with a physical system—"that particle"—the operational principle applies to the system. It is a scientific statement because one can devise an experiment to verify the statement, for instance by measuring the position of the particle (in "this coordinate system") at two subsequent times and dividing the distance between these points by the time taken for the particle to move from one position to the other.

Example 2. "I am moving with respect to space." This statement deals with a physical system—me—and thus the operational principle applies to the statement. However, it is not a scientific statement because no one has been able to devise a physically realizable experiment which will detect (uniform) motion with respect to "space."

Example 3. "The square root of four is two." This statement deals with a mathematical abstraction rather than with a physical system. Therefore the operational principle does not apply to it.

The question whether or not the operational principle gives the most suitable or practical definition of scientific statements about physical systems belongs to the field of the philosophy of science. Suffice it to say here that the operational principle, expressed in this form or some other form, has been enormously *fruitful* in physics. Its application has resulted in many advances, such as those in the fields of quantum mechanics and relativity. In these chapters we shall use the operational principle to develop part of the theory of relativity.

Questions

11-4 Consider the difficulties in determining the "instantaneous velocity" of a particle in such a way as to satisfy the operational principle. Is such a definition possible?

11-5 Consider the following statements. To which of these statements does the operational principle apply? Which of the statements to which the operational principle does apply can be said to be scientific statements?

This book is one inch thick.
The sun blew up two minutes ago.
Here is a ten-horsepower motor.
The kinetic energy of that particle is 10 joules.
The child is father of the man.
This statue is beautiful.
My hat is green.
Thou shalt not kill.
Two plus two is four.
Two apples plus two apples equals four apples.

11.2 THE UNIQUE ROLE OF LIGHT. In a vacuum a flash of light is the fastest message carrier. This gives to the light flash a unique position among message carriers. What is light?

In Chapter 5 we discussed the concept of an *electric field* which is produced by the presence of charged bodies. In the analysis of that chapter the charged bodies responsible for electric fields were at rest, so that the fields did not change with time. Such unchanging—or static—electric fields are called *electrostatic* fields.

Suppose that two charged particles are placed some distance apart and initially at rest with respect to one another. It is possible to measure or to calculate the *electrostatic* force on either particle due to the presence of the electrostatic field set up by the other particle. Assume that both particles are constrained as in Fig. 11-1*a* so that they are not accelerated by this electrostatic force.

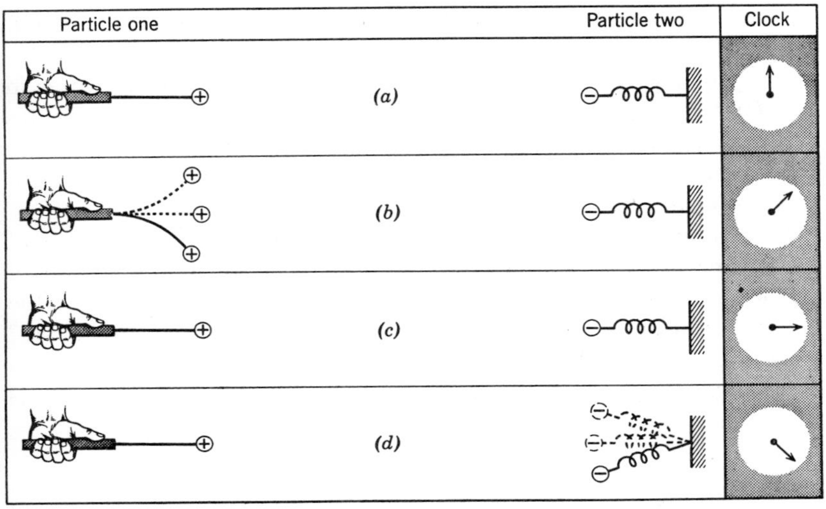

Fig. 11-1. Thought experiment. Propagation of an electrical disturbance. (*a*) Both particles are at rest. (*b*) Particle one is wiggled by hand. (*c*) Interval in which both particles are again at rest. (*d*) Particle two responds to wiggle at later time.

Now suppose that particle one is suddenly wiggled or oscillated by an outside force for a short time. Will particle two feel *immediately* the change in field due to the change in position of particle one? If this experiment is carried out, it is found that particle two does *not* respond immediately but rather responds after a time interval which is proportional to the distance between the charged particles. In fact, if we measure the distance between the particles and divide it by the interval of time between the forced oscillation of particle one and the responding oscillation of particle two, then the result is equal to the speed of light. (We assume that this experiment takes place in a vacuum.)

We conclude that the disturbance in the electric field caused by the forced oscillation of particle one does not arrive instantaneously at particle two but rather that this field disturbance *propagates* or travels at the speed of light from one place to another.

Questions

11-6 How could you use a third charged particle to demonstrate that the speed of propagation of the electrical disturbance between particles one and two has a constant value during its trip?

11-7 In Fig. 11-1*b* is the electric field at the negative charge given by Eq. (5-9),

$$\mathbf{E} = \frac{1}{4\pi\epsilon_0}\frac{q\hat{r}}{r^2} \tag{5-9}$$

where q is the charge of the positively charged particle? If not, is Eq. (5-9) invalid?

11-8 Some energy is certainly required to oscillate particle two as in Fig. 11-1*d*. That energy must have come from particle one. Where is this energy during the interval pictured in Fig. 11-1*c*? Does the disturbance of the electric field carry energy? How must the law of conservation of energy be changed to take this into account?

11-9 Suppose that another charged particle is located to the left of particle one in Fig. 11-1. Would it also respond to the oscillation of particle one? What conclusions do you draw about the shape of the disturbance in the electric field set up by the oscillation of particle one? According to this picture, can all the energy delivered to the electrical disturbance by particle one be delivered to particle two? What happens to any that is left over?

You will learn in studying magnetism that one way a magnetic field can be produced is by a changing electric field. Since a changing electric field is involved in the "electric field disturbance" caused by the changing position of particle one, it might be expected that magnetic fields would also be associated with this disturbance; they are. Changing magnetic fields can be detected experimentally in such disturbances. Because the motion of charged particles produces changing electric *and* magnetic fields, the resulting disturbances are called *electromagnetic disturbances* or *electromagnetic waves*. The velocity of propagation of electromagnetic waves can be calculated from more advanced theory. The calculated value agrees well with the experimental one and is equal to the velocity of a flash of light. In fact, *light itself is an electromagnetic disturbance.* How does light differ from other electromagnetic disturbances?

Thus far nothing has been said about "how fast" particle one is made to oscillate. The simplest kind of oscillation is harmonic oscillation in which the displacement y varies with the sine or cosine of the time.

$$y = A \sin \omega t = A \sin 2\pi \nu t$$

where ν is the frequency in cycles per second and ω is the angular frequency in radians per second. This is the simplest kind of oscillation because it is the only kind which can be described in terms of a single frequency. Electromagnetic waves can be produced experimentally by charges oscillating harmonically as slowly as a few cycles per second or less and as fast as a hundred billion cycles per second. The equipment used to generate any one of these frequencies may be rather sophisticated and expensive, but it has as its output simply a set of charges oscillating at the designed frequency. Electromagnetic waves in this range of frequencies are used (in order of ascending frequency) for standard radio broadcast, television and fm broadcast, microwave relays, and radar. Figure 11-2 shows an experiment in the propagation of an electromagnetic disturbance using a radar transmitter and receiver instead of the charged particles of Fig. 11-1. Reflecting "dishes" are used to focus the waves. This experiment is much more easily carried out than the one using charged particles.

It is difficult to find a mechanism to vibrate charged particles, even electrons, at frequencies greater than about one hundred billion cycles per second. A different type of mechanism must be used. Electromagnetic

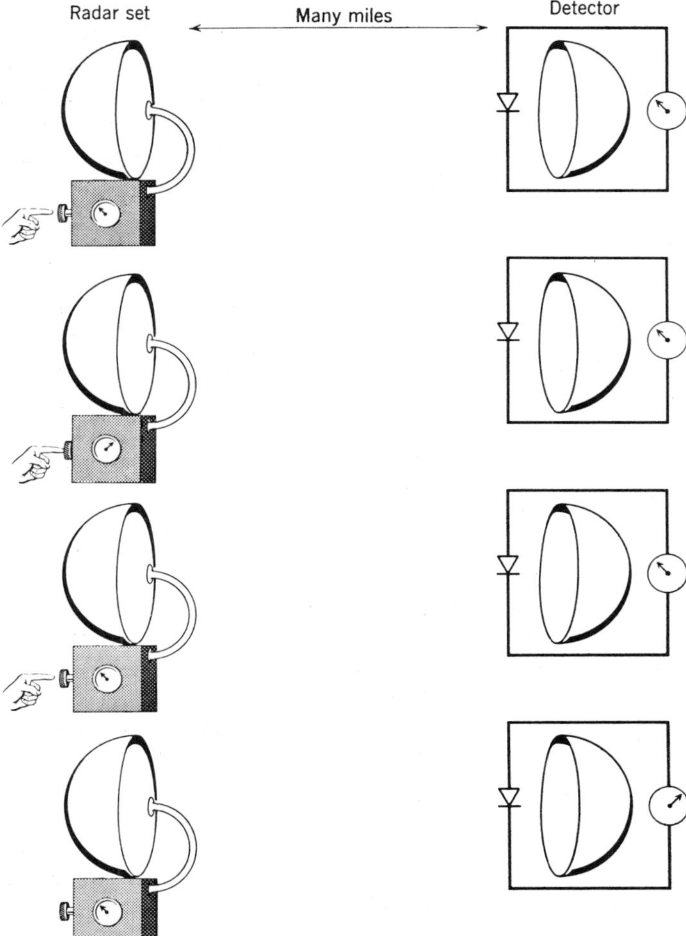

Fig. 11-2. Experiment of Fig. 11-1 carried out using radar.

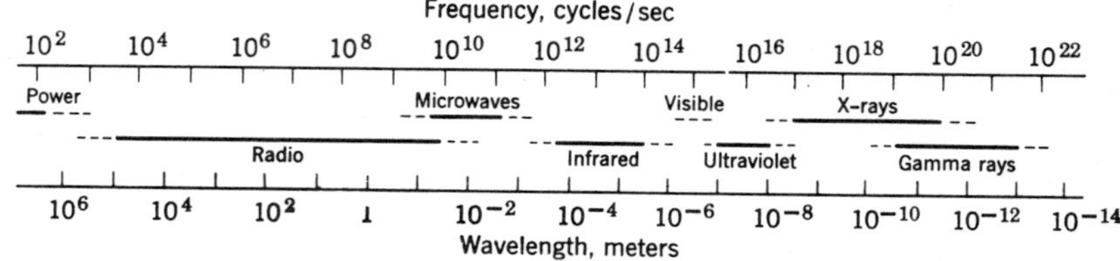

Fig. 11-3. The electromagnetic spectrum. Note that the wavelength and frequency scales are logarithmic.

waves of higher frequencies are produced by instruments called masers, by hot incandescent bodies (such as the filament in an incandescent light bulb), by atomic transitions (such as in the sodium or mercury vapor lamps). The human eye is sensitive to electromagnetic waves in the narrow range of frequencies between 4.3×10^{14} and 7.5×10^{14} cps. This is called *light*. Different frequencies of light in this range appear to our eyes as different *colors*. White light is a mixture of light of several or many frequencies in this range. So-called X-rays, and gamma rays released in some nuclear reactions, are electromagnetic waves of even higher frequency. Every electromagnetic wave in this wide spectrum of frequencies moves with the same speed in a vacuum. This speed, called the *speed of light*, is given the symbol c and has the value 2.9979×10^8 m/sec. The value 3×10^8 m/sec is sufficiently accurate for our purposes and will be used in this and the next two chapters. Many materials, including gases, will transmit electromagnetic waves of only a given range or ranges of frequencies. In many of these materials the velocity of propagation may be different for different frequencies. In no material does light move faster than in a vacuum. Figure 11-3 is a chart of the electromagnetic spectrum.

Question

11-10 The wavelength of a harmonic electromagnetic wave is defined as the distance between two adjacent "crests" in the wave at any instant. Wavelength is sometimes given the symbol λ (the Greek "lambda"). Show that an electromagnetic wave of frequency ν (Greek "nu") has a wavelength $\lambda = c/\nu$, where c is the velocity of light. What is the wavelength of a radio wave of frequency one megacycle (1 Mc)? a light wave of frequency 6×10^{14} cps? an X-ray of frequency 10^{19} cps?

Some properties of light which are important for our later study are summarized below. The careful theoretical and experimental proof of these properties belong to texts on electricity and magnetism, optics, and atomic physics.

1. *Reflection.* When electromagnetic waves fall on an object they are

transmitted through the object, absorbed by it, or reflected from it. Usually the interaction involves all three. Most materials reflect electromagnetic waves of some frequencies and absorb or transmit electromagnetic waves of other frequencies. For instance, when a "red" object is illuminated by white light, it reflects light of a range of frequencies which the eye sees as red and transmits or absorbs other frequencies within the light spectrum. In the experiments which follow we shall assume that, *when an object reflects electromagnetic waves, it does so at the same instant that the waves impinge upon it.*

2. *Travel in a straight line.* Electromagnetic waves travel in a straight line in a vacuum. Operationally this means that by using apertures it is possible to produce a *beam* or *ray* of electromagnetic radiation which will then be observed to move along a straight path. In addition to straight line travel in a vacuum, electromagnetic radiation travels in a straight line in any uniform medium such as air or water, but, in general, is bent at the interface between two different media, such as at the surface of a pond. Even in a uniform medium or a vacuum, electromagnetic waves do not travel strictly in a straight line in the presence of a gravitational field. However, the predicted departure of the path of light from a straight line at the surface of the earth due to the presence of the earth's gravitational field is so small as to be undetectable. In defining a narrow beam or ray by means of small apertures, the apertures must be somewhat larger than a wavelength of the electromagnetic wave which is to form the beam. If the aperture is smaller than a wavelength, the radiation will spread out rather than form a beam.

3. *Energy and momentum.* Energy is carried by an electromagnetic wave in small "packets" or "quanta" of magnitude $h\nu$, where ν is the frequency of the wave and h is a constant called Planck's constant, which has the value 6.624×10^{-34} joule-sec. These quanta of radiation are called *photons.* No smaller non-zero amount of energy can be emitted or absorbed at this frequency. The quantum of *momentum* carried by a single photon has the value $h\nu/c$. No smaller non-zero amount of momentum can be transferred to a particle with which the electromagnetic wave interacts.

Question

11-11 Approximately how narrow a beam of radiation can be formed at a frequency of 1 Mc/sec? at a frequency of 100 Mc/sec? at a frequency of 6×10^{14} cps?

Class Discussion Question

11-12 Up to now we have assumed that we can observe an object without disturbing its motion in the process of observation. Suppose that we are observing a very small body with light of wavelength 6000 Å. If the maximum permissible velocity change due to this process of observation is 1 mm/sec, what is the mass of the least massive object which can be observed under these circumstances? Assume that the process of observation involves the reflection of a single photon and that a single photon can be detected by the apparatus. Compare the mass of this object to the masses of the proton and the electron. Could you extend the definition of a "particle" to include many objects too small to be seen by the unaided human eye? Condense items 1 and 2 in the summary of Sec. 3.12 to a single item.

11.3 A SINGLE OBSERVER. THE RADAR WORLD. In this section we shall set up an "experiment in principle" for observing the motion of objects in two dimensions which will satisfy the operational principle even for objects which move with speeds approaching that of light. The goal of this analysis will be simply the description of the motion of these objects by a single observer. The description of this motion by two or more observers will be considered in Chapter 12. The equations of motion for these objects will be considered in Chapter 13.

Suppose we have a very large flat horizontal plane. At the center of this plane, in a position we shall take to be the origin of an inertial polar coordinate system (see Sec. 6.1), there sits a single observer. This observer has a clock next to him and also a light flasher. When the observer pushes a button on the light flasher, a flash of white light is emitted in all directions, On the plane are several objects which reflect light. It is midnight of the darkest night, so that the observer can see an object only by sending out a light flash and watching for the reflection from the object. The different objects may be distinguished from one another by the different colors they reflect.*

For the present, suppose that all the objects on the plane are at rest with respect to the observer. The observer can tell the *direction* of a given object by the direction in which he sees a reflection of the color appropriate to the object. He can tell the *distance* of the object from him (and therefore from the origin of the coordinate system) by measuring the length of time which elapses between the flashing of the light flasher and the return of the reflected flash. He calculates this distance by using the measured speed of light and *assuming* that this speed is the same in all directions. For instance, if 1 sec elapses between his flash and the return of the reflected flash, the light has traveled a total distance $D = ct = 3 \times 10^8$ m and the

* Any apparent change in the color of an object due to the Doppler shift can be allowed for when a method is devised below for measuring the velocity of the object. For the relativistic Doppler shift see Project XI at the end of Chapter 13.

object must be half this distance away, or 1.5×10^8 m. For distances much smaller than this the observer may require a photosensitive device to detect the return flash and automatic equipment to record the much smaller time interval between the sending of the flash and the return of the reflection. Such equipment is available.

Questions

11-13 How does the observer verify that any given object is stationary?

11-14 Modify the oscilloscope clock of Sec. 10.2 for use as a distance-measuring device. This clock will be connected to the flasher and to a photocell which produces an electrical signal when it detects a returning flash of light.

We have used electromagnetic pulses in the frequency range of visible light in order to stay as near as possible to the conventional meaning of the word "observe." There is no reason why electromagnetic pulses of different frequency should not be used with detectors of radiation other than the human eye. Since this general method of pulse and reflection is used in radar detection, we shall call the picture which our observer has of his surroundings the *radar world.*

Now suppose that the objects begin to move around on the plane. By using repeated flashes the observer will be able to illuminate any one object in successive positions and locate these positions in terms of direction and distance in the polar coordinate system.

Here is a crucial question: Suppose that the observer locates a given object at a certain position with a light flash. *At what time* was the object at the position determined by the observer? Since the object is observed to be moving, the observed position will change with time. The only clock in use is the clock next to the observer. The observer must thus derive the time at which the object was at the observed location by using the readings on his own clock. In measuring the distance to the object, the observer has already assumed that the speed of light is known, is constant, and is the same in all directions. Using these assumptions once more, he may surmise that the light flash takes as long to reach the object as it does to return to him from the object. (We have already assumed that the process of reflection is instantaneous.) Hence the object reflects the flash of light at a time halfway between the time the flash is emitted and the time the reflected flash is received. In other words, if the observer's clock reads t_f when the flasher is fired and t_r when the reflected flash is received, the time on his clock at which he calculates the reflection to have taken place is

$$t_f + \frac{t_r - t_f}{2}$$

In this way the observer can determine a sequence of positions for a moving object as a function of time on his clock. The velocity of the object may be defined as the vector change in position divided by the elapsed time. The acceleration may be defined as the vector change in velocity divided by the elapsed time. The limit-taking processes usually associated with the concepts of instantaneous velocity and acceleration will depend operationally on the maximum repetition rate of the flasher or on the minimum resolving time of the detector used to receive the reflected flashes.

An "experiment in principle" has been constructed which can be used to describe the motion of rapidly moving objects on a plane. The *radar world*, which consists of the observer's description of these motions, conforms to the operational principle. We shall refer to this method of observing objects as the *method of reflected flashes*.

Several cautions concerning the radar world should be expressed. In the first place, although the acceleration of an object can be measured, this does not necessarily mean that $\mathbf{F} = m\mathbf{a}$ if the object is traveling faster than one-tenth the speed of light. The laws of motion derived in the previous chapters are valid only for relative speeds less than one-tenth the speed of light. We shall see later that two observers in rapid relative motion will, in general, measure different accelerations for the same object; consequently, the equation $\mathbf{F} = m\mathbf{a}$ loses its unique meaning in its present form. In Chapter 13 we shall show how meaning may be restored by using a new formalism.

In the second place, the radar world is defined as *the picture which the observer has of his surroundings*. Thus far this picture has been derived exclusively by means of reflected flashes. Later we may wish to devise further "experiments in principle" which will widen the scope of the radar world, but the following questions cannot be answered by experiments using the present equipment and therefore cannot yet be called scientific questions.

What is *really* happening on the plane?

Where are the objects which are not at present under observation?

When an object is under observation, where is it between illuminations by the flasher?

What is the actual instantaneous velocity of the object as defined by the equation

$$\mathbf{v} = \lim_{\Delta t \to 0} \Delta\mathbf{r}/\Delta t$$

The method of reflected flashes is not the only possible way to observe objects on a plane. Another method, for instance, is simply to watch these objects visually in sunlight. Both of these methods conform to the operational principle. However, these two methods lead to different pictures of the motion of objects, as you will show in Project X. This difference is due to the finite speed of light. In setting up the radar world, the finite speed of light is allowed for in calculating positions and times. In the visually perceived "sunlight world" we assume that objects are where we see them *at the time when the light reaches us.* Since the laws of motion of a particle have a simpler form when its motion is described in the radar world, we shall devote ourselves to developing this method.

11.4 SIMULTANEITY OF EVENTS FOR A SINGLE OBSERVER. What does the observer in fact observe? He observes a returning flash of light which has been reflected from some object on the plane. Strictly speaking, it is the reflection of light by the object which is "seen" by the observer. The *event* which is seen by the observer is this reflection. More technically, an *event* is an occurrence on the plane which can be seen by the observer. A reflection of a flash of light by an object on the plane is such an event. Another event might be the emission of a light flash by one of the objects on the plane which carries its own light flasher. The job of the observer is to *locate* these events. This process of location involves not only space coordinates but also the time coordinate.

Questions

11-15 With his present procedures can the observer locate in space and time the flash of light which *originates* from one of the objects on the plane? What scientific statements *can* he make about this event?

11-16 The observer says, "By means of a reflected flash of light I have located an object 4×10^{10} cm due south which had this position 1 sec ago." Do you believe him?

11-17 The observer's description of the "location of an event" includes both position and time. What are the "locations of events" which are inaccessible to the observer at or before any given time?

11-18 Consider only events which occur along the polar axis. In the coordinate system in Fig. 11-4 the horizontal axis represents the position of an event on the polar axis. The location of the observer at the present is at the origin of this diagram. The vertical axis corresponds to time, with the present located at the origin. On the diagram, what is the locus of all possible past events occurring on the polar axis which

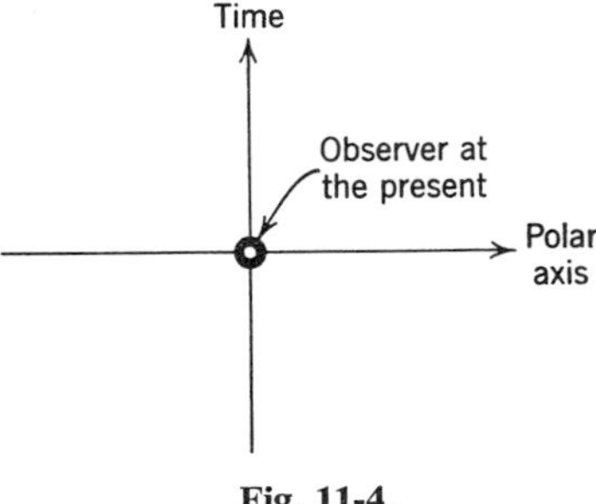

Fig. 11-4.

could have been seen by the observer before the present? What is the locus of all possible past events occurring on the polar axis which could *not* have been seen by the observer before the present?

It will be very important in our later study to be able to determine which events a given observer views as being *simultaneous*. For instance, in synchronizing two clocks it will be important to start them both simultaneously. What events will our observer take to be simultaneous?

Certainly the observer will *not* assume that if flashes emitted by two different objects reach him at the same time they were emitted simultaneously. It could be that one object was much farther away than the other and emitted its flash earlier. If, however, the observer has determined the distance to an object on the plane by the method of reflected flashes, he will have no difficulty in calculating the exact time at which this object emitted a flash using the time at which he receives this flash. *By definition*, two such events will be called simultaneous if the observer calculates that they occurred at the same time on his clock.

Questions

11-19 Show that, if the observer receives at time t_2 a flash from an observed direction but from an unknown source, the most he can say about the time t_1 and distance d_1 at which the flash was emitted is given by the equation

$$d_1 = c(t_2 - t_1)$$

11-20 Objects of different colors are placed along the polar axis at various distances from the observer. Each of these objects has a light flasher which emits light of the same color as it reflects (e.g., the red object has a red flasher, etc.). By means of the method of reflected flashes the observer determines that all the objects are at rest and he measures the distance to each one of them. The flashers of various objects are flashed in pairs, and the observer is to determine whether or not the pairs of flashes occur simultaneously. Demonstrate in detail how he could make this determination.

11-21 By the method of reflected flashes the observer determines that all the positions of an object lie along a path given by the set of equations

$$r = r_1 + v_1 t$$

$$\theta = 0$$

where r_1 has the value 10^9 m and v_1 has the value 10^7 m/sec. When the observer's clock reads 100 sec, a flash arrives from the object. At what time did the object emit the flash? What was the position of the object at that time?

11-22 In answering the last question, is it possible that the observer will have to interpolate the position of the object between two positions determined by the method of reflected flashes? Is such an interpolation justified? Is there some way that it can be avoided?

11-23 Continuing with Question 11-21, an object which the observer observes to be at rest at a distance of 10^9 m from the origin emits a flash of light which the observer receives when his clock reads 95 sec. Will the observer calculate that the flashes from the stationary object and the moving one were emitted *simultaneously*?

11-24 In Fig. 11-5 the * represents the space-time location of the emission of a flash of light on the polar axis which the observer receives at the present. The location of the observer at the present is at the origin of this diagram. Draw a curve representing the locus of all possible events (flashes or reflections) on the polar axis which the observer would say (at the present) had occurred simultaneously with the * event. Continue the curve to include all events which the observer will say (at any time in the future) occurred simultaneously with *.

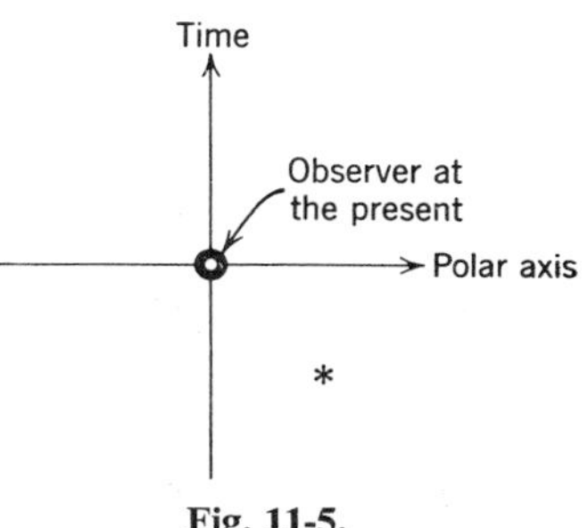

Fig. 11-5.

The poet Matthew Arnold speaks of "a darkling plane swept with confused alarms of struggle and flight, where ignorant armies clash by night."† After a first reading it may seem that our large, flat plane immersed in darkness and swarming with racing, flashing objects is in a greater uproar than Matthew Arnold's battlefield. The purposes of these sections have been to demonstrate in a simple physical situation the use of light flashes and a single clock to make observations of distant objects which may be in rapid motion, to introduce the concepts of *event* and *simultaneity* in their operational forms, and, most important of all, to condition you to think critically about every statement made by the observer to see if it can be made to conform to the operational principle. The next chapter will test every such skill you have, because the introduction of a second observer carrying a second clock and flasher will take us far from the world of common experience to the heart of the subject of relativity.

† Matthew Arnold, *Dover Beach;* see any respectable anthology of English poetry.

EXERCISES

11-1 Below are two sets of hypothetical observations taken on a single object by an observer using the method of reflected flashes. For each set:

(*a*) Plot the path of the object. Is this path a straight line?

(*b*) What is the average speed of the particle in the interval of observation?

(*c*) Does the particle accelerate during the interval of observation?

Graph paper and a compass may be useful in solving this problem.

	t_f = time of flash, in microseconds	t_r = time of return of reflection, in microseconds	θ = polar angle of returned flash, in degrees
SET I	5.53	14.47	150
	12.26	16.74	120
	15.26	19.74	60
	17.53	26.47	30
SET II	0.53	9.47	150
	17.46	21.94	120
	21.74	26.22	60
	24.53	33.47	30

11-2 An object starts from the origin of a polar coordinate system at a time $t = 0$. All its later positions as determined by the method of reflected flashes lie along the path given by the set of equations

$$r = At$$

$$\theta = \pi t_2/(t + t_1)$$

where A has the value 10^7 m/sec and t_1 has the value 1 sec. At some later time on the observer's clock a flash emitted by the object arrives at the observer from a direction $\theta = \pi/2$. When was the flash emitted? What time does the observer's clock read when he receives the flash?

chapter 12

The description of events by two observers

12.1 THE DESCRIPTION OF EVENTS BY TWO OBSERVERS AT REST. Suppose that there are two observers on our broad flat plane. Each observer has his own clock and light flasher. We shall call the two observers Mr. A and Mr. B and shall refer to the positions and equipment of these observers by the same letters (for instance, point A, clock B, etc.). For the present suppose that the two observers are at rest with respect to one another and that both verify that they are at rest with respect to an inertial reference frame.

Question

12-1 Show that the two observers, using their clocks and light flashers, can each verify that they are at rest with respect to one another if both clocks run uniformly.

Can the observers set their clocks to read the same time and adjust them to run at the same rate? Suppose that in a previous experiment using a stationary measuring rod, a mirror, and Mr. A's clock, the speed of light on a round-trip path has been measured. Suppose also that Mr. A's clock is to be taken as the standard of time.

Questions

12-2 Give a set of instructions for the measurement of the speed of light on a round-trip path using a light flasher, a stationary measuring rod, a mirror, and a clock.

12-3 Using the flasher, measuring rod, and one or more mirrors, how can you make a test to determine whether or not clock A runs *uniformly*?

In defining uniformity operationally in this case, what is your standard of uniformity? Can you design a clock made of a measuring rod and two mirrors?

Now Mr. A measures the distance d to Mr. B, using the method of reflected flashes. He then telegraphs the information about this distance d to Mr. B together with the information that at some prearranged time, say ten o'clock, he will emit a flash of light, which we shall call the *synchronizing flash*. Mr. B prepares for the synchronizing flash by stopping his clock and setting it for ten o'clock plus d/c seconds. When Mr. B observes the synchronizing flash, he starts his clock. The two clocks are now said to be *synchronized*.

Of course, this is not the only way that synchronization of clocks can be defined. One might think, for instance, that if Mr. A originally had two clocks, verified that they ran at the same rate while they were together at his position, and then had the second clock carried to Mr. B the two clocks would still be synchronized. Indeed, we could *define* synchronization of clocks in this way if we chose. Notice, however, that this definition makes use of a clock in motion relative to A during its transfer from Mr. A to Mr. B. We have not yet compared observations of clocks in relative motion. When we do so in Sec. 12.4, we shall see that this definition of synchronization will not give the same result as the one given above for stationary clocks. The definition using clocks relatively at rest and a synchronizing flash is adopted because it will lead later to a simpler description of the motion of particles.

Questions

12-4 Devise an operational method for adjusting Mr. B's clock to run at the same rate as Mr. A's clock.

12-5 After Mr. B's clock has been adjusted to run at the same rate as Mr. A's clock, show that Mr. B will agree with Mr. A on the distance between them.

12-6 Suppose that Mr. A emits a light flash at ten o'clock and at every second thereafter. If Mr. B is satisfied to time other events with an accuracy of plus or minus 1 sec, show how he can use the flashes from Mr. A and a simple counter to tell time as long as he remains stationary at a known distance from Mr. A.

12-7 Show that the synchronizing procedure outlined above will allow any number of clocks which are stationary with respect to Mr. A at any point on the plane to be synchronized to read the same time as Mr. A's clock.

12-8 Define the phrase "same time" in the last question in such a way as to satisfy the operational principle.

12-9 Demonstrate that, once their clocks are synchronized and running at the same rate, Mr. *A* and Mr. *B* will agree on the round-trip average speed of light.

Class Discussion Question

12-10 Show that, if the two synchronized clocks at *A* and *B* are used to measure the speed of light on a one-way path between them, the results would not show any difference in this speed between the two directions *A* to *B* and *B* to *A* even if this difference existed.

Suppose that by agreement between the observers the position of Mr. *A* is taken to be the origin of a polar coordinate system and the direction from *A* to *B* is taken as the direction of the polar axis as shown in Fig. 12-1. If both Mr. *A* and Mr. *B* observe another stationary object by the method of reflected flashes, will they agree on its coordinates in this polar coordinate system? Mr. *B*, of course, will have to measure the direction and distance of the object from his position and then use some kind of geometry to deduce the direction and distance of the object from *A*. The direction and distance of the object from *A* are by definition the polar coordinates of the object. What kind of geometry must Mr. *B* use in order to predict correctly the direction and distance of the object which will be measured by Mr. *A*? This can be determined only by experiment. Experiment shows that if Mr. *A* and Mr. *B* are at rest with respect to one another, Mr. *B* must use *plane Euclidean geometry* in order to predict correctly the direction and distance at which Mr. *A* will observe the object.

Questions

12-11 Using the preceding result, show by symmetry arguments that if Mr. *A* and Mr. *B* are to agree on the coordinates of objects in *three* dimensions, Mr. *B* must use *solid* Euclidean geometry to transform his observations in order to predict correctly the observations of Mr. *A*.

12-12 Mr. *B* is at a distance of 100 m from Mr. *A* along the polar axis. Mr. *B* sends out a flash and receives a blue reflection after an interval of 6 μsec at an angle of 90 degrees from the polar axis. What are the polar coordinates of the blue object?

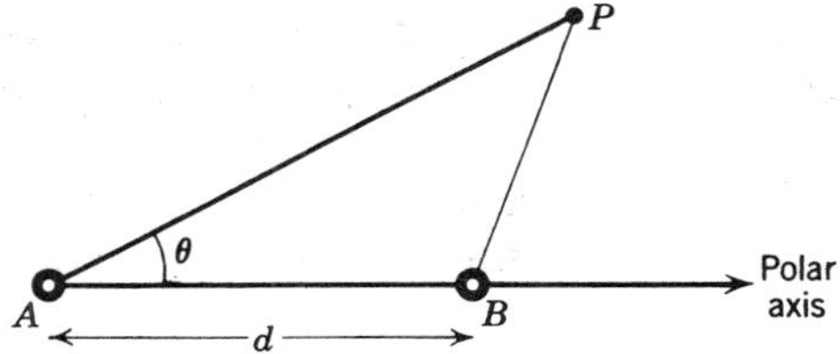

Fig. 12-1. Location of a stationary object *P* by two observers relatively at rest.

Now suppose that Mr. A and Mr. B agree on the coordinates of a stationary object. If this object emits a flash of light, will the two observers be able to agree on the *time* at which the flash was emitted? Since they can agree on the *coordinates* of the object, they must be able to calculate the distance of the object from each one of them. These calculations must agree, because if they did not Mr. A and Mr. B would not have been able to agree on the coordinates of the object. Since the speed of light measured by each of them has the same value, the time taken for the flash to reach either one of them must be agreed upon as well. Since their two clocks are synchronized, the time the flash was emitted will be agreed upon by the two observers.

Since the two observers can agree on the time an event occurred (if they know the spatial coordinates of the event), they will be able to agree whether or not two events are *simultaneous* even if these two events do not occur at the same place.

Questions

12-13 Mr. A and Mr. B agree that two objects are stationary at the following polar coordinates: red at $r = 300$ m, $\theta = 90°$, and green at $r = 400$ m, $\theta = -90°$. Mr. B is located 300 m from Mr. A along the polar axis. Mr. B receives flashes from these two objects in the sequence green-red separated by a time interval of 0.1 μsec. Will Mr. B determine that the flashes were emitted simultaneously? What time interval will separate the flashes at A?

12-14 Show that it follows from the foregoing that, if any number of additional observers are placed about the plane at rest with respect to Mr. A, their clocks can be synchronized with respect to Mr. A's clock and that after this is done every clock will be synchronized with every other clock. Show also that every one of these observers will be able to agree on the coordinates of a given stationary object as calculated by using the method of reflected flashes and on the time a given event occurs if the spatial coordinates of the event are known. Finally, show that two events which appear to be simultaneous for one of these observers will be simultaneous for all of these observers.

12-15 Use the results of the previous question, suppose that no point on the plane is a distance greater than d from the nearest observer, and suppose that the position of an event is known only by the position of the observer nearest to that event. Show that under these circumstances the uncertainty in the time of occurrence of any event will be equal to or less than d/c. Can you set up a satisfactory definition of *simultaneous* under these circumstances?

The description of motion of a moving object consists in locating the positions of the object at given times. From these determinations an observer can calculate the vector velocity and acceleration of the object during any time interval. Since Messrs *A* and *B* can agree on the coordinates of an object at any time, they will agree on the series of positions which the object occupies as a function of time. Therefore they will agree on the vector velocity and acceleration of the object. Thus their descriptions of the motion of an object will agree.

In summary, two or more observers who are stationary with respect to one another can agree on the following:

that they are at rest with respect to one another;
the distance between them;
what time it is;
the coordinates of another stationary object;
the time of an event (if its coordinates are known);
whether or not two events are simultaneous (if their coordinates are known);
the position, vector velocity, and vector acceleration of a moving object as functions of time.

These statements may be summarized by saying that *observers A and B, who are at rest with respect to one another, can agree on the radar world of either of them.*

12.2 ASSUMPTIONS CONCERNING TWO OBSERVERS IN UNIFORM RELATIVE MOTION. In this section we shall begin to analyze the case of two observers in uniform relative motion by considering the assumptions to be used in this analysis. We shall consider only observers who are at rest with respect to inertial reference frames (which themselves may be in uniform relative motion). For this reason the properties which all inertial reference frames have in common will form an important part of the assumptions. An observer who is at rest with respect to an inertial reference frame will be called an *inertial observer.*

Try to see the physical basis for each of the following assumptions, and make sure you understand what each assumption does *not* say.

1. *Assumption generalized from experiment.* The laws of physics are the same in every inertial reference frame. No law of physics can be used to distinguish between inertial reference frames.

   a. The average speed of light on a go-and-return path will be the same when measured in any inertial reference frame and will not depend on the state of motion of the light source. No contradiction results from assuming that this speed is the same in all directions.

b. In a *field-free* inertial reference frame no experiment can be devised which will indicate a unique or preferred *direction* with respect to that frame. We shall consider only experiments which are described with respect to such field-free inertial reference frames.

2. Two events which occur at the same place and are observed to occur simultaneously by one observer will be observed to occur simultaneously by every observer.

3. In the experiments which follow, observers will be assumed to interact only by means of light flashes and to leave each other otherwise unaffected by their presence. Forces on observers and other objects due to the light flashes will be assumed to alter their motion by only negligible amounts.

4. We shall consider only experiments in which the physical properties of measuring devices when observed in a reference frame in which they are at rest do not depend on the past history of these measuring devices.

We have already used result 1a in constructing the radar world and in demonstrating what two observers can agree upon if they are at rest with respect to one another. Assumption 1 does *not* say that two inertial observers in relative motion will measure the same electric or magnetic or gravitational fields in a given region or that they will agree about the distance between two events or the time between these two events. What it does say is, for example, that the motion of particles as seen from the two systems will obey laws which are the same in the two systems. Phenomena occurring in a closed system are independent of any uniform motion of the system as a whole.

The phrase "*field-free* inertial reference frame" in 1b needs to be explained. By a field-free frame we mean one in which there are no static electric or magnetic fields and no detectable gravitational fields. We have seen (Question 5-30) that a uniform gravitational field cannot be detected in an inertial reference frame which is in "free fall" in the gravitational field. Such a reference frame is "field-free" if there are no static electric or magnetic fields in it.

It was shown in Chapter 10 that two observers in uniform relative motion may not be able to agree about whether or not two given events occur simultaneously. Assumption 2 deals with one case in which all such observers *can* agree that two events are simultaneous. If two events occur closely enough to one another in space, then communication between the positions of the two events by means of light flashes can take place in an arbitrarily short time. For sufficiently small separations there will be no ambiguity about whether or not the two events took place simultaneously. Since communication under these circumstances is essentially instantaneous, the agreement on simultaneity is the same as in the classical limit of low velocities. Light flashes originating from two events which occur at the same place and simultaneously when seen at that place will arrive simultaneously at every observer, no matter how distant he is from the point of occurrence or how fast he is moving with respect to other observers. Hence all observers will agree on the simultaneity of two events which occur at the same place.

Assumption 3 assures that the motion of particles and observers is not changed by the process of observing them. For elementary particles such as protons or electrons the truth of this assumption cannot be taken for granted. See Sec. 11–2.

We are trying to show how the relative motion of an observer influences his description of events and objects. Assumption 4 is an attempt to limit consideration to effects of relative motion only, rather than effects of past history.

Up to now all observers have been at rest with respect to our "broad flat plane." One might conclude that in what follows any observer can check to see if he is in motion with respect to the plane merely by dragging a finger on the ground. This is not to be permitted. Only *relative* motion can be detected. Therefore you may wish to think of the plane as a geometrical construct in interstellar space, so that the phrase "the velocity of a particle with respect to the plane" will have no operational meaning.

Using the results of the last section and the assumptions of this section, we shall now carry out a series of "thought experiments" which will demonstrate how two observers in uniform relative motion describe a common occurrence. Since we shall be able to deduce the results of these experiments without actually carrying them out, these results will be derived rather than dependent on further experiments for their derivation. The fact that further experiments support these results increases our confidence in the assumptions we have made.

12.3 AGREEMENT OF TWO OBSERVERS ON THEIR RELATIVE VELOCITY AND ON DISTANCES PERPENDICULAR TO THE DIRECTION OF RELATIVE MOTION. Suppose that two identical observers A and D are each in a field-free inertial reference frame but that A and D are approaching each other (see Fig. 12-2). Each observer uses the same standard of length (derived, for instance, from the wavelength of the orange-red line from a krypton 86 sample at rest in his frame; see Sec. 2.5) and the same standard of time (derived, for instance, from the time it takes a flash of light to make a round trip between two parallel mirrors stationary in his frame and located a prescribed distance apart). Assumption 1 postulates that these standards are the same for both observers.

Now suppose that by the method of reflected flashes A determines that D is approaching him with uniform velocity $\mathbf{v}$ along a straight line collision course. Now D will observe A approaching him too. The question is this: If D measures the velocity and direction of A's approach, will he observe A approaching him along a straight line collision course, and will his measure of the magnitude of the relative velocity agree with A's measure of the magnitude of the relative velocity?

First of all, consider the direction of approach of A as seen by D. D *must* see A approaching along a straight line collision course. Suppose that he did not; this would imply some lack of symmetry with respect to the line AD in the reference frame of D introduced by either the uniqueness of some particular direction in space or by some asymmetry in the past histories of A or D. The first possibility is excluded by Assumption 1b, and the second possibility is excluded by Assumption 4. Hence, if A sees that D is approaching on a straight line collision course, D will see A approaching on a straight line collision course.

Fig. 12-2. Radar world of A.

Now D will also agree with A on the magnitude of the relative velocity, because of the symmetry between A and D. The two observers are identical, their past pistories will not affect the result (Assumption 4), and the directions in the inertial reference frame of each of them are equivalent. In fact, there would be no way to distinguish this situation from the one in which the labels A and D were interchanged. Hence the two must agree on the magnitude of the relative velocity.

We shall set up a coordinate system for our next thought experiment (see Fig. 12-3). A is at rest at the origin of this inertial coordinate system. A observes D approaching him with velocity $\mathbf{v}$ down the x-axis. Observer B is at rest a distance y_0 up the y-axis from A. B sees E approaching *him* with the same velocity $\mathbf{v}$ along a line which is parallel to the x-axis. D sees E in a direction perpendicular to the x-axis and at rest with respect to him. From these conditions and the previous results and assumptions it follows that:

1. The presence of B and E will not influence the descriptions which A and D have of each other's motion. Similarly the presence of A and D will not influence the description which E and B have of each other's motion (Assumption 3).

2. From 1 and the results of the previous experiment, it follows that A and D will be able to agree on the magnitude of their relative velocity and the line along which it lies. The same holds for agreement between E and B on the magnitude of their relative velocity and the line along which it lies.

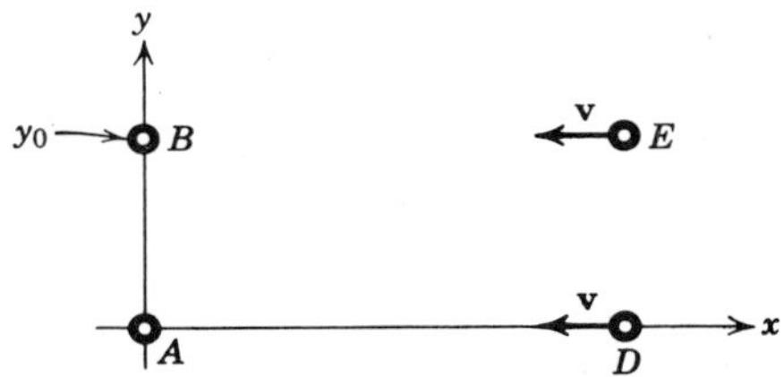

Fig. 12-3. Radar world of A and B.

3. Since A and B are at rest with respect to one another and therefore can agree on the velocity of any other object in the plane (Sec. 12.1), A will agree with B that E is approaching B with velocity $\mathbf{v}$ along a line parallel to the x-axis and B will agree with A that D is approaching A along the x-axis with a velocity $\mathbf{v}$.

4. It follows from 2 and 3 that A and E can agree on *their* relative velocities and the lines along which these velocities lie. The same holds for agreement between B and D on their relative velocities. In other words, two observers in uniform relative motion can agree on the magnitude of the relative velocity between them and the lines along which these velocities lie *even if these velocities are not collinear*.

5. A and B will agree that the perpendicular distance between the paths of E and D is y_0.

6. By symmetry arguments similar to those of the last experiment, D and E will also agree that the distance between them is y_0.

Question

12-16 Demonstrate the result 5 and present the symmetry arguments of step 6.

The result of step 6 is an important one. It means that A, B, C, and D all agree on the distance y_0 between D and E which is perpendicular to the direction of relative motion of the observers. If a measuring rod of length y_0 were laid between D and E, all four observers would agree on the length of this measuring rod. The result is that *inertial observers in uniform relative motion will agree on the results of measurement of distances perpendicular to the direction of their relative motion.*

Question

12-17 Show that D and E would agree with A and B that the distance between A and B is also y_0.

The results derived so far in this chapter do not seem very surprising. In essence, they are the same results found in classical mechanics but more rigorously derived. The surprises begin now.

12.4 DILATION OF TIME. PROPER TIME. Now we can derive, with a single thought experiment, two of the most important results of the theory of relativity. Observers A and B have verified that they are at rest with respect to each other, this time they have chosen the direction of the x-axis to lie from A to B, and they have synchronized their clocks by the method outlined in Sec. 12.1. (See Fig. 12-4.) Now A and B see D and E moving toward them in a negative x-direction, with D coming down the x-axis with velocity $\mathbf{v}$ and E moving along a parallel path a perpendicular distance y_0 away also with velocity $\mathbf{v}$ (see Fig. 12-4). From the results of our previous thought experiment, all four observers agree that the perpendicular distance between the paths of D and E is y_0.

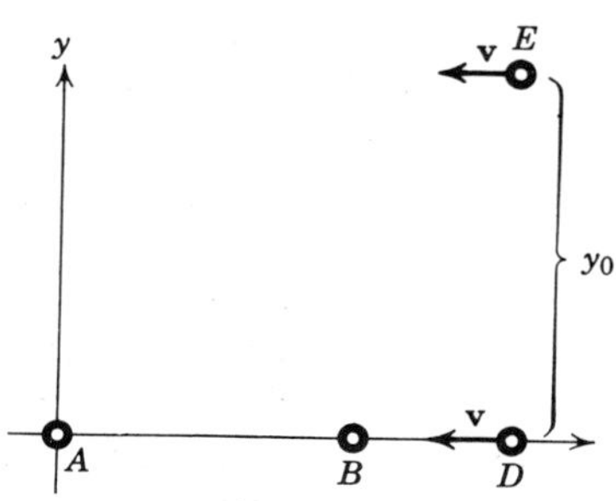

Fig. 12-4. Radar world of A and B.

Now the thought experiment will proceed as follows: When D and B coincide, there is emitted from that point a flash which is reflected from E. The distance between A and B is adjusted by trial and error so that when D and A coincide they both receive the reflected flash from E. Both D and B will agree that the flash is emitted simultaneously with their coincidence because these two events (the coincidence and the emission of the flash) occur at the same place (Assumption 2). Similarly both D and A will agree that the flash returns to them from E simultaneously with *their* coincidence. In other words, we have two sets of simultaneous events which all four observers agree are simultaneous.

Question

12-18 Show that A will agree with D and B on the simultaneity of the emission of the flash and the coincidence of D and B. Show that B will agree with D and A on the simultaneity of the coincidence of D and A and the arrival at that point of the flash reflected from E.

Our problem will be to calculate the value of the time interval in the two systems between the coincidence of B and D (and the emission of the flash) and the coincidence of A and D (and the arrival there of the flash reflected from E). We shall find that this time interval is different when measured in the two systems and that this difference can be traced directly to the fact that the speed of light is the same for the two sets of observers.

First let us look at the experiment as seen by D, shown in Fig. 12-5. He sees A and B approaching him with speed v. When B reaches him, a

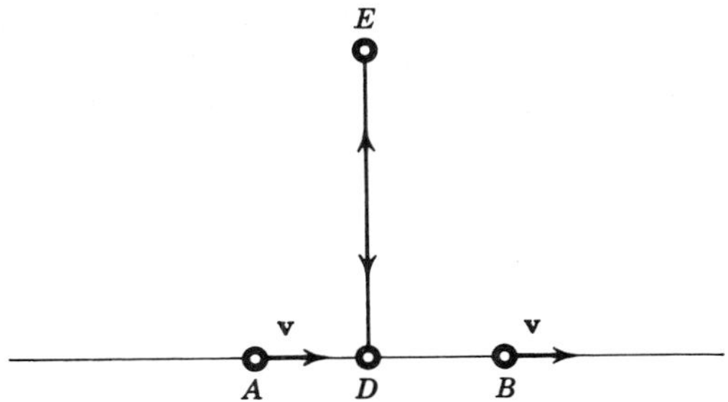

Fig. 12-5. View of path of light flash as seen by D and E.

flash of light is emitted which travels along the straight line from D to E and then is reflected back again along the same straight line, reaching D at the same time A reaches him. The elapsed time between the two events is simply twice the distance between D and E divided by the speed of light c. We shall call this time interval $\Delta\tau$. The reason for distinguishing this time by the Greek letter tau will become apparent below.

$$\Delta\tau = \frac{2y_0}{c}$$

or, solving for y_0,

$$y_0 = \frac{c\,\Delta\tau}{2} \tag{12-1}$$

The picture which A and B have of the experiment is a little more complicated. To them that part of the light front which is to be reflected from E will travel along a path inclined from the vertical, and the return of the reflected flash from E to A will be inclined from the vertical in the other direction (see Fig. 12-6). If A and B have previously synchronized their clocks, they can time the interval Δt which it takes for D to travel from B to A. Since they see D moving with a speed v, the distance from

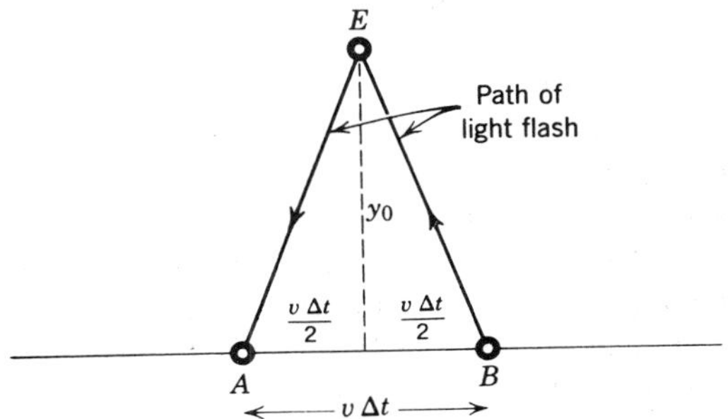

Fig. 12-6. View of path of light flash as seen by A and B.

A to B must have the value $v\,\Delta t$. Using the Pythagorean theorem, they can calculate the total distance which the light flash has traveled between the two events. This distance must be equal to $c\,\Delta t$.

$$c\,\Delta t = 2\sqrt{(v\,\Delta t/2)^2 + y_0{}^2} \tag{12-2}$$

The solution of this equation for y_0 gives

$$y_0 = (c\,\Delta t/2)\sqrt{1 - v^2/c^2} \tag{12-3}$$

Question

12-19 Carry out the steps between Eqs. (12-2) and (12-3).

Remember that A, B, D, and E all agree that the distance y_0 between D and E has one and the same value. Hence we can equate the expressions for y_0 in Eqs. (12-1) and (12-3).

$$c\,\Delta\tau/2 = (c\,\Delta t/2)\sqrt{1 - v^2/c^2}$$

or, more simply,

$$\Delta\tau = \Delta t\sqrt{1 - v^2/c^2} \tag{12-4}$$

This is a remarkable result. Equation (12-4) says that the interval of time between the coincidence of B and D and the coincidence of A and D will be shorter as measured on a clock traveling with D than it will be as measured on clocks traveling with A and B. This difference has nothing to do with differences in the clocks of A and D. At the beginning of Sec. 12.3 we postulated that these clocks are identical. By looking at the derivation, it is easy to see that the reason for the difference in the time interval measured in the two frames is that between the two coincidences the light path as seen in the frame of D is shorter than the light path as seen in the frame of A and B. Since the velocity of light is the same when measured in each reference frame, this means that the time interval between the coincidences cannot be the same when measured in the two frames.

One thing should be made perfectly clear: Although the time interval as measured in the two frames is different, *there is no disagreement about the reading of clocks in the different frames when these clocks are in coincidence.* When D and B are in coincidence, they can record the readings on each other's clocks without ambiguity and both will agree on the readings of both clocks. The same can be done between the clocks of D and A when they coincide. Observer D will agree that the difference between the reading on clock B when he passes it and the reading on clock A when he passes it has the value Δt. Similarly the difference between the reading which B takes of clock D at their coincidence and the reading which A takes of clock D at their coincidence will have the value $\Delta\tau$. Hence, although there is a difference in the time interval as measured in the two frames, this difference is not based on any disagreement about the actual readings on clocks.

It will be useful later on to use what is called the *proper time* (sometimes called the *local* time). The proper time between two events is defined as the time between these events as measured in an inertial reference frame in which the two events occur at the same place. In the thought experiment above, observer D sees his coincidence with B and with A occurring at the same place. Therefore the interval $\Delta\tau$ is the proper time interval between these two events. We shall use the Greek letter τ ("tau") to refer to proper times or time intervals. If two events occur at the same place in a given inertial reference frame, the two events will be said to be *proper in that frame*, and the inertial reference frame in which two events occur at the same place will be called the *proper frame* with respect to the two events. Finally a *proper clock* is a clock which is at rest in the proper frame with respect to two events.

Equation (12-4) can be used to calculate the proper time between two events if the distance between the two events and the time between them is known, as measured in any inertial reference frame. The calculation is done by finding the uniform velocity of a second inertial reference frame in which the two events would occur at the same place and substituting that velocity into Eq. (12-4).

Questions

12-20 In a particular inertial reference frame two events occur a distance 12×10^8 m apart and are separated by a time interval of 5 sec. What is the proper time interval between the two events?

12-21 In a particular inertial reference frame two events occur a distance 6×10^8 m apart and are separated by a time interval of 2 sec. What is the proper time interval between these two events?

12-22 In a particular inertial reference frame two events occur a distance 6×10^8 m apart and are separated by a time interval of 1 sec. What is the proper time interval between these two events? Be careful.

12-23 What is the relationship between two events if the proper time interval between them cannot be defined? Show that a proper time interval can always be defined for events which coincide with consecutive positions of a moving particle.

12-24 The statement is sometimes made that "The proper clock runs slower than any other clock." Explain what this means, and discuss the conditions under which it is true.

The circumstance that A and B measure a different time interval between the two events than D and E measure is often referred to as the *dilation of time*. To dilate means to stretch. This does not mean that a given inertial observer can stretch time as measured on clocks which are at rest in his own reference frame. The dilation of time refers to the difference in the time interval between two events as measured on *different* clocks which are in uniform relative motion with respect to one another.

We have shown that clock D appears to run slow as seen by A and B. One might criticize this conclusion by making the statement that, if the relations between the two coordinate systems are symmetrical, clocks A and B should appear to run slow as seen by D—*and in fact this statement is correct*. The lack of symmetry in the results of the present experiment is due to the fact that observers A and B both compare their measured time intervals with readings on the *same clock* D as it passes, whereas observer D compares his measured time intervals with readings on *different clocks* A and B as they pass in turn. The apparent paradox will be resolved in Sec. 12.6, where it will be shown that D observes clocks A and B to be out of synchronism with each other in his frame.

Question

12-25 In a given sample of μ mesons (elementary particles produced in some nuclear reactions), half will decay to other elementary particles in 1.5 μsec measured with respect to a reference frame in which the μ mesons are at rest. Half of the remainder will decay in the next 1.5 μsec, and so on. Consider μ mesons produced by the collision of cosmic rays with gas nuclei in the atmosphere at a height of 30 km above the surface of the earth. If the μ mesons move vertically downward with a velocity nearly that of light, approximately how long will it take them to reach the earth as measured by an observer at rest on the surface of the earth? If there were no time dilation, approximately what fraction of the μ mesons produced at a height of 30 km would remain undecayed by the time they reached the earth? If it is determined experimentally that one-eighth of the initial number have not decayed at the surface of the earth, what is the vertical velocity of the μ mesons with respect to the surface of the earth? Assume that they all move with the same velocity. This very striking effect was used as an early proof of time dilation.

12.5 LORENTZ CONTRACTION. PROPER LENGTH. Another important result can be derived from the previous thought experiment with little extra work. A and B on the one hand and D on the other hand agree about their relative speed v. Now D observes B and A to go past him in turn with this speed. He measures a time interval $\Delta\tau$ between the time B

passes him and the time A passes him. From these two pieces of information he concludes that the distance Δx between A and B must be given by the formula

$$v = \frac{\Delta x}{\Delta \tau}$$

On the other hand, B and A observe D to go past each of them in turn with speed v. They, however, measure the time which D takes to go from B to A to have the value Δt. Hence they conclude that the distance Δx_0 between them is given by the formula

$$v = \frac{\Delta x_0}{\Delta t}$$

Equating the two expressions for v and using Eq. (12-4), we have

$$\frac{\Delta x_0}{\Delta t} = \frac{\Delta x}{\Delta \tau} = \frac{\Delta x}{\Delta t \sqrt{1 - v^2/c^2}}$$

The Δt cancels from both sides and we have

$$\Delta x = \Delta x_0 \sqrt{1 - v^2/c^2} \tag{12-5}$$

This equation says that the distance between A and B as measured by them is *longer* than the distance between them as measured by D. If a meter stick were laid between A and B and at rest with respect to them, then as this meter stick moved past observer D it would appear in the radar world of D to be shorter than a meter stick which is stationary with respect to him. This apparent foreshortening of distances in the direction of relative motion is called the *Lorentz contraction*. We have already shown that distances *perpendicular* to the direction of relative motion appear to be the same in the radar worlds of observers in the two frames.

The value of the length of a measuring rod as measured in an inertial reference frame in which it is at rest is called the *proper length*. There is no ambiguity about such a measurement because the measurement is carried out on an object which is at rest in that reference frame and thus under conditions which satisfy the assumptions of classical mechanics. In the previous thought experiment the proper length between A and B is the length Δx_0 measured by them. We shall use the subscript zero to indicate lengths which are proper lengths. Notice that in the previous experiment the proper length is measured in a reference frame different from that in which the proper time is measured.

Question

12-26 Explain the following statement and discuss the conditions under which it is true. "The proper length of a rod is longer than any other length of that rod."

The use of the symbol Δ which prefixes x and t in the last two sections should not be taken to mean that these quantities are necessarily small. By letting y_0 and Δx_0 get smaller proportionally, both Δx and $\Delta\tau$ can indeed be made as small as desired. On the other hand, by letting y_0 and Δx_0 get larger proportionally, the values of Δx and $\Delta\tau$ can be made as large as desired. The only caution which must be observed is that y_0 and Δx_0 be kept in such a proportion that the flash reflected from E will return to D just as D coincides with A.

Class Discussion Question

12-27 Consider the situation pictured in Fig. 12-7. The relative positions and motions of observers A, B, D, and E are as in Fig. 12-6, but the origin of the coordinate system has been shifted to observer C. Observer C is at rest with respect to A and B, while observer F is at rest with respect to D and E. The coordinates y_A and x_A can have any constant value. Clocks A, B, and C are synchronized to each other in the reference frame in which they are at rest, and clocks D and F are synchronized in the reference frame in which they are at rest. Show that observer F will observe the same proper time interval as observer D between the coincidence of D and B and the coincidence of D and A. Show that observer C will observe the same time interval between these coincidences as observer A. Show that observer C will agree with observers A and B on the proper length of a rod laid at rest between A and B. Show that observer F will agree with observer D on the Lorentz-contracted length of this rod. You have shown that *the time interval between events and the observed lengths of rods in the radar worlds of observers in uniform relative motion depends only on the relative positions of these events and rods and on the direction of relative motion of the coordinate systems of these observers, and not on the choice of the origins of these coordinate systems.*

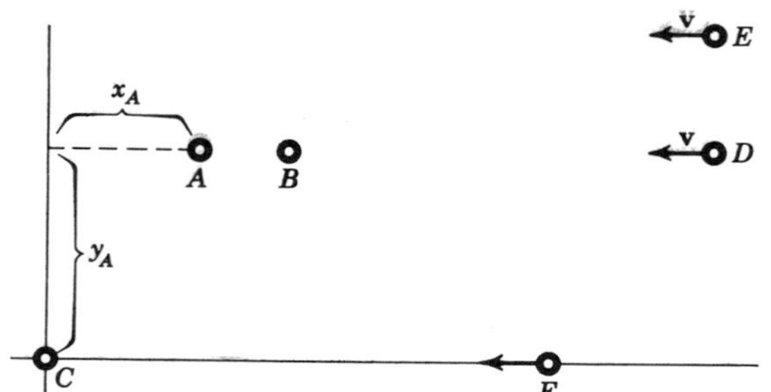

Fig. 12-7. Radar world of A, B, and C; used to demonstrate that time dilation and Lorentz contraction are independent of x- and y-coordinates of events and measuring rods.

Fig. 12-8. Radar world of A, B, and C.

12.6 THE RELATIVITY OF SIMULTANEITY AND THE RELATIVE SYNCHRONIZATION OF CLOCKS. In this section we shall analyze more formally a thought experiment similar to that of the lightning bolts striking both ends of a moving train first discussed in Sec. 10.3. We shall see again that observers who are in uniform relative motion will not always be able to agree on which events are simultaneous if these events occur at different places. By studying this disagreement more carefully, we shall show that it results in a disagreement about the synchronization of clocks.

Suppose that observers A, B, and C are equally spaced along a line and are all at rest with respect to one another in an inertial frame as in Fig. 12-8. The distance between A and B and the distance between B and C have both been measured to be equal to x_0, and the clocks of all three observers have been synchronized to read the same time in their coordinate system. Now suppose that observer D approaches the three stationary observers with velocity $\mathbf{v}$ along the line on which they lie. Things have been so arranged that D will coincide with B at exactly twelve noon on clock B. Observers A and C will agree that D coincided with B at twelve noon on their clocks. By prearrangement, A and C each emit a flash at exactly twelve noon on their clocks. (These correspond to the lightning bolts of Sec. 10.3.) Because B lies halfway between A and C, the flash of light from each of them will arrive at B simultaneously. Will these two flashes arrive at D simultaneously? No, because D will have moved past B toward A before he sees the flash from A. This flash from A must pass D *before* it arrives at B. Similarly, the flash from C must arrive at D *after* it passes B. Since the two flashes arrive at B simultaneously as seen from all frames (since the arrivals occur at the same place), they cannot arrive simultaneously at D.

Now what does D observe? First of all, as he approaches B he can be plotting the positions of A and C by the method of reflected flashes. When he coincides with B, he will predict that A and C are equidistant from him. However, we know from the previous section that D will measure the distance from A to C to be equal to $2x_0\sqrt{1 - v^2/c^2}$. Hence when D coincides with B he predicts that both A and C are a distance $x_0\sqrt{1 - v^2/c^2}$ away. Observer D reasons that, if A and C were to emit their flashes of light simultaneously at the instant when he coincides with B, these two flashes should arrive at his position simultaneously, since they would start at points equidistant from him. Since these two flashes do *not* arrive at his position simultaneously, *D concludes that the flashes were not emitted simultaneously from A and C.* Now, observers A and C maintain that their clocks read the same time (twelve noon) when the flashes were emitted. Observers who are at rest with respect to D but who were near A and C at the time the flashes were emitted will verify that both clocks A and C read twelve noon when the flashes were emitted. Therefore the only conclusion open to D is that the clocks at A and C were not synchronized with that at B.

The situation, then, is that observer B measures the clocks at A and C to be synchronized with his own and he sees the emission of the flashes from A and C take place simultaneously. On the other hand, observer D does not observe that the flashes from A and C are emitted simultaneously and concludes from this and other evidence that the clocks at A and C cannot be synchronized with the clock at B. Notice again that there is no disagreement about the reading on any clock. D can read the clock at B when he coincides with it, and other observers at rest with respect to D can verify that the clocks at A and C read twelve noon when the flashes are emitted.

Let us look more closely at the lack of synchronism which D observes between clocks A and B. We shall use primes on the time symbols to represent times measured on clocks A, B, and C, and no primes on the time symbols to represent times measured on clock D. Let all times be measured with respect to twelve noon and let D set his clock to twelve noon as he passes B. Then, if t_e' represents the time at which A emits the flash as measured on clock A, we have $t_e' = 0$ since the emission occurs at twelve noon on this clock. What we wish to find is the time t_e at which D surmises the flash must have been emitted from A. The value of t_e will be equal to the lack of synchronism which D sees between clocks A and B.

First of all, when will the flash emitted by A arrive at D? If we call this time t_1' as measured on clock A or B, then the distance vt_1' traveled by D in this time plus the distance ct_1' traveled by the flash of light in this time must add up to the distance between A and B.

$$vt_1' + ct_1' = x_0 \quad \text{or} \quad t_1' = \frac{x_0}{c + v}$$

The time interval between the coincidence of B and D and the reception of the flash at D is a proper time interval to D because both events occur at the same place in his reference frame. Hence A and B can use Eq. (12-4) to predict correctly the time t_1 which clock D will read when the flash is received by D.

$$t_1 = t_1'\sqrt{1 - v^2/c^2} = x_0 \frac{\sqrt{1 - v^2/c^2}}{c + v} \tag{12-6}$$

Now let us go back a bit in time. As D passes B, he predicts that A is a distance $x_0\sqrt{1 - v^2/c^2}$ away from him. Since t equals zero at this instant by definition and since D sees A approaching with speed v, observer D will say that the distance of A from him as a function of time is given by the expression $x_0\sqrt{1 - v^2/c^2} - vt$. Now D asks himself, "How far away was A when he emitted the flash?" Since D receives the flash at a time t_1, the expression for the distance of the flash front from him must have been $c(t_1 - t)$ At the instant at which the flash was emitted, the distance of A from D was equal to the distance of the flash front from D Call this time t_e. Then, equating the two expressions above, we have

$$x_0\sqrt{1 - v^2/c^2} - vt_e = c(t_1 - t_e)$$

Solve for t_e.

$$t_e = \frac{t_1 - (x_0/c)\sqrt{1 - v^2/c^2}}{(1 - v/c)}$$

Now substitute for t_1 from Eq. (12-6) and simplify.

$$t_e = \frac{x_0}{c}\sqrt{1 - v^2/c^2}\left[\frac{1}{1 - v^2/c^2} - \frac{1}{1 - v/c}\right]$$

$$= \frac{x_0}{c}\sqrt{1 - v^2/c^2}\left[\frac{-v/c}{1 - v^2/c^2}\right]$$

$$t_e = \frac{-x_0 v/c^2}{\sqrt{1 - v^2/c^2}} \qquad (12\text{-}7)$$

This is the lack of synchronism between clocks A and B according to the calculations of D. Notice that x_0 is the proper distance between A and B, i.e., the distance measured in the frame in which they are at rest. The minus sign means that D thinks the flash was emitted from A *before* the coincidence of D with B, i.e., *before* $t = 0$. Since observer A stoutly maintains that he emitted the flash at twelve noon exactly, observer D must conclude sadly that the clock carried by A is set too fast (i.e., set ahead) by an amount t_e compared to clock B.

Questions

12-28 Show by a similar derivation that D sees the clock at C to be set too slow (i.e., set back) by a time equal in magnitude to the same t_e when compared to clock B.

12-29 According to D, how far away from him was A when the flash was emitted from A? According to D, how far away from him was C when the flash was emitted from C?

12-30 Demonstrate that D will see all clocks which are moving with A and are on a line through A perpendicular to the x-axis to be out of synchronism with B by the same amount. Show that D and B will agree on the simultaneity of events which take place along a line perpendicular to their relative velocity vector.

Since the previous thought experiment could be carried out for a series of clocks which are at rest with respect to B and synchronized in the frame of B but different proper distances away, we conclude that D would observe those clocks farther ahead of him to be set farther ahead of clock B, and those clocks farther behind him to be set farther back with respect to clock B, all by an amount given by Eq. (12-7) with a change of sign for those behind.

Notice carefully that D can set his clock to read the same time as *any one clock* (in this case clock B) in the frame of B at any given time. Thereafter the clock B by which he has set his clock will appear to D to run slow. Other clocks at rest in the frame of B and synchronized with each other in the frame of B will also appear to D to run slow at the same rate as clock B; but, in addition, they will appear to D to be set ahead of or behind the reference clock B by an amount given by Eq. (12-7), where x_0 is the proper distance between these clocks measured in the frame of B in which they are at rest (positive x_0 measured in the direction of motion of D).

12.7 THE LORENTZ TRANSFORMATION.* Now we have enough information so that, if we know where and when an event occurs with respect to one reference frame, we can predict correctly where and when it will occur in another reference frame.

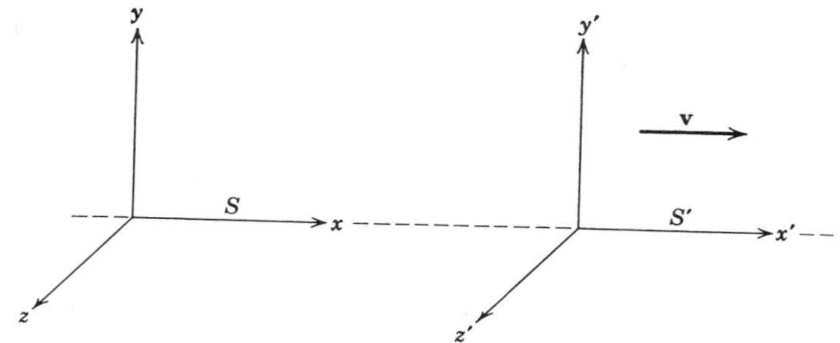

Fig. 12-9. Two inertial reference frames in uniform relative motion.

* For a careful development of the Lorentz transformation equations from experimental results see H. P. Robertson, "Postulate vs Observation in the Special Theory of Relativity," *Reviews of Modern Physics*, **21**, 378 (July 1949).

Consider two inertial reference frames in uniform relative motion with relative speed v. Suppose that their x-axes coincide and that their y- and z-axes point in the same directions respectively. Call the xyz frame *frame S*, and the $x'y'z'$ frame *frame S'*. We shall take the frame S to be at rest and frame S' to be moving to the right, as in Fig. 12-9. Time measured in frame S will have the symbol t; time measured in frame S' will have the symbol t'. By definition, $t = t' = 0$ when the origins of the two systems coincide. Now suppose that there occurs an event which in frame S has the space coordinates (x, y, z) and time t. What will be the coordinates and time of occurrence of the same event in frame S'?

First of all, observers at rest in the two frames will agree on the y- and z-coordinates of the event.

$$y' = y$$

$$z' = z$$

The transformation of the x-coordinate is less simple. At the time t at which the event occurs in frame S, observers in S measure that the origin of frame S' has moved a distance vt in the x-direction. Hence the difference between the x-coordinate of the event and the x-coordinate of the origin of S' *as measured in frame* S is given by $x - vt$. This is not, however, the coordinate x' of the event as measured in S', because of the Lorentz contraction of distances in the x-direction.

Suppose that a measuring rod lies in the x'-direction and at rest in the frame S' in such a way that one end of this measuring rod coincides with the $y'z'$ plane, and the other end coincides with the event being observed when this event occurs. The length of this rod will be x', the x'-coordinate of the event in S'. Since the rod is at rest in S', we see that the distance x' is a *proper distance*. The corresponding distance $x - vt$ measured in frame S is not a proper distance because in that frame the origin of S' is a moving point. Equation (12-5) can be used to relate the proper distance x' between the event and the origin of S' as measured in S' to the distance $x - vt$ between the event and the origin of S' as measured in S.

$$x' = \frac{x - vt}{\sqrt{1 - v^2/c^2}}$$

This is the transformation equation for the x-coordinates of the event.

Now for the transformation of time. The clocks moving with each frame are synchronized in their own frame to read $t = t' = 0$ when the origins of S and S' coincide. We know the relation between the times measured on the two clocks at the *origins* of S and S' because they coincide at $t = t' = 0$. From Sec. 12.4, the observer at the origin of S' sees the clock at the origin of S running slow so that $t' = t/\sqrt{1 - v^2/c^2}$, where t is measured on the clock at the origin of frame S. In addition, the observer in S' sees a difference of synchronism between the clock at the origin of S and a clock which is at the position of the event but at rest in S. From Sec. 12.6, the observer in S' has to add

$$(-xv/c^2)/\sqrt{1 - v^2/c^2}$$

Hence the observer in S' sees the event occurring at a time

$$t' = \frac{t - xv/c^2}{\sqrt{1 - v^2/c^2}}$$

In summary, if an observer in S observes an event with the coordinates x, y, z, and t, he can predict correctly that an observer in S' will observe the event to have the coordinates x', y', z', and t', given by the equations

$$\begin{aligned} x' &= \frac{x - vt}{\sqrt{1 - v^2/c^2}} \\ y' &= y \\ z' &= z \\ t' &= \frac{t - xv/c^2}{\sqrt{1 - v^2/c^2}} \end{aligned} \tag{12-8}$$

Questions

12-31 Show that in the limit as v/c goes to zero, Eqs. (12-8) take the form one would expect in classical mechanics.

12-32 From Eqs. (12-8) show that the inverse transformation has the form

$$\begin{aligned} x &= \frac{x' + vt'}{\sqrt{1 - v^2/c^2}} \\ y &= y' \\ z &= z' \\ t &= \frac{t' + x'v/c^2}{\sqrt{1 - v^2/c^2}} \end{aligned} \tag{12-9}$$

Explain carefully what this inverse transformation says. If you wish to test your understanding of the derivation of (12-8), derive (12-9) by the same method.

In order to save time, space, and typesetting charges, the symbols β and γ are defined in relativity as follows:

$$\beta = v/c \qquad \text{where } \beta \text{ is positive}$$

$$\gamma = \frac{1}{\sqrt{1 - v^2/c^2}} = \frac{1}{\sqrt{1 - \beta^2}} \tag{12-10}$$

In terms of these symbols, the transformation equations have the form

$$\begin{aligned} x' &= \gamma(x - vt) = \gamma(x - \beta ct) \\ y' &= y \\ z' &= z \\ t' &= \gamma(t - \beta x/c) \end{aligned} \tag{12-11}$$

and the inverse transformation equations have the form

$$\begin{aligned} x &= \gamma(x' + vt') = \gamma(x' + \beta ct') \\ y &= y' \\ z &= z' \\ t &= \gamma(t' + \beta x'/c) \end{aligned} \tag{12-12}$$

The transformation equations, (12-8) or (12-11), and the inverse transformation equations, (12-9) or (12-12), are called the *Lorentz transformation equations.* If we know the space and time coordinates of an event in one inertial reference frame, we can use the Lorentz transformation equations to predict correctly the space and time coordinates of the same event in another inertial reference frame which is in uniform relative motion with respect to the first. Notice that both space and time coordinates are involved in the transformations of both the x-coordinates and the time. The sharp distinction in classical mechanics between space and time does not exist in these equations. In Chapter 13 we shall show how it is possible to find a single expression describing the "location of an event" involving both space and time on which all inertial observers in uniform relative motion can agree.

Questions

12-33 In my inertial coordinate system a flash of light is emitted from a position $x = y = z = 1000$ m at a time $t = 5$ sec. Another observer moves past me in the positive x-direction at a velocity 0.8 that of light. He coincides with the origin of my reference frame at $t = 0$. What will be the space and time coordinates of the event in his reference frame? Check your answer by using the inverse transformation to give again the coordinates of the event in my reference frame.

12-34 Show from the transformation equations that if two Lorentz transformations with relative velocities given by β_1 and β_2 respectively are carried out consecutively, the result is the same as a single Lorentz transformation with relative velocity β given by the expression

$$\beta = \frac{\beta_1 + \beta_2}{1 + \beta_1\beta_2} \tag{12-13}$$

12-35 Suppose that a particle is at rest in an inertial frame S''. With respect to frame S', the particle is moving in the positive x-direction with velocity v_2. With respect to frame S, the origin of frame S' is moving in the positive x-direction with velocity v_1. The x-axis of frame S and frame S' coincide. From the results of the last question, find the velocity of the particle in frame S. Using the values $v_2 = v_1 = 0.8c$, resolve the paradox of Question 2-20 in Chapter 2. Show that no reference frame can be found by consecutive Lorentz transformations in which the speed of a given particle is greater than the speed of light if the speed of this particle is less than the speed of light in *any* such frame.

EXERCISES

12-1 An event occurs at a position x, y, z and at a time t in frame S given by each entry in the accompanying table. Find the position and time of each event in a frame S' which moves in the positive x-direction of frame S with constant speed $v = 0.8c$. The x-axes of the two frames lie along a common line, and the origins of the two frames coincide at $t = t' = 0$. Find the *proper time* between the coincidence of the origins and each event for those cases in which this proper time can be defined.

Event	x, meters	y, meters	z, meters	t, seconds
1	0	0	0	0
2	10^8	0	0	1
3	10^9	0	0	1
4	10^9	10^9	10^9	1
5	-10^9	10^9	10^9	1
6	$\frac{3}{8} \times 10^9$	10^{16}	10^{12}	1
7	$-\frac{3}{8} \times 10^9$	10^2	0	1
8	2.4×10^8	0	0	1
9	2×10^9	10^9	0	10
10	0	0	3×10^9	10

12-2 Two events occur at the same place in my inertial reference frame and are separated by a time of 3 sec. What is the spatial distance between these two events in an inertial reference frame moving with uniform relative velocity with respect to my frame and in which the events are separated by a time of 5 sec?

12-3 A meter stick moves along its own length with constant velocity with respect to frame S. The length of this meter stick is measured by determining the locations of its endpoints at the same time in frame S. Show that the Lorentz contraction of the meter stick will be observed.

12-4 A runner with a 100-ft pole held parallel to his direction of motion enters a barn 50 ft long which is open at both ends. Can the sliding doors at both ends of the barn be closed in such a way that the runner and pole are shut in the barn before the pole collides with the exit door of the barn? Explain carefully how both an observer standing in the barn and the runner will interpret the outcome of this experiment.

12-5 Explain why the result of the experiment of Sec. 12.4 is not symmetrical for observers *A* and *D*. Show quantitatively that the result obtained in that section can be explained by using expressions for time dilation and the relative synchronization of clocks.

12-6 Using the concepts of time dilation and relative synchronization of clocks, resolve Einstein's train paradox described in Sec. 10-3.

12-7 Suppose that two clocks *A* and *B* at rest with respect to one another and 1.6×10^6 km apart (about one million miles) are "synchronized" by the following method: A third clock *C* originally near *A* and at rest with respect to *A* is found to run at the same rate as clock *A*. Clock *C* is then removed from *A* in a direction opposite to the direction of *B* from *A* and accelerated to a speed of 4.5×10^4 m/sec (about 100,000 mph) toward *A*. As *C* passes *A*, it is moving with constant velocity toward *B*. Clock *C* is set to read the same time as clock *A* as they pass one another. Clock *C* then travels with constant velocity toward *B*. As clock *C* passes *B*, clock *B* is set to read the same time as clock *C*. Assuming that the period of acceleration has not changed the rate at which clock *C* runs after the acceleration is over, calculate the difference in the setting between clock *B* under these circumstances and the setting derived by the method of synchronization using flashes of light presented in Sec. 12.1.

12-8 In a given sample of π^+ mesons half will decay to other elementary particles in 18 nanoseconds measured with respect to a reference frame in which the π^+ mesons are at rest. Half of the remainder will decay in the next 18 nanoseconds, and so on. In a certain proton synchroton π^+ mesons are produced when a proton beam strikes an aluminum target *inside* the accelerator. If there were no time dilation and if no mesons were removed from the resulting beam by collisions, what is the greatest distance from the target at which half of the mesons would remain undecayed? If in fact $\gamma = 15$ (Eq. 12-10), what is the distance from the target at which half the mesons will remain undecayed?

PROJECT X. THE VISUAL APPEARANCE OF RAPIDLY MOVING OBJECTS

THE RIGID BODY IN THE THEORY OF RELATIVITY. Consider two observers A and D who are each at rest with respect to an inertial reference frame but in uniform relative motion with respect to one another. Suppose that observer D makes a "square rigid body" by fastening four meter sticks together in such a way that he observes this construction as a square which is at rest in his radar world. (You may consider in the following argument that all observers determine the position and shape of the "square" from the positions of four objects of different colors at the four corners of the square.) If this "square rigid body" moves past Mr. A with relative velocity $\mathbf{v}$ in such a way that two opposite edges are parallel to $\mathbf{v}$, show that the "square" will appear as in Fig. X-1*b* in the radar world of A What lengths will each side of this figure have in the radar world of A if $v/c = 0.8$?

Problems

X-1 Suppose that the diagonal of the "square rigid body" lies along the direction or relative motion. Draw the radar worlds of D and A for this case. Show that the following statements are true: A "rigid body" of any shape which is at rest in the radar world of D will have every dimension parallel to the direction of relative motion foreshortened by a factor $\sqrt{1 - v^2/c^2}$ in the radar world of A and every dimension perpendicular to the direction of relative motion unchanged. If a body stationary in D is observed to be rigid in the radar world of D, then it will be observed to be rigid in the radar world of all observers in uniform relative motion with respect to D. On the other hand, the shape of the rigid body will in general be different in the radar worlds of these different observers.

X-2 Show that the following statements are true: If a body which is observed to be rigid in the radar world of observer D is observed to be rotating slowly without translational motion in this radar world, it will *not* be observed to be a rigid body in the radar worlds of all observers in uniform relative motion with respect to observer D. A body which is originally stationary and which originally appears rigid in the radar world of observer D will not continue to appear rigid if it is accelerated at a small rate in the radar world of observer D. It will appear to D to be shrinking in the direction of relative motion as it accelerates.

Clearly, the concept of a rigid body will have to be redefined in the theory of relativity. Since there is no ambiguity about the shape or dimensions of

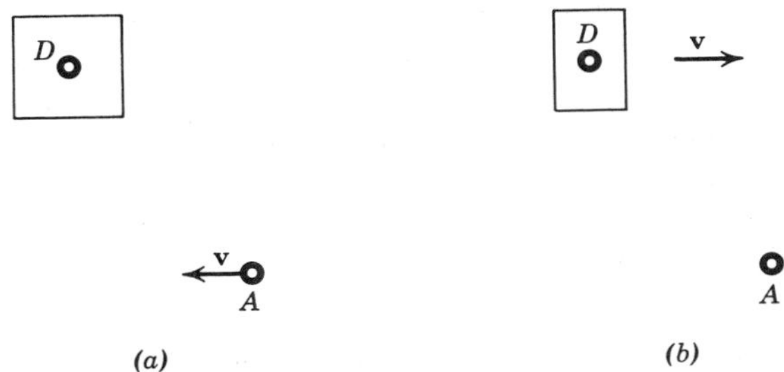

Fig. X-1. (*a*) Radar world of *D*. (*b*) Radar world of *A*.

a rigid body if it is at rest and not accelerating in the radar world of a given observer, we shall build our definition of a rigid body about this circumstance. This definition will apply only to rigid bodies which are neither accelerating nor rotating in an inertial frame.

Definition. A system of particles is said to constitute a *rigid body* in the theory of relativity if, and only if, an inertial reference frame can be found such that every particle in the system of particles remains at rest in the radar world of an observer at rest in that reference frame. The *proper shape* of a rigid body is defined as the shape of the body observed in the radar world of this same observer.

In the example used above, the square constructed out of meter sticks is a rigid body by this definition and has the proper shape of a square. *Whenever we are describing the proper shape of a rigid body we shall use a capital first letter.* Thus a "Square" means a rigid body which has the shape of a square in an inertial reference frame in which the rigid body is at rest and has no acceleration or rotation. Using the Lorentz transformation equations, we can find the proper shape of a rigid body if we know its shape, velocity, and orientation in the radar world of an inertial observer in which the rigid body is moving with constant velocity.

Problems

X-3 Discuss the shape of a Cube in the radar worlds of observers in uniform relative motion in different directions with respect to the axes of this Cube.

X-4 In my radar world I observe a rigid body which appears to be a cube moving with one face perpendicular to the direction of its velocity in my frame. I measure its velocity to be four-fifths that of light. What is its proper shape?

Notice that the definition of a rigid body does not apply to so-called rigid bodies which are accelerating or rotating with respect to inertial reference frames. Perhaps a new definition of a rigid body might be constructed by using an accelerating or rotating reference frame in which the body is at rest. However, the theory of relativity does not deal with accelerating or rotating reference frames, so we shall omit consideration of rigid bodies under these circumstances.*

REVIEW: OBSERVATION OF RIGID BODIES IN THE RADAR WORLD. The radar world of an inertial observer was defined in Sec. 11.3 as the picture which an inertial observer obtains of his surroundings by the method of reflected flashes, using a single flasher and a single clock. Suppose that a Square moves as in Fig. X-1*b* with respect to observer *A*. One way that observer *A* can determine the positions of, say, the four corners of the Square at a given time on his clock is by the following method (again, you may consider that four objects, all of different colors, are at four corners of the Square). First, by a series of reflected flashes he determines that all four corners have the same uniform velocity **v**. Second, he sends out a single flash which is reflected by all four corners and by which he can determine the position of each corner *at the time on his clock at which the flash reached each corner*. This time will be different for different corners because they will be different distances from observer *A*. Third, he can use the known constant velocity of each corner and its position at the known time at which it reflected the last flash of light to calculate the position of each corner at any earlier time. In this way he can determine the positions which all four corners occupied *simultaneously* at any earlier time on his clock.

In Sec. 12.1 the concept of simultaneity was enlarged to show how any number of observers who are relatively at rest can synchronize their clocks so that they will all calculate that a given event occurred at the same time on their clocks. Now observer *A* can use a set of such observers relatively at rest with respect to him and with clocks synchronized to his to determine in a more direct manner the position and shape of the moving Square in his radar world. He simply arranges things by trial and error so that four of his observers coincide with the four corners of the Square simultaneously on their clocks. Then they can tell him at what time this

* Following the usage of V. Fock (*The Theory of Space Time and Gravitation*, Pergamon Press, New York, 1959), we shall refer to the description and laws of motion of particles in inertial frames as the *theory of relativity*. Elsewhere this is often called the *theory of special relativity*. The description and laws of motion of particles in gravitational fields and in accelerated frames we shall call the *theory of gravitation*. Elsewhere this is often called the *general theory of relativity*.

coincidence occurred. Suppose they tell him of this coincidence by each emitting a flash of light. Knowing the positions of his observers and that their flashes were emitted simultaneously, he has all the information needed to locate the rigid body at that instant.

The resulting picture of the rigid body which Mr. A obtains by either of these equivalent methods is called the radar world of A. Figure X-1*b* represents a possible result of such an observation.

Problem

X-5 Will observer D riding with the Square agree that the four observers at rest with respect to Mr. A emitted their flashes simultaneously?

THE VISUAL APPEARANCE OF RAPIDLY MOVING RIGID BODIES. THE SUNLIGHT WORLD. From 1905 when Einstein published his paper on relativity* until 1959 it was generally assumed that, if a Cube *illuminated by sunlight* should pass by an observer, the Lorentz contraction could be seen by the observer if he watched visually as the Cube went by him. In 1959 James Terrell† pointed out that the visual observation of a rigid body illuminated by sunlight is quite a different experimental circumstance than the use of flashes to construct what we have called the radar world. Terrell showed that Mr. A's visual observation of a rapidly moving rigid body could be interpreted as a *rotation* of the body without contraction. Let us see how this might come about.

Suppose that a Cube whose edge has the proper length l_0 moves with uniform velocity $\mathbf{v}$ in the radar world of A in such a way that one edge of the Cube lies parallel to $\mathbf{v}$. Consider the radar world pictures of this Cube at the point of nearest approach of the Cube to Mr. A as observed by Mr. D riding with the Cube, and by Mr. A past whom the Cube is moving. The two radar worlds are pictured in Fig. X-2. The radar world of either observer could be obtained experimentally from the location of four flashes originating from four corners E, F, G, and H simultaneously in the frame of the observer in question.

What will the Cube look like to observer A if it is illuminated with sunlight? Terrell's central insight was that the sunlight view which observer A has of the Cube is determined not by light rays which left the corners E, F, G, and H simultaneously in the frame of A but *by light rays which arrive at observer A simultaneously*. After all, what you see visually at any instant consists of light rays which enter your eye at that instant irrespective of when they left their source. A striking example of this is the view of the stars which we have from the earth. Our view of the sun

* A. Einstein, *Annalen der Physik*, **17,** 891 (1905), translated in *The Principle of Relativity* by A. Einstein and others, Dover Publications, Inc., New York.

† James Terrell, *Physical Review*, **116,** 1041 (1959).

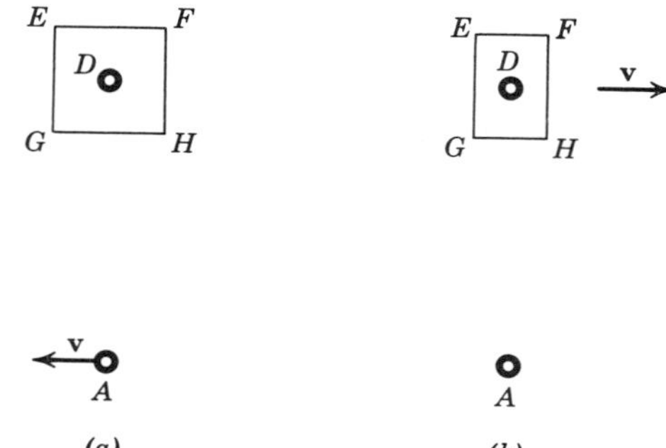

Fig. X-2. (*a*) Radar world of *D*. (*b*) Radar world of *A*.

now is really a view of the sun as it was about eight minutes ago. Our view of very distant stars now (using a powerful telescope) is really a view of those stars as they were billions of years ago. Yet both are what we see simultaneously at the present time in our frame of reference.

In what sequence will the rays of light have to leave corners *E*, *F*, *G*, and *H* of the Cube in Fig. X-2 in order to arrive simultaneously at the position of *A*? The lower corners *G* and *H* are equidistant from *A* in Fig. X-2*b*, so that light leaving these corners simultaneously as measured in the frame of *A* will arrive at *A* simultaneously. Show that observer *A* will observe the edge *GH* to be $\sqrt{1 - v^2/c^2}$ times the proper length l_0 of this edge observed in the radar world of *D*. On the other hand, the light arriving at *A* from corner *E* simultaneously with light from *G* will have been emitted earlier than the light from *G*. How much earlier? If the Cube has an edge of length l_0 as seen by observer *D*, then the edge *EG* will have the *same* length l_0 in the radar world of observer *A* because this direction is transverse to the relative velocity **v**. In the frame of *A* it will take light l_0/c seconds to travel down the back of the cube. Hence the light from *E* left l_0/c seconds before light which arrives at *A* from *G* at the same time. In this time the Cube has moved a distance $v(l_0/c)$. The observer at *A* will therefore be able to see corner *E*. In fact, the projection of side *EG* seen by observer *A* will be vl_0/c meters long. We have already seen that the bottom edge will appear to be $l_0\sqrt{1 - v^2/c^2}$ meters long. Hence observer *A* will have the visual view of the cube shown in Fig. X-3.

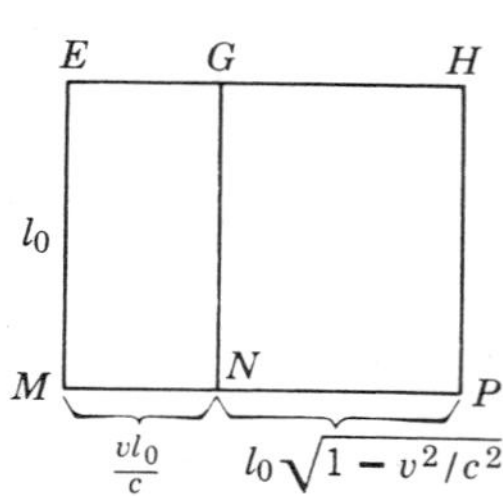

Fig. X-3. Visual view of the Cube seen by observer *A* when the Cube appears to him in a direction perpendicular to its direction of motion.

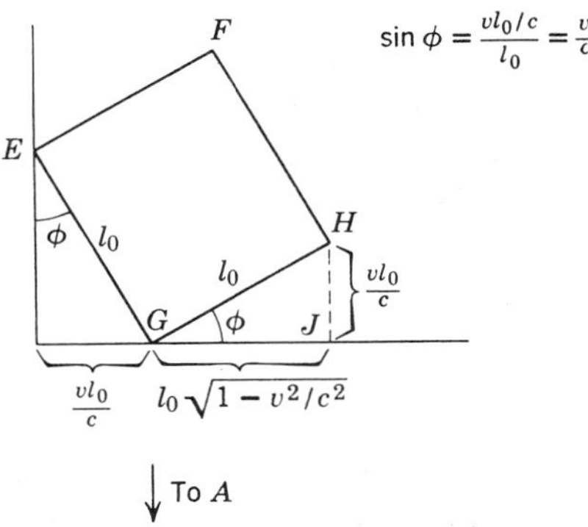

Fig. X-4. Apparent tilt of whole Cube *EFGH* as it passes observer *A*.

Problem

X-6 Show that the corners of the Cube marked *M*, *N*, and *P* in Fig. X-3 are correctly placed in that figure.

Using Fig. X-4, show that the view of the Cube of Fig. X-3 is the same as observer *A* would have of an *undistorted* cube which is rotated through an angle ϕ whose sine is v/c. This is the result found by Terrell.

Problems

X-7 Calculate the angle of apparent rotation ϕ under the above circumstances if $v = 4500$ m/sec (about 10,000 mph). What does the Cube look like to Mr. *A* if v is very close to c? At the time on *A*'s clock at which he sees the Cube in the position described above, what is the location of the Cube in his radar world? If you ask Mr. *A* this question, how long will it be before he can verify his answer by direct observation?

X-8 Is the Lorentz contraction of the Cube *real*? If so, why does Mr. *A* not *see* it in the case treated above? If not, why does Mr. *A observe* it in his radar world?

The objection may be raised that, if this rotation were actually observed by observer *A*, he should see corner *H* a little farther away from him than corner *G* and corner *E* a little nearer to him than in the unrotated state. It is true that Mr. *A* would not see such changes in depth. However, the perception of depth involves stereoscopic vision, i.e., the use of two eyes in different locations. In the examples treated in this project the observation must be carried out from a single location, so that the view seen by Mr. *A* must be a *one-eyed view*. We shall assume also that the Cube or other object subtends a small angle at the eye of Mr. *A* so that the location of the Cube or other object involves only a *single* direction from *A*.

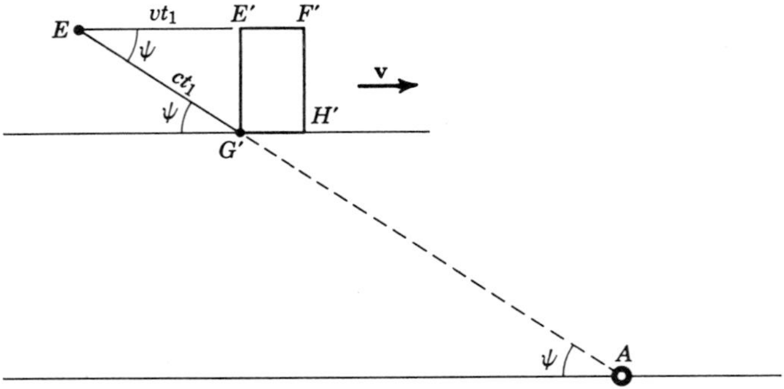

Fig. X-5. Location of Cube at which back side *EG* first becomes visible to observer *A*. Rectangle *E′F′G′H′* is Mr. *A*'s radar world picture of the Cube.

Stereoscopic vision and large angles of observation introduce complicated distortions in the image of the object which will not be treated here.*

Clearly the visual appearance of the Cube in the example above differs from the picture of the Cube obtained in the radar world of Mr. *A*. In the radar world the Cube is contracted along its direction of motion but not rotated, whereas in visual appearance the Cube is rotated but not contracted. We shall call the visual appearance of his surroundings seen in sunlight by any inertial observer the *sunlight world* of that observer. The *time* which the observer attaches to an event in his sunlight world we shall take to be the time on his clock at which he actually sees that event. In constructing a radar world, on the other hand, an observer assumes that a distant event occurs before he observes it and attaches a previous time to that event according to the time which he calculates it takes for a flash of light emitted from the event to reach him.

An observer may, of course, see his sunlight world by using *any* source of light, not just the sun; or the objects he sees may themselves be luminous. Either of these types of illumination may utilize electromagnetic radiation of frequencies other than those in the visual range, and detectors other than the human eye. All such methods of illumination are included in the phrase the *sunlight world.*

In the previous example it was found that Mr. *A* could see the back side of the Cube obliquely when the Cube appeared in a direction perpendicular to its velocity vector. Where does observer *A* see the Cube to be located when he can first see this back side? The situation is pictured in Fig. X-5. The rectangle *E′F′G′H′* represents Mr. *A*'s radar world picture of the Cube at a time when a ray of light which left corner *E* at an earlier time just passes corner *G′*. The angle ψ is the angle which this ray of light

* See J. Terrell, *ibid.* See problem **X-12** below.

will make with the direction anti-parallel to **v** when it reaches observer A. We shall call this angle ψ the *direction of observation* or the *angle of observation*. Mr. A will begin to observe the back side of the Cube under the circumstance that $EG'A$ is a straight line. Suppose that it takes a time t_1 for the light to move from E to G'. In that time the Cube will have moved a distance vt_1, represented by the line EE' in Fig. X-5. The angle $E'EG$ is ψ, so we may write

$$\cos\psi = \frac{vt_1}{ct_1} = \frac{v}{c} \tag{X-1}$$

Hence Mr. A will begin to see the back side of the Cube when the cosine of the direction of observation ψ is equal to v/c.

Problem

X-9 Interpret Eq. (X-1) in the cases in which $v \to 0$ and in which v is almost equal to c.

What view does Mr. A have of the bottom edge GH at the instant when he begins to see the back side? The answer can be derived by using Fig. X-6. Rectangles $E'F'G'H'$ and $E''F''G''H''$ represent subsequent positions of the Cube in the radar world of A. In this radar world the Cube has a height l_0 equal to its proper height but a length l equal to $l_0\sqrt{1 - v^2/c^2}$. Line JH'' is drawn perpendicular to line $G'A$. It is assumed that the angle subtended at A by light from H'' and J is so small that the distance $H''A$ is equal to the distance JA. In this case, light which leaves

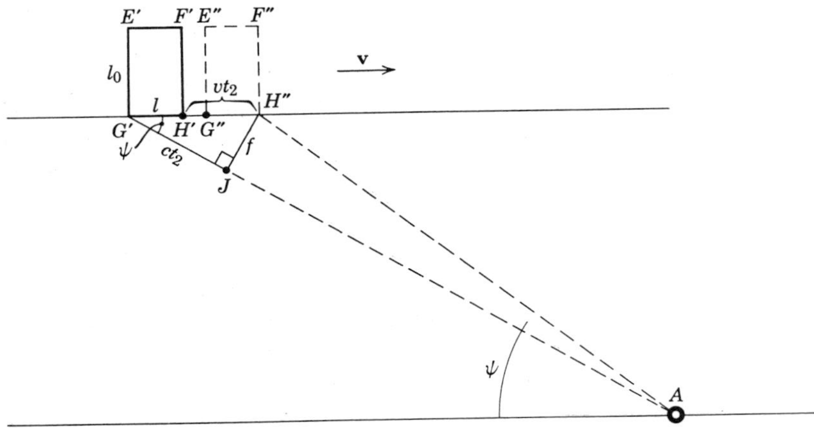

Fig. X-6. Appearance of lower edge of Cube. Rectangles $E'F'G'H'$ and $E''F''G''H''$ represent subsequent positions of the Cube in the radar world of A.

points H'' and J simultaneously will arrive at observer A simultaneously. Show that, if it takes a time t_2 for light to move from G' to J while the corner H moves from H' to H'', observer A will see the bottom edge to have the projection JH'' which we shall call f.

From Fig. X-6,

$$\frac{f}{ct_2} = \tan \psi \tag{X-2}$$

and

$$\frac{ct_2}{l + vt_2} = \cos \psi \tag{X-3}$$

Solve Eq. (X-3) for t_2.

$$t_2 = \frac{l \cos \psi}{c - v \cos \psi} \tag{X-4}$$

Solve Eq. (X-2) for f and substitute the value of t_2 from Eq. (X-4).

$$f = ct_2 \tan \psi = \frac{cl \cos \psi \tan \psi}{c - v \cos \psi}$$

$$f = \frac{cl \sin \psi}{c - v \cos \psi} \tag{X-5}$$

But l is the contracted length of the Cube in the radar world of A. Its value is $l_0\sqrt{1 - v^2/c^2}$, where l_0 is the proper length of an edge of the Cube (in an inertial reference frame in which the Cube is at rest). Hence Eq. (X-5) becomes

$$f = \frac{l_0\sqrt{1 - v^2/c^2} \sin \psi}{1 - (v/c) \cos \psi} \tag{X-6}$$

This equation for f is valid for any angle of observation ψ. Now we wish to calculate f for the position of the Cube at which Mr. A first sees the back side of the Cube. From Eq. (X-1) this occurs when $\cos \psi = v/c$. Show that in this case

$$f = \frac{l_0\sqrt{1 - v^2/c^2}\sqrt{1 - v^2/c^2}}{1 - v^2/c^2} = l_0 \tag{X-7}$$

This equation says that Mr. A sees the bottom edge of the Cube to have its full (uncontracted) length. In other words, Mr. A sees the Cube in this position directly from the bottom. Once again the Lorentz contraction of the Cube is not observed in the sunlight world of Mr. A.

It is possible to start with Eq. (X-6) and show that at any direction of observation in which Mr. A sees the Cube it will appear to be rotated through some angle ϕ, and then to calculate this angle. Equation (X-6) was derived for any angle of observation. To begin, let us find the apparent angle of rotation ϕ of an undistorted Cube which will give the same value of f as does Eq. (X-6). From Fig. X-7 we see that

$$l_0 \sin(\phi + \psi) = f \tag{X-8}$$

Substitute this value for f into Eq. (X-6), take the arcsine of both sides of this equation, and show that

$$\phi = \arcsin\left[\frac{\sqrt{1 - v^2/c^2}\,\sin\psi}{1 - (v/c)\cos\psi}\right] - \psi \tag{X-9}$$

This equation gives the apparent angle of rotation ϕ of an undistorted Cube as a function of its velocity in the radar world of observer A and the direction of observation ψ with respect to observer A. In deriving this equation we *assumed* that there would be apparent rotation without distortion for all angles ψ. In order to check this assumption we can use it again to calculate the apparent angle of rotation of the front edge of the cube FH. Figure X-8 is used in this calculation. Once again the rectangle $E'F'G'H'$ represents the Cube in the radar world of Mr. A. Line KH'' is drawn perpendicular to $F'A$. Once again it is assumed that the angle subtended by KH'' at A is small enough that the distance KA is equal to the distance $H''A$. If it takes a time t_1 for light to move from F' to K while the corner H moves from H' to H'', observer A will see the front edge to have the projection $H''K$ which we shall call h. Using right triangles $LH''K$ and $LH'F'$, show that

$$h = \frac{l_0[\cos\psi - (v/c)]}{1 - (v/c)\cos\psi} \tag{X-10}$$

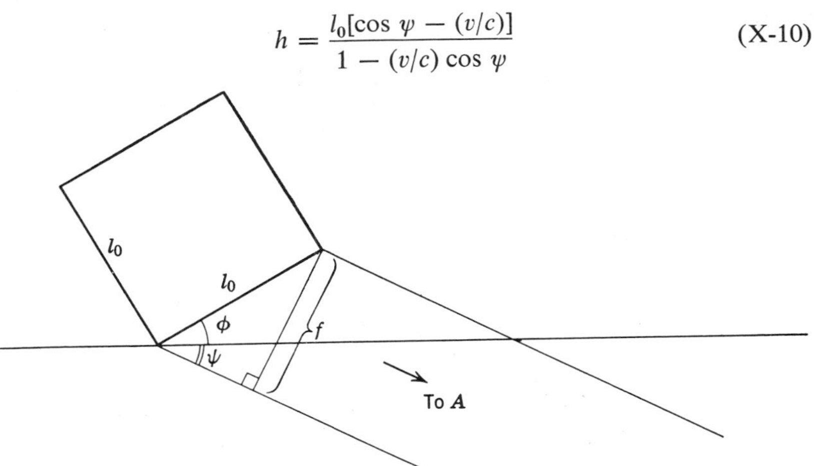

Fig. X-7. Calculation of the angle of apparent rotation of an undistorted Cube which will give the same value of the projection f as does Eq. (X-6).

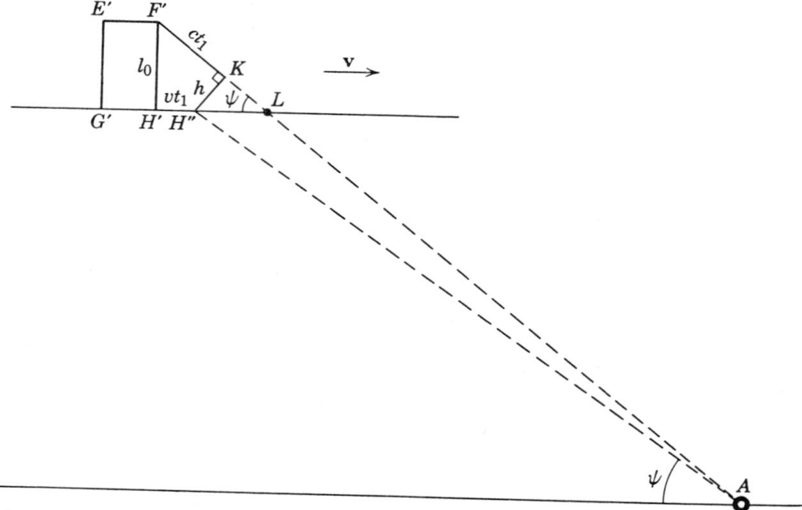

Fig. X-8. Calculation of the apparent length h of the Cube edge $F'H'$ in the sunlight world of Mr. A. Rectangle $E'F'G'H'$ represents the Cube in the radar world of Mr. A.

If we assume again that Mr. A will interpret this projection as due to an apparent rotation of an undistorted Cube through an angle ϕ, we have, from Fig. X-9,

$$\cos(\phi + \psi) = \frac{h}{l_0} \tag{X-11}$$

Using Eqs. (X-10) and (X-11), find the angle of apparent rotation

$$\phi = \arccos\left[\frac{\cos\psi - (v/c)}{1 - (v/c)\cos\psi}\right] - \psi \tag{X-12}$$

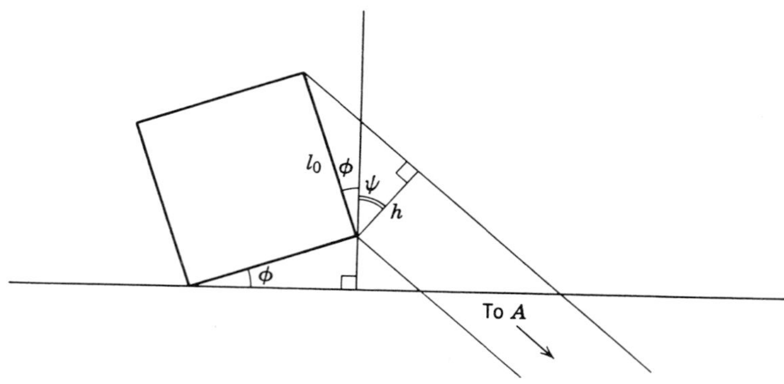

Fig. X-9. Calculation of angle of apparent rotation ϕ of undistorted Cube which will give the same value of h as Eq. (X-10).

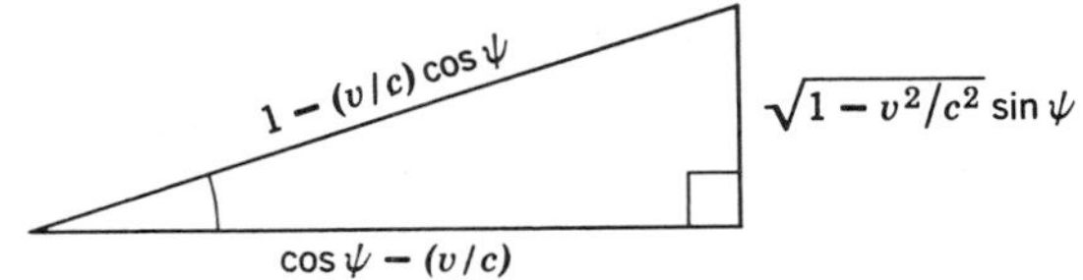

Fig. X-10. Demonstration that Eq. (X-13) is correct.

If this angle of apparent rotation is the same as that of Eq. (X-9), we will have demonstrated that the assumption of apparent rotation is a consistent one. The angles ϕ from Eqs. (X-9) and (X-12) will be the same if the following equation is valid.

$$\arcsin\left[\frac{\sqrt{1 - v^2/c^2}\,\sin\psi}{1 - (v/c)\cos\psi}\right] = \arccos\left[\frac{\cos\psi - (v/c)}{1 - (v/c)\cos\psi}\right] \qquad \text{(X-13)}$$

Show that this equation is correct by showing that the triangle in Fig. X-10 is a right triangle.

Since Eq. (X-9) and Eq. (X-12) are equivalent, either one can be used

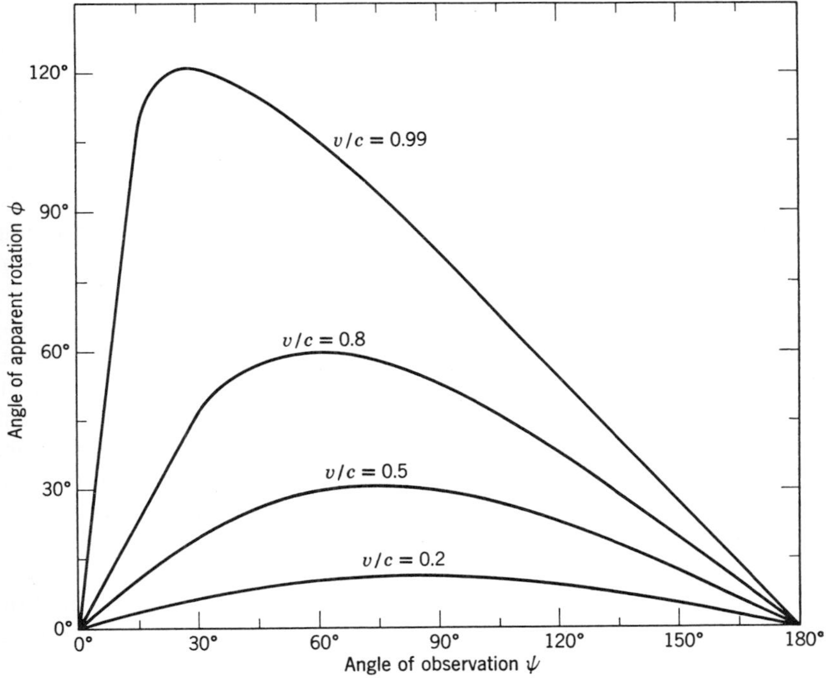

Fig. X-11. Graph of $\phi = \arccos\left[\dfrac{\cos\psi - (v/c)}{1 - (v/c)\cos\psi}\right] - \psi.$

to calculate the angle of apparent rotation ϕ of the cube as seen by Mr. A once values of v/c and ψ are given. Since there are no square roots in Eq. (X-12), this one will be easier to use. Figure X-11 shows this angle of apparent rotation as a function of ψ for several values of the ratio v/c, using Eq. (X-12).

Problem

X-10 Demonstrate that every point on the edges and faces of the Cube, not only the corners, participate in the apparent rotation.

A rigid body of any proper shape can be considered to be made up of a large number of small Cubes. The analysis above can be applied to each of these Cubes. The result is that in the sunlight world of A any rigid body will have the apparent rotation given by Eq. (X-9) or (X-12) *provided* that the angle subtended by the entire object at observer A is small, as was assumed in the previous derivation.

Problems

X-11 Suppose observer A lies directly in the path of a Cube which approaches him with constant velocity $\mathbf{v}$ in his radar world. Demonstrate that the Cube will look bigger to him at any given time in his radar world than in his sunlight world as it approaches, and bigger to him in his sunlight world than in his radar world as it recedes. Define an *apparent magnification* of the object in the sunlight world, and work out an approximate expression for this apparent magnification of any object under these circumstances as a function of its distance from the observer in his radar world and the ratio v/c. Show that under these circumstances the velocity of the approaching Cube as observed in the sunlight world of Mr. A will not be the same as the velocity of the approaching Cube as observed in the radar world of Mr. A. Show also that, if the approaching and receding velocities are observed to be the same in the radar world of Mr. A, the approaching and receding velocities in the sunlight world of Mr. A will *not* be the same. Work out expressions for the approaching and receding velocities in the sunlight world of Mr. A if the approaching and receding velocities in the radar world of Mr. A are the same and are equal to $\mathbf{v}$. If the straight line path of the Cube does not pass through point A but passes by a perpendicular distance b away and if the velocity $\mathbf{v}$ of the Cube in the radar world of A is constant, show that in the sunlight world of A the Cube will appear to approach with a velocity greater than $\mathbf{v}$, will appear to decelerate as it approaches, passes, and recedes, and will recede with a velocity less than $\mathbf{v}$. *This is the reason why the sunlight world is not convenient for developing the laws of motion of a particle.*

X-12 Suppose that the angle subtended by a large rigid body at the position of the observer is *not* small. Show how for purposes of analysis the rigid body may be considered to be made up of small Cubes which *do* subtend a small angle at the position of the observer. The analysis of this section may now be applied to each of these Cubes. Describe the kinds of apparent distortion you would expect in this larger rigid body as a result of the violation of the assumption of small subtended angles. Consider first the apparent distortion due to differential apparent rotation of different parts of the large rigid body, using Fig. X-11. Consider next the added apparent distortion due to different apparent velocities of different parts of the large rigid body, using the results of Problem X-11. Suppose that you are riding very very fast down a street along whose sides are both individual houses and uninterrupted store-fronts. How would the passing view look to you?

WHAT IS REALLY HAPPENING? If a Cube moves past an observer with a large constant velocity as measured in his radar world, then in his radar world the Cube appears to be contracted in its direction of motion, while in the sunlight world of the observer the Cube appears to be rotated without distortion. If the angle subtended by the Cube at the position of the observer is not small, the Cube will appear to twist and writhe in the sunlight world as it passes by.

What is the Cube *really doing* under these circumstances?

The operational principle tells us that this is not a scientific question unless the experimental method by which it is to be answered is specified. If the experiment is to be carried out according to the instructions, "Look at it with one eye," then the results of the experiment will be what we have called the sunlight world. If the experiment is to be carried out according to the instructions, "Bounce flashes of light off distinguishable objects at the corners of the Cube and locate the positions of these corners at the same time as calculated by using the measured velocity of the Cube, the speed of light, and the directions of the returning flashes," the results of this experiment will be what we have called the radar world. There are other experimental methods by which the Cube can be observed. These other methods may lead to still different pictures of the Cube, as you will show below.

Each of the "worlds" which corresponds to a different method of observation can be said to be real in the sense that it is *scientific* as defined by the operational principle. The word *real* has no other scientific meaning when applied to physical systems. This does not exclude the possibility that the word *real* may have different but still useful meanings in other fields of human endeavor.

The results of this project have not yet been tested experimentally. Since they follow directly from the Lorentz transformation equations (which have been verified experimentally in many ways) and from simple geometrical arguments, it is hard to see how these results could be in error. However, because in the past the majority of physicists have been known to proceed for long periods of time using results and assumptions which were either incorrect or operationally meaningless or both, we should not claim too much for the results of this project until some experimental verifications are in hand.

Problem

X-13 An inertial observer is instructed to send out a single flash of light in all directions and to take as the position of each object which reflects this flash the *direction* in which the reflection is observed and the *distance* as calculated from the length of time between the flash and the return of the reflection from that object, using the speed of light (assumed to be the same in all directions). Define the *one-flash world* to be the picture which this observer obtains of his surroundings by this method The *time* to be assigned to this configuration is the time of the emission of the flash on his clock. Demonstrate that, if all objects are at rest, the one-flash world is the same as the radar world of the same observer. Show that the two worlds are not the same if objects move about with respect to this observer. Show that a Cube which moves past the observer appears to be distorted in the one-flash world. Work out qualitatively the nature of this distortion, and give quantitative results for one or two apparent positions of the Cube. You may carry this analysis as far as you or your instructor desires. At a particular time on the observer's clock determine the relative location of a moving Cube in the radar world, the sunlight world, and the one-flash world of the observer.*

* C. W. Sherwin, *American Journal of Physics*, **29**, 67 (1961).

chapter 13

The relativistic laws of motion of a particle*

13.1 THE *S* REFERENCE FRAMES AND THE REFERENCE EVENT. In this chapter we shall be dealing with a particular set of reference frames. We shall call this particular set the *S-reference frames*, or more simply the *S-frames*. By definition, the S-reference frames have the following characteristics.

1. All S-frames are inertial reference frames. That is, the equation $\mathbf{F} = m\mathbf{a}$ is true for particles in each S-frame under the conditions in which classical mechanics is valid.
2. All S-frames are in uniform relative motion with respect to one another.
3. The x-axes of all S-frames lie along a common line.
4. The y-axes of all S-frames lie in a common plane (i.e., they point in the same direction). The z-axes of all S-frames lie in a common plane.
5. The S-frames are all free of gravitational fields. That is, no static gravitational fields can be detected by instruments which are at rest with respect to these frames in the regions in which experiments are to be carried out. It is found experimentally that in reference frames which satisfy conditions 1 and 5, light moves in straight lines with constant velocity on a go-and-return path.
6. The origins of the S-frames are chosen so that they all coincide at some instant. This coincidence we shall call the *reference event*. Thus in

* The notation of this chapter conforms largely to that of V. Fock in *The Theory of Space Time and Gravitation*, New York, Pergamon Press, 1959. The principal change in this chapter has been the use of superscripts instead of subscripts on the components of the world point of an event.

every S-frame the spatial coordinates of the reference event is

$$x = y = z = 0.$$

7. We choose the time $t = 0$ in every S-frame as the time of the reference event. Since a procedure has already been worked out for synchronizing any clock at rest in an inertial reference frame with a clock at the origin of that frame, the reference event can be used to synchronize every clock at rest in every S-frame with respect to the clock at the origin of the same frame.

In property 5 we allow the presence of electric and magnetic fields, because we shall deal in this chapter with the motion of uncharged particles only, and it is an *experimental result* that electric and magnetic fields do not affect either the motion of uncharged particles or the propagation of light.*

In distinguishing between particular members of the set of S-frames we shall use primes, so that one particular frame may be labeled S, a second frame may be labeled S', a third frame may be labeled S'', and so forth. In order to make the signs in the transformation equations come out correctly, it will be assumed that the origin of frame S' moves in the positive x-direction in frame S, that the origin of frame S'' moves in the positive x-direction in frame S', and so forth.

Phrases such as "an observer in S" or "a clock in S" will be taken to be shorthand for the phrases "an observer at rest with respect to frame S" and "a clock at rest with respect to frame S" respectively.

In this chapter an event will be described in any S-frame by its location and time in the *radar world* of an observer at the origin of that S-frame. We shall make no further use of the sunlight world presented in Project X.

Questions

13-1 Suppose that a flash of light is given off in all directions from the reference event. If you are an observer in S, describe how you can use this flash to synchronize all the clocks which are at rest with respect to your frame.

13-2 After the synchronization of clocks has taken place in frame S, will an observer in another frame S' agree that the clocks in S are synchronized?

13-3 Show how the definition of an *inertial frame* precludes the possibility that the relative velocity of any two S-frames is greater than the velocity of light.

* It is assumed that gradients of the electric and magnetic fields are so small that forces exerted on any permanent or induced dipole moments of the uncharged particles are negligible.

13-4 What is the significance of the fact that in classical mechanics it is sufficient to have a "reference particle" whereas in special relativity it is necessary to have a "reference event"?

13.2 THE WORLD POINT OF AN EVENT. Given the space and time coordinates of two events in one S-frame, we have found out in Chapter 12 how to predict correctly the space and time coordinates of the same two events in any other S-frame. Clocks at rest in the two frames will not always agree on the magnitude of the time interval between the two events, and measuring rods at rest in the two frames will not always agree on the distance between the two events. Although it is perfectly possible to describe events accurately in different frames, using the Lorentz transformation equations, it is inconvenient and not very elegant because the description will depend on the particular S-frame from which the two events are observed. It would be much more convenient if there were some measure of the relationship between two events on whose value the observers in every S-frame could agree. This measure might involve both space and time relations between the two events.

Such a measure is found by considering the fact that the speed of light is the same for the observers in every S-frame (Assumption 1a, Sec. 12.2). This means that a flash of light emitted from a point will spread out from that point in the form of a sphere as seen by observers in every S-frame.

Questions

13-5 Define carefully the operational meaning of the statement that the flash of light will spread out "in the form of a sphere" for a particular inertial observer. How can he observe that part of the sphere which is moving away from him?

13-6 Show that as this sphere of light spreads out the observer in every S-frame will see the center of this sphere to be stationary in his frame.

In terms of two events, if the first event is the emission of the flash and the second event is its reception at some other point which, with respect to some frame S, has the coordinates Δx, Δy, Δz and occurs at a time Δt later with respect to the first event, then the equation for the spreading sphere of light in that frame will be

$$(\Delta x)^2 + (\Delta y)^2 + (\Delta z)^2 = c^2\,(\Delta t)^2$$

no matter what the coordinates of the second event in this system are. Since the same flash will look spherical in every S-frame, we may write the same equation for a second frame S', using primes to indicate measurements with respect to frame S'.

$$(\Delta x')^2 + (\Delta y')^2 + (\Delta z')^2 = c^2 (\Delta t')^2$$

Now, in general, observers in S and S' will measure different values for either side of these two equations because of their disagreements concerning the synchronization of clocks and the lengths of measuring rods in the two systems. However, observers in *both* S-frames will agree that the following expressions are equal to zero.

$$c^2 (\Delta t)^2 - (\Delta x)^2 - (\Delta y)^2 - (\Delta z)^2 = 0$$
$$c^2 (\Delta t')^2 - (\Delta x')^2 - (\Delta y')^2 - (\Delta z')^2 = 0$$

This combination of space and time coordinates gives the same value for both coordinate systems. In this case the value is zero.

Using this clue and the Lorentz transformation equations, it is easy to show that for *any* two events observed from frames S and S'

$$c^2 (\Delta t)^2 - (\Delta x)^2 - (\Delta y)^2 - (\Delta z)^2 = c^2 (\Delta t')^2 - (\Delta x')^2 - (\Delta y')^2 - (\Delta z')^2 \tag{13-1}$$

Questions

13-7 Use the Lorentz transformation equations to show that Eq. (13-1) is correct.

13-8 Show that, for any two arbitrary events, either side of Eq. (13-1) will not always be equal to zero.

13-9 Describe the physical situations corresponding to a negative and to a positive value for either side of Eq. (13-1).

We have found a measure of the relationship between two events on whose value all inertial observers in uniform relative motion can agree. If we are dealing with S-frames and one of these events is the reference event, then Eq. (13-1) becomes

$$c^2t^2 - x^2 - y^2 - z^2 = c^2t'^2 - x'^2 - y'^2 - z'^2 \tag{13-2}$$

Hereafter the coordinates of an event, x, y, z, t (primed or unprimed), in any S-frame will be assumed to be taken with respect to the reference event (which occurs at the origin of every S-frame at a time defined to be zero).

Now we shall define the *world point of an event* in any S-frame in terms of its four "components."

$$\begin{aligned} x^0 &= ct \\ x^1 &= x \\ x^2 &= y \\ x^3 &= z \end{aligned} \tag{13-3}$$

The component of an event with the superscript zero in any S-frame is c

times the time of the event in that frame. The components with the superscripts 1, 2, and 3 are the x, y, and z spatial coordinates respectively of the event in that frame. *Notice carefully* that superscripts are not exponents; that is, x^2 now means y, not "x squared." In order to distinguish an exponent from a superscript, we shall always write an exponent outside parentheses. Thus in this new notation Eq. (13-2) becomes

$$(x^0)^2 - (x^1)^2 - (x^2)^2 - (x^3)^2 = (x^{0'})^2 - (x^{1'})^2 - (x^{2'})^2 - (x^{3'})^2 \quad (13\text{-}4)$$

The four components of the world point of an event are sometimes said to constitute a *four-vector*, and the world point of an event is sometimes called the *four-vector position* of the event.

The *square of the world distance* s^2 of an event from the reference event is defined by the equation

$$s^2 = (x^0)^2 - (x^1)^2 - (x^2)^2 - (x^3)^2 \qquad \text{definition} \qquad (13\text{-}5)$$

The world distance is sometimes called the *four-vector distance* or the *interval*. Comparing Eqs. (13-4) and (13-5), we see that *the square of the world distance of any event from the reference event is the same for observers in every S-frame*, or, more succinctly, *the square of the world distance to any event is the same in every S-frame*. Any quantity which is the same in all S-frames is called *Lorentz invariant* because it is invariant under a Lorentz transformation. Thus the square of the world distance to any event is Lorentz invariant.

Notice that the coordinates of the world point of an event in a given S-frame include both the spatial and the time coordinates of the event, so that the single world point describes completely the location of the event in space and time in that S-frame. Observers in different S-frames may fail to agree on some of the separate coordinates of the world point of an event, but they will all agree on the value of the square of the world distance of this event from the reference event.

One more matter of notation. The symbol $r^2 = (x^1)^2 + (x^2)^2 + (x^3)^2$ is reserved for the square of the *spatial* distance of a given event from the origin of the S-frame (at any time), and the symbol

$$(\Delta r)^2 = (\Delta x^1)^2 + (\Delta x^2)^2 + (\Delta x^3)^2$$

for the square of the spatial separation of two different events in that frame. On the other hand, the symbol $s^2 = (x^0)^2 - (x^1)^2 - (x^2)^2 - (x^3)^2$ refers to the square of the world distance of an event from the reference event in any S-frame, and the symbol

$$(\Delta s)^2 = (\Delta x^0)^2 - (\Delta x^1)^2 - (\Delta x^2)^2 - (\Delta x^3)^2$$

refers to the square of the world distance between two different events.

The value of s^2 for any event and of $(\Delta s)^2$ for any two events will be the same in all S-frames. The value of r^2 for any event and of $(\Delta r)^2$ for any two events will usually be different for different S-frames. Notice also that

$$s^2 = (x^0)^2 - r^2$$

and

$$(\Delta s)^2 = (\Delta x^0)^2 - (\Delta r)^2 \tag{13-6}$$

Questions

13-10 In frame S the spatial coordinates of a given event are

$$x = y = z = 10^9 \text{ m}$$

The event occurs at a time $t = 100$ sec in this frame. What is the square of the spatial distance to this event from the origin? What is the square of the world distance to this event? What are the squares of the spatial and world distances to another event which occurs at the same spatial coordinates at a time $t = 1$ sec?

13-11 The square of the world distance between two events is 9×10^4 m^2. In frame S the spatial distance between these two events is 400 m. What is the time interval between these two events in frame S? In a frame in which this time interval is three times as great, what will be the spatial separation between these two events?

13-12 Show that, if the world components of event number one are x^0, x^1, x^2, x^3 with respect to the reference event and if the world components of event number two are Δx^0, Δx^1, Δx^2, Δx^3 with respect to event number one, then the world components of event number two with respect to the reference event can be found by adding separately the components of event number one to the respective components of event number two taken with respect to event number one.

13.3 THE SUMMATION CONVENTION. One of the advantages of using the superscripts in the coordinates of the world point of an event is that any one of these coordinates can be indicated by the symbol x^α, where α can take on any one of the values $\alpha = 0, 1, 2,$ or 3. Now let us define another symbol e_α as follows.

$$e_0 = 1, \quad e_1 = e_2 = e_3 = -1 \qquad \text{definition} \tag{13-7}$$

Then Eq. (13-5) can be written

$$\begin{aligned} s^2 &= (x^0)^2 - (x^1)^2 - (x^2)^2 - (x^3)^2 \\ &= e_0(x^0)^2 + e_1(x^1)^2 + e_2(x^2)^2 + e_3(x^3)^2 \\ &= \sum_{\alpha=0}^{3} e_\alpha(x^\alpha)^2 \end{aligned} \tag{13-8}$$

where $\sum\limits_{\alpha=0}^{3}$ means the sum over the index α from 0 to 3. Because of the factor e_α the first term of this sum is positive and the rest are negative.

With one more slight modification we can present this equation in a simple and elegant form. Suppose we define components x_α with a subscript as follows.*

$$x_\alpha = e_\alpha x^\alpha \quad \text{for } \alpha = 0, 1, 2, \text{ or } 3 \qquad \text{definition} \tag{13-9}$$

The process of multiplying x_α by e_α is called *lowering the index*. Then Eq. (13-8) can be written

$$s^2 = \sum_{\alpha=0}^{3} (e_\alpha x^\alpha)(x^\alpha) = \sum_{\alpha=0}^{3} x_\alpha x^\alpha \tag{13-10}$$

In order to simplify the notation Einstein devised a *summation convention.* According to this summation convention, if two symbols, *one with a subscript and the other with the same superscript*, are multiplied, then by definition this product is to be summed over all four values of the index. As an example,

$$x_\alpha x^\alpha = \sum_{\alpha=0}^{3} x_\alpha x^\alpha \qquad \text{definition}$$

Whenever such a summation is not to be carried out, we shall label it "no summation." For instance, Eq. (13-9) should be written

$$x_\alpha = e_\alpha x^\alpha \qquad \text{no summation} \tag{13-9}$$

Using the summation convention, Eq. (13-10) may be written

$$s^2 = x_\alpha x^\alpha$$

and Eq. (13-4) becomes

$$x_\alpha x^\alpha = x_\alpha' x^{\alpha\prime}$$

Whenever a symbol has a Greek index (α, β, δ, . . .), we shall assume that this index can take on the values 0, 1, 2, or 3 and that summations involving Greek indices are over the same values. On the other hand, whenever a symbol has a Roman index (i, j, k, . . .), we shall assume that this index can take on only the values 1, 2, or 3 and that summations involving Roman indices are over these same three values. Thus the components of s are written x^α and the components or r are written x^i. Similarly,

$$s^2 = x_\alpha x^\alpha$$

whereas

$$r^2 = -x_i x^i$$

* The professional will recognize that we are introducing *covariant notation* without mentioning that term explicitly.

Questions

13-13 Write out each of the components x^α, each of the components x_α, each of the components x^i, each of the components x_i. Does $x_0 = x^0$? Show that $s^2 = x_0 x^0 + x_i x^i$.

13-14 Show that $x^\alpha = e_\alpha x_\alpha$ (no summation, of course, because both are subscripts). The process of multiplying x_α by e_α is called *raising the index*.

13.4 THE WORLD VELOCITY. The goal of our analysis of events in various S-frames is the description of the motion of a particle and the derivation of the laws of mechanics for this motion for the case in which the particle moves at velocities approaching that of light. Thus far our description has been of events rather than of particles. As a particle moves about, what events can we use to describe its motion? These events can be the arrival of the particle at particular locations in any frame S. In order to make these events observable by other observers in frame S or in other S-frames, they can be signaled by a flash of light from the location at which the particle has arrived and at the instant of this arrival.

The description of motion of a particle will certainly involve a determination of its *velocity*. What meaning can velocity have under relativistic conditions? The classical definition of velocity involves dividing the vector displacement of the particle by the time interval required for this displacement for very short time intervals. In the case of relativistic mechanics the distance separating the two events which describe two consecutive locations of a particle and also the time interval between these two events will depend on the relative state of motion of the observer so that the value of the observed velocity will be different for different observers. Once again, this definition of velocity is quite adequate to describe the motion of a particle in a single inertial reference frame, but it is neither very convenient nor very elegant when trying to compare the descriptions of this motion with respect to two or more S-frames.

Question

13-15 In frame S a particle moves with uniform speed $v = \Delta y/\Delta t$ along the y-axis. Show that in a frame S' the y' component of the velocity of the particle will have some value v' between the value v and zero.

One measure of "distance" between two events which would be agreed on by observers in every S-frame is the world distance between these events. An incremental *world displacement* might be used in the numerator in defining a "world velocity." The components of this world velocity might be of the form $\Delta x^\alpha/\Delta t$. But what about the value of the time interval Δt in the denominator? The measured length of this time interval will depend on the relative motion of the observer. Is there any measure of the time interval between two events on which all observers in uniform relative motion can agree? Certainly. They can all agree on the *proper* time interval between two events. Remember that the proper time interval between two events is defined as the time interval measured in that inertial frame in which the two events occur *at the same place.* Most S-frame observers will have to carry out a mathematical calculation to derive the proper time interval between two events from their own observations of these events, but the observers in every S-frame will agree on the proper time so calculated.

Let us see how such a calculation of proper time would be carried out. Suppose that in some frame S two events are separated by a distance Δr and a time Δt. What will be the proper time between these two events? In the first place, we know from Eq. (12-4) that the proper time $\Delta\tau$ will be related to the time Δt by the equation

$$(\Delta\tau)^2 = \left[1 - \frac{v^2}{c^2}\right](\Delta t)^2 \qquad (13\text{-}11)$$

where v is the magnitude of the uniform relative velocity between the frame S and the frame in which the two events occur at the same place. But the value of this speed must be given by $v = \Delta r/\Delta t$, since observers in a frame moving with that speed in the direction connecting the two events would see those two events occurring at the same place. Substituting this value for v into Eq. (13-11), we have

$$(\Delta\tau)^2 = \left[1 - \frac{1}{c^2}\left(\frac{\Delta r}{\Delta t}\right)^2\right](\Delta t)^2$$

$$= \frac{1}{c^2}\left[c^2(\Delta t)^2 - (\Delta r)^2\right]$$

$$= \frac{1}{c^2}\Delta x_\alpha \Delta x^\alpha$$

$$(\Delta\tau)^2 = \frac{(\Delta s)^2}{c^2} \qquad (13\text{-}12)$$

where the summation convention is assumed in the next-to-last expression.

Questions

13-16 What are the proper time intervals between the pairs of events described in Questions 13-10 and 13-11?

13-17 Show that the square of the proper time interval between two events which describe two consecutive locations of a particle will always be positive.

13-18 Show that the proper time interval between the emission of a light flash and its reception is zero.

Using the world displacement of a particle and the proper time interval, we can define an average world velocity for the particle. The components of this average world velocity will be $\Delta x^\alpha/\Delta\tau$, where $\alpha = 0, 1, 2$, or 3. The *instantaneous world velocity* involves a limit-taking process in which the proper time interval between events describing the world displacement of the particle is made smaller and smaller. The components of the instantaneous world velocity will be given by

$$V^\alpha = \lim_{\Delta\tau\to 0} \frac{\Delta x^\alpha}{\Delta\tau} = \frac{dx^\alpha}{d\tau} \qquad \alpha = 0, 1, 2, \text{ or } 3 \qquad \text{definition} \quad (13\text{-}13)$$

Because the world velocity has four components in any S-frame it is sometimes called the *four-vector velocity*. When referring to the components of the conventional velocity $v^i = dx^i/dt$ in a particular S-frame, we shall use lower-case letters and call them components of the *spatial velocity* of the particle to distinguish them from components of the world velocity. The quantity $v = \sqrt{(v^1)^2 + (v^2)^2 + (v^3)^2}$ will be called the *spatial speed* of the particle.

Questions

13-19 Show that in a particular S-frame the components of the world velocity of a particle are given by

$$\begin{aligned} V^0 &= \frac{c}{\sqrt{1 - v^2/c^2}} \\ V^i &= \frac{v^i}{\sqrt{1 - v^2/c^2}} \qquad i = 1, 2, \text{ or } 3 \end{aligned} \qquad (13\text{-}14)$$

where v is the spatial speed of the particle in that frame and v^1, v^2, and v^3 are the x, y, and z components respectively of the spatial velocity of the particle in this frame. Show that in the limit of low velocities $V^i \to v^i$.

13-20 A particle moves with constant spatial velocity from the position $x = y = z = 10^8$ m to the position $x = y = z = 2 \times 10^8$ m in 1 sec when observed in frame S. Find the components of the world velocity in this frame.

13-21 Show that $V_\alpha V^\alpha = c^2$, where, by definition, $V_\alpha = e_\alpha V^\alpha$ (no summation); i.e., that the square of the magnitude of the world velocity is Lorentz invariant. Show that this implies that V^0 is a function of the other three components V^i. From Question 13-19, show what this function is.

13-22 Show that the transformation equations which relate the components V^α of the world velocity of a particle in frame S to the components $V^{\alpha'}$ of the world velocity of the same particle in frame S' are

$$\begin{aligned} V^{0'} &= \gamma(V^0 - \beta V^1) \qquad & V^{2'} &= V^2 \\ V^{1'} &= \gamma(V^1 - \beta V^0) \qquad & V^{3'} &= V^3 \end{aligned} \qquad (13\text{-}15)$$

where the v which enters β and γ is the relative spatial speed of the two S-frames.

13-23 By a procedure similar to that used in defining the world velocity, define the components A^α of the world acceleration of a particle. Show that for very low velocities the last three components of the world acceleration are equal to the respective components of the spatial acceleration of the particle. Find the value of the summation $A_\alpha A^\alpha$, where $A_\alpha = e_\alpha A^\alpha$ (no summation), and show that the square of the magnitude of the world acceleration is Lorentz invariant. Show that $V_\alpha A^\alpha = 0$, where, by definition, $V_\alpha = e_\alpha V^\alpha$ (no summation). Derive the transformation equations for the components of the world acceleration between two S-frames.

13.5 THE WORLD MOMENTUM.

In a similar fashion we can define the *world momentum* of a particle as the product of the mass and the world velocity. For the mass we shall take the mass as measured at low relative velocities according to the procedure of Sec. 3.10. This is called the *rest mass* or the *proper mass*. We shall use the common symbol m for the rest mass.

The components of the world momentum are defined as

$$P^\alpha = mV^\alpha = m\,\frac{dx}{d\tau} \qquad \alpha = 0, 1, 2, \text{ or } 3 \qquad \text{definition} \quad (13\text{-}16)$$

When referring to the components of the conventional momentum $p^i = mv^i$ in a particular S-frame, we shall use lower-case letters and call them components of the *spatial momentum* to distinguish them from components of the world momentum.

Questions

13-24 Write out the components of the world momentum in a particular S-frame in terms of the spatial velocity and spatial momentum of the particle in this frame. Show that $P_\alpha P^\alpha = m^2c^2$, where, by definition, $P_\alpha = e_\alpha P^\alpha$ (no summation), i.e., that the square of the magnitude of the world momentum is Lorentz invariant. Show that at low velocities the last three components of the world momentum are equal to the respective components of the spatial momentum of the particle.

13-25 Show that the equations for the transformation of the components of world momentum between two S-frames are

$$\begin{aligned} P^{0\prime} &= \gamma(P^0 - \beta P^1) & P^{2\prime} &= P^2 \\ P^{1\prime} &= \gamma(P^1 - \beta P^0) & P^{3\prime} &= P^3 \end{aligned} \tag{13-17}$$

where the v which enters β and γ is the relative spatial speed of the two S-frames.

13.6 THE RELATIVISTIC ENERGY. Thus far in this chapter we have been devising convenient symbols for describing the motion of a particle, using the material of Chapter 12. No new physical result has been derived. In the remainder of this chapter we shall investigate these symbols to see in what way they can be used to describe the motion of a particle whose spatial speed approaches that of light.

In the first place, what is the physical meaning of the zeroth component of the world momentum? This component has the form

$$P^0 = m\frac{dx^0}{d\tau} = mc\frac{dt}{d\tau} = \frac{mc}{\sqrt{1 - v^2/c^2}} \tag{13-18}$$

where use has been made of Eq. (12-4). In order to discover what physical meaning this expression might have, let us investigate its form for very small velocities. This should give some clue to the corresponding quantity in the classical limit. Expanding the denominator by using the binomial theorem, we have

$$\frac{1}{\sqrt{1 - v^2/c^2}} = \left(1 - \frac{v^2}{c^2}\right)^{-1/2} = 1 + \frac{1}{2}\frac{v^2}{c^2} + \frac{3}{8}\frac{v^4}{c^4} + \frac{15}{48}\frac{v^6}{c^6} + \cdots$$

For very small relative velocities only the first two terms will be important. In this approximation P^0 becomes

$$P^0 = mc\left[1 + \frac{1}{2}\frac{v^2}{c^2}\right] \qquad \frac{v}{c} \ll 1$$

This can be written in a very suggestive form, namely,

$$P^0 = \frac{1}{c}\,[mc^2 + \tfrac{1}{2}mv^2] \qquad \frac{v}{c} \ll 1 \tag{13-19}$$

The second term in the brackets is simply the classical kinetic energy of the particle. So P^0 is somehow related to the energy. But, what is the first term in the brackets? It has the units of energy but does not depend on the state of motion of the particle. Einstein called it the *rest energy* of the particle. In the next section we shall see Einstein's remarkable interpretation of the significance of the rest energy.

Returning to the general case of Eq. (13-18) in which the speed of the particle in a given S-frame is *not* very much less than the speed of light, we can factor the right side of Eq. (13-18) in the same way as the right side of Eq. (13-19).

$$P^0 = \frac{1}{c}\left[\frac{mc^2}{\sqrt{1 - v^2/c^2}}\right] = \frac{1}{c}(\gamma mc^2)$$

By analogy to Eq. (13-19) we define a *total relativistic energy* W by the equation

$$W = \frac{mc^2}{\sqrt{1 - v^2/c^2}} = \gamma mc^2 \qquad \text{definition} \qquad (13\text{-}20)$$

so that Eq. (13-18) becomes

$$P^0 = \frac{W}{c} \qquad (13\text{-}21)$$

Since relativistic energy will include the rest energy defined above, we define the *relativistic kinetic energy* T by the equation

$$W = mc^2 + T$$

or

$$T = W - mc^2 = mc^2(\gamma - 1) \qquad \text{definition} \qquad (13\text{-}22)$$

Notice that *the kinetic energy T is equal to $\frac{1}{2}mv^2$ only for very low velocities.* Notice also that no potential energy terms have been included. Such terms might arise from interactions of masses with gravitational fields or interactions of charges with electric or magnetic fields. Such interactions are assumed to be absent in the present discussion.

Questions

13-26 Show that the total relativistic energy of a particle will depend on the particular S-frame from which it is observed. Is the rest energy Lorentz invariant?

13-27 The definition of relativistic kinetic energy in Eq. (13-22) has not yet been demonstrated to correspond to the measured kinetic energy of rapidly moving particles. Show how the results of the experiment outlined in Sec. 10.2 could be used to carry out this demonstration. Show that the qualitative results of that experiment are what one would expect if Eq. (13-22) gives correctly the kinetic energy of electrons.

13-28 A few cosmic ray particles have been observed which have a kinetic energy as high as 10^{19} eV. How long will it take a proton of this kinetic energy to cross our galaxy as measured on a clock carried with the proton? The rest mass of the proton is 1.67×10^{-27} kg. The diameter of our galaxy is approximately 100,000 light-years.

13-29 Show that

$$(P^0)^2 = (P)^2 + m^2c^2$$

or that (13-23)

$$W^2 = (P)^2c^2 + m^2c^4$$

where $(P)^2 = (P^1)^2 + (P^2)^2 + (P^3)^2$. (We shall use this relation in Project XI.)

13.7 THE CONSERVATION OF MOMENTUM AND OF MASS-ENERGY. In classical mechanics when two or more particles interact, the component of the total linear momentum of all the particles in each Cartesian direction is conserved. Is the same true of each component of the world momentum in relativistic mechanics? We have not learned how to describe the electric or magnetic or gravitational interactions of particles in relativistic mechanics, but let us consider the special case of a system of particles each of which is initially too far from any other particle in the system to interact in any of these ways; then let us consider the system of particles again after they have interacted and are once again too far apart to interact with one another. For the present we shall deal only with processes in which no light or other electromagnetic radiation is absorbed or given off, so that this radiation will not contribute or absorb momentum or energy during the interaction. If P_i^{α} refers to a particular component of the world momentum of particle i before the interactions and $\bar{P}_k^{\alpha}$ (note the bar) refers to the same component of the world momentum of particle k after the interaction, a law of conservation of world momentum would read

$$\sum_{i=1}^{N} P_i^{\alpha} = \sum_{k=1}^{N'} \bar{P}_k^{\alpha} \qquad \alpha = 0, 1, 2, \text{ or } 3 \tag{13-24}$$

where N is the number of particles present before the interaction and N' is the number of particles present after the interaction. Notice that Eq. (13-24) stands for four equations, one for each component α of the world momentum. It is assumed that the components of world momentum on each side of Eq. (13-24) are measured with respect to the same S-frame, because the separate components of world momentum are not Lorentz invariant.

We have not proved Eqs. (13-24). They represent an educated guess based on the symbolism we have developed. They must be verified experimentally. This verification is complete and striking and extends to a wider range of circumstances than we considered in developing Eqs. (13-24).

1. The equations have been verified in elastic nuclear collisions at relativistic velocities. Under these circumstances it is found that the spatial

momentum and the classical kinetic energy of the interacting particles are not necessarily conserved, but the components of world momentum are conserved.

2. The equations are correct even in nuclear reactions in which electromagnetic radiation is given off or absorbed, provided one includes in the momentum and energy terms the momentum and energy carried off by or absorbed from the electromagnetic radiation.

3. The equations are correct even if N is not equal to N', that is, if there are a different number of particles after the interaction than before. This can occur when particle-anti-particle pairs are created or annihilated or when nuclear or atomic particles are split apart or fused together.

We showed in the last section that the zeroth component of the world momentum can be considered to be $1/c$ times the relativistic energy. The relativistic energy of a particle is made up of two parts: a rest energy mc^2 and a relativistic kinetic energy. According to Eqs. (13-24) with $\alpha = 0$, the *total* relativistic energy of a system of particles will be conserved in the reactions we have considered. This conservation law applies to the rest energy and the kinetic energy of the system taken together, *not separately*. Thus is raised the possibility that, if the total rest mass of the particles after the interaction is less than the total rest mass of the particles before the collision, the difference will be converted to kinetic energy of the products. In fact, if a total rest mass Δm is lost, then from Eqs. (13-21), (13-22), and (13-24) an additional kinetic energy equal to $\Delta T = (\Delta m)c^2$ will appear in its place. If electromagnetic radiation is given off, it may carry off some of the energy (and momentum) released. If this is taken into account by letting the symbol ΔE represent the kinetic energy *plus* the radiant energy released when a mass Δm is lost during a reaction, we obtain Einstein's famous equation,

$$\Delta E = (\Delta m)c^2 \tag{13-25}$$

Since the velocity of light is so large, the total energy released can be very large even for a very small change in the total rest mass of the system.

Because of the possibility of converting rest mass to energy and the reverse, the first of Eqs. (13-24) is called the *law of conservation of mass-energy*. The entire set of expressions is called the *law of conservation of momentum and mass-energy*.

Questions

13-30 In a certain nuclear reaction the products of the reaction have a total rest mass which is 1 g less than the total rest mass of the reactants. How much energy in joules, is produced in this reaction? If 4.2×10^9 joules of energy are released in the explosion of one ton of TNT, how many tons of TNT would be required to release as much energy as the conversion of 1 g of rest mass to kinetic energy?

13-31 When 1 kg of hydrogen gas combines chemically with 8 kg of oxygen gas, 1.2×10^8 joules of energy are released. Show that the fractional change in rest mass corresponding to this much energy is so small as to be undetectable. Sensitive chemical balances can detect a relative change in mass of about 1 part in 10^7.

13-32 A particle moving along the x-axis of an S-frame strikes another particle which is initially at rest. All motion after the collision is along the x-axis. No change in rest mass accompanies the collision. Set up the Eqs. (13-24) for this collision in terms of the components of the spatial velocities of the two particles. You will find the solution of these equations for the final velocities of the two particles to be rather involved. The project at the end of this chapter presents elegant methods for solving collision problems such as this one.

13.8 THE DESCRIPTION OF MOTION OF A PARTICLE. THE WORLD LINE. Suppose that a particle of rest mass m moves about as observed from frame S. Using the method of reflected flashes, an observer in S can observe the particle in consecutive positions and find the coordinates of the world point of the particle, $x^0 = ct$, $x^1 = x$, $x^2 = y$, $x^3 = z$, at any time t on his clock. The locus of world points occupied by the particle as it moves about is called the *world line* of the particle in frame S. An example of a world line for a particle whose spatial motion takes place in the xy plane is shown in Fig. 13-1. The quantity $x^0 = ct$

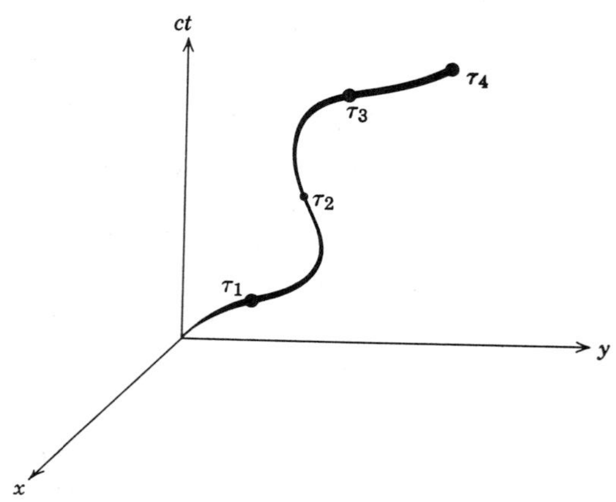

Fig. 13-1. Possible world line for a particle moving in the xy plane starting from the origin at $t = 0$. Note that the vertical axis is ct.

has been plotted on the vertical axis. For simplicity we have chosen the origin of frame S to coincide with the position of the particle at time $t = 0$, although this choice is not necessary. (Remember that the origins of *all* S-frames coincide at $t = 0$.) The graph of a world line for a particle moving in three spatial dimensions would require a four-dimensional plot and hence cannot be visualized.

Question

13-33 Describe qualitatively the position, spatial velocity, and spatial acceleration of the particle in Fig. 13-1 as a function of time in frame S.

Now the observer in S wishes to construct the components of the instantaneous world velocity and world momentum of the particle in his frame. To do this he needs to know the proper time interval between two subsequent positions of the particle. In fact, what he *really* wants to know is the *incremental* proper time interval $d\tau$ between two closely spaced positions of the particle. He can approximate this increment by illuminating the particle with his flasher as rapidly as his flasher will go and noting the time interval dt in his frame between the adjacent positions of the particle. Then, using Eq. (12-4), he can find $d\tau$.

$$d\tau = dt\sqrt{1 - v^2/c^2} \tag{13-26}$$

where v is the instantaneous spatial speed of the particle in his frame. If the components of the world displacement of the particle in his frame during the time interval dt (corresponding to the proper time interval $d\tau$) are dx^0, dx^1, dx^2, and dx^3, then the components of the world velocity of the particle in his frame are $dx^0/d\tau$, $dx^1/d\tau$, $dx^2/d\tau$, and $dx^3/d\tau$. The components of the world momentum of the particle in his frame are $m\,dx^0/d\tau$, $m\,dx^1/d\tau$, $m\,dx^2/d\tau$, and $m\,dx^3/d\tau$.

Question

13-34 In my inertial frame a particle of rest mass m follows a curve given by the equations

$$x = \frac{x_1 t}{t_1 + t}$$

$$y = v_1 t$$

$$z = 0$$

where x_1, v_1, and t_1 are constants. Find the equations for the world line of this particle in my frame, and the components of the world momentum at any time t.

Now suppose that the arrival of the moving particle at different locations is signaled by the emission of a light flash from each location at the instant of coincidence. If each coincidence and the emission of the flash occur at the same place and occur simultaneously for one observer, they will occur simultaneously for all observers (Assumption 2, Sec. 12.2). The emission of these flashes will all occur at the same place for an observer riding on the particle. An observer in S can calculate the proper time interval between two of these flashes.

If the particle emits a series of flashes closely spaced in proper time, then the interval of proper time between any two consecutive flashes can be calculated by the observer in S. Each such interval will have to be calculated from Eq. (13-26) by using the instantaneous spatial speed v of the particle and assuming that this speed is constant between flashes. By adding up the increments of proper time calculated in this way, the total proper time elapsed between the first and the last flash can be calculated, and for small enough time intervals the calculation of this total elapsed proper time will give the same result in every S-frame. If the origins of the S-frames are chosen in such a way that they not only coincide with each other but also with the particle at $t = 0$, then any point on the path of the particle can be characterized by a unique *proper* time as shown in Fig. 13-1. If a flash of light is emitted by the particle at any point, observers in every S-frame will agree on the proper time at which the flash was emitted. In each S-frame the calculation of the proper time can be symbolized by integrating Eq. (13-26).

$$\tau = \int_0^t \sqrt{1 - v^2/c^2}\, dt \tag{13-27}$$

where the spatial speed v of the particle in that frame may be a function of time.

Questions

13-35 A particle leaves the origin of frame S at $t = 0$ and thereafter moves with a speed given by the expression

$$t_1/(t_1 + t) = \sqrt{1 - v^2/c^2}$$

where t_1 is a constant. Find an equation for the proper time corresponding to time t in frame S. If t_1 has the value 100 sec, find the proper time τ corresponding to the time $t = 200$ sec on the clocks in frame S.

13-36 Set up but do not solve the equation for the proper time corresponding to a point on the path of the particle described in Question 13-34 in terms of the time t measured in that frame.

Observers in every S-frame can agree on the proper time corresponding to any point on the path of a moving particle if the proper time for some initial point on this path is given. If the particle moves with constant spatial velocity, the proper time corresponding to any point on its path will be equal to the time read at that point on a clock carried with the particle if the clock was set with the others at the initial point. We know this because under these circumstances we can find an inertial reference frame in which the particle is at rest, and in this frame the arrival of the clock at every point on its path occurs at the same place. Hence a clock carried with the particle will measure proper time *provided that the particle moves with constant spatial velocity.*

Now suppose that the particle moves with spatial velocity which changes in either magnitude or direction or both; that is, suppose that the particle experiences an acceleration. The proper time interval between an initial point on its path and some subsequent point can still be calculated by using Eq. (13-27),

$$\tau = \int_0^t \sqrt{1 - v^2/c^2}\, dt \tag{13-27}$$

in any S-frame, in which the particle occupies this subsequent point at a time t. This proper time interval will be agreed upon by observers in all S-frames.

Suppose that an accelerated particle carried a clock. Between two points on its path, will this clock read the same proper time interval calculated by using Eq. (13-27)? The answer is *not necessarily*. There is no way to predict how a given clock will behave when it experiences acceleration unless the details of the clock's construction are taken into account. Some clocks may read proper time, some may not. Our standard of time, the ephemeris second, is related to the period of revolution of the earth around the sun. If the sun were suddenly moved with a large acceleration, this particular timekeeping mechanism would be ruined. On the other hand, the atomic "vibrations" which govern atomic clocks are much less affected by acceleration of the atoms.

We may, if we wish, *define* an *acceleration-proof clock* to be one which reproduces the proper time interval given by Eq. (13-27) when it is carried with a moving particle, where v is the instantaneous speed of the clock in a particular S-frame. Whether or not we can find a real clock to correspond to this idealization will depend on the state of technology and the accelerations involved in a particular experiment. Even if no such clock can be found, Eq. (13-27) is a perfectly "operational" definition of proper time on which all S-frame observers can agree.

13.9 THE WORLD FORCE AND THE RELATIVISTIC LAWS OF MOTION OF A PARTICLE. In classical mechanics the time derivative of the vector momentum of a particle is equal to the resultant vector force acting on the particle. We can set up a corresponding expression for the proper time derivative of the world momentum. The physical meaning of this equation will have to be shown by further analysis. As before, the time derivative is taken with respect to the proper time, on which observers in every S-frame can agree. We shall *define* the components of this derivative to be the components of the *world force*, sometimes called the *four-vector force* or the *Minkowski force*.

$$\frac{dP^\alpha}{d\tau} = F^\alpha \qquad \alpha = 0, 1, 2, \text{ or } 3 \qquad \text{definition} \tag{13-28}$$

Questions

13-37 Show that in frame S the last three components of the world force have the form

$$\frac{1}{\sqrt{1 - v^2/c^2}} \frac{d}{dt}\left[\frac{m\, dx^i/dt}{\sqrt{1 - v^2/c^2}}\right] = F^i \qquad i = 1, 2, \text{ or } 3 \tag{13-29}$$

where v is the spatial speed of the particle in this frame. Show that as $v/c \to 0$ these equations become equal to the corresponding classical expressions.

13-38 Show that, for any world force, $V_\alpha F^\alpha = 0$.

13-39 Show that in frame S the zeroth component of the world force is equal to $1/c$ times the proper time rate of increase of the total relativistic energy of the particle. Show that in a reference frame in which the particle is instantaneously at rest this zeroth component is equal to zero.

13-40 Show that the transformation equations for the components of the world force between S-frames are

$$\begin{aligned} F^{0\prime} &= \gamma(F^0 - \beta F^1) \qquad & F^{2\prime} &= F^2 \\ F^{1\prime} &= \gamma(F^1 - \beta F^0) \qquad & F^{3\prime} &= F^3 \end{aligned} \tag{13-30}$$

where the v which enters γ and β is the relative speed of the two frames. Show that the square of the magnitude of the world force $F_\alpha F^\alpha$ is Lorentz invariant. Here $F_\alpha = e_\alpha F^\alpha$ (no summation).

Equation (13-28) is simply a definition of the world force. The zeroth component of this world force in any S-frame is the $1/c$ times the proper time rate of change of the relativistic energy of the particle in that frame, as you showed in Question 13-39. In Questions 13-37 and 13-39 you showed that in a reference frame in which the particle is (instantaneously) at rest, the last three components of the world force are equal to the components of the force discussed in classical mechanics, and that under these circumstances the zeroth component of the world force is equal to zero. This is not surprising, since in the limit of low velocities the laws of motion of a particle must become the classical laws of motion. We shall call the last three components of the world force in a reference frame in which the particle is instantaneously at rest the components of the *proper force*. We shall use the lower-case symbols f^1, f^2, and f^3 to represent the x, y, and z components of the proper force respectively. The three components of the proper force are equal to the components of the force applied to the particle according to the laws of classical mechanics. The zeroth component of the world force in this frame is equal to zero. We must now find a relation between the proper force and the world force.

Let us consider an example. A spring balance is attached to a particle of rest mass m initially at rest, and a force of one newton as read on the spring balance is applied to the particle in the positive x-direction. Now there is no ambiguity about the reading on the spring balance in any S-frame. Every observer can take a picture of the spring balance scale at his leisure, and every such picture will show the pointer indicating "one newton." Will this value of the applied force be equal to the x-component of the *world force* in every S-frame? Looking at the transformation equation (13-30), we see that the answer is no, because the magnitude of the x-component of the world force depends on the relative state of motion of the reference frame, while the reading on the spring balance does not. Let frame S be the S-frame in which the particle was initially at rest. Let frame S' be the S-frame in which the particle is instantaneously at rest at a particular time. In frame S' the particle will respond to the spring balance force according to the laws of classical mechanics because this corresponds to the limit of low velocity. The reading on the spring balance corresponds to the proper force component f^1. In this case the other two components of proper force f^2 and f^3 are equal to zero. From the inverse transformation equations corresponding to Eqs. (13-30), we can find the components of the world force in frame S in which the particle was initially at rest.

$$F^0 = +\beta\gamma f^1$$
$$F^1 = \gamma f^1$$
$$F^2 = F^3 = 0$$

where the v which enters β and γ is the spatial speed of the particle in the positive x-direction in frame S (or the spatial speed of frame S in the negative x-direction in frame S'). Using Eq. (13-28), the equation of motion in the x-direction is

$$\gamma f^1 = F^1 = \frac{d}{d\tau}(P^1)$$

Multiply through by $1/\gamma = \sqrt{1 - \beta^2}$.

$$f^1 = \sqrt{1 - \beta^2}\, F^1 = \sqrt{1 - \beta^2}\, \frac{d}{d\tau}\,(P^1)$$

But, from Eq. (13-26), $dt\,\sqrt{1 - \beta^2} = d\tau$, so this equation becomes

$$f^1 = \sqrt{1 - \beta^2}\, F^1 = \frac{d}{dt}\left[\frac{m\,dx/dt}{\sqrt{1 - \beta^2}}\right]$$

Thus we must identify the components of force applied according to the classical laws of mechanics to be equal to $\sqrt{1 - \beta^2}$ *times the corresponding component of the world force.* This result is easily generalized to include the application of y and z components of proper force f^2 and f^3 applied by a spring balance with respect to a frame S in which the particle is moving with velocity v.

$$f^i = \sqrt{1 - \beta^2}\, F^i = \frac{d}{dt}\left[\frac{m\,dx^i/dt}{\sqrt{1 - \beta^2}}\right] \qquad i = 1, 2, \text{ or } 3 \qquad (13\text{-}31)$$

Question

13-41 Complete the derivation of Eqs. (13-31).

Example 1. A particle of rest mass m is initially at rest at the origin of frame S. At $t = 0$ a spring balance exerts a force f^1 on the particle in the x-direction as measured on the spring balance. The reading on the spring balance is kept constant for all time. Find an expression for the velocity of the particle in frame S as a function of time.

Solution. Start with Eq. (13-31) with $dx^1/dt = v$.

$$f^1 = \frac{d}{dt}\left[\frac{mv}{\sqrt{1 - v^2/c^2}}\right]$$

Multiplying through by dt and integrating, we have, since f^1 is a constant,

$$\frac{mv}{\sqrt{1 - v^2/c^2}} = \int_0^t f^1\, dt = f^1 t \qquad (13\text{-}32)$$

The solution of this equation for v is

$$\frac{v}{c} = \frac{1}{\sqrt{1 + (mc/f^1 t)^2}} \qquad (13\text{-}33)$$

which is the desired expression.

Questions

13-42 Carry out the steps between Eq. (13-32) and Eq. (13-33).

13-43 Show that for short times Eq. (13-33) reduces to the usual classical expression.

13-44 Show that for very long times the velocity of the particle in frame S will approach but will not exceed the velocity of light.

13-45 Show that in frame S', which is instantaneously at rest with respect to the particle at a particular time, the acceleration has its classical value. The observer in S will agree that the clock and measuring rods instantaneously at rest with respect to the particle give this classical value for the acceleration. How does the observer in S interpret this difference in acceleration measured in the two systems?

Example 2. A particle is held on a circular path by a string of negligible mass one end of which is fixed at the origin of an S-frame. What is the tension in the string at the origin?

Solution. By symmetry the tension in the string will be the same at all points in the path of the particle. Suppose that the particle moves in the xy plane, and consider an instant at which the particle moves in the positive x-direction. At this instant the proper force in the y-direction, f^2 (as measured by a spring balance in the string), is equal to the tension in the string. Since the speed of the particle is constant, Eq. (13-31) becomes

$$f^2 = \frac{m}{\sqrt{1-\beta^2}}\frac{d^2(x^2)}{dt^2}$$

where $d^2(x^2)/dt^2$ is the acceleration of the particle on its circular path as measured in frame S. If the particle moves in a circle of radius R, this acceleration is simply v^2/R and the tension f is given by

$$f = (f^2) = \frac{m}{\sqrt{1-v^2/c^2}}\frac{v^2}{R}$$

13.10 ELECTRIC AND MAGNETIC FORCES IN THE THEORY OF RELATIVITY. The acceleration of atomic and nuclear particles to relativistic speeds usually involves the use of electric and magnetic forces. We have avoided mentioning electric and magnetic forces while developing the theory of relativity, because we have described these forces even for low particle velocities in only the most rudimentary manner consistent with the development of classical mechanics. If such forces are considered relativistically, it is found that electric and magnetic fields cannot be separated but must be combined in an appropriate way. This combination must be in such a form that it can relate the four components of the world position of a charged particle and the four components of its world velocity to the four components of the world force exerted on the particle by the "electromagnetic field." The necessary combination of electric and magnetic fields involves the use of *tensors*. Through use of the electromagnetic tensor, the laws of electricity and magnetism (which we have not studied in this book) can be expressed in a simple and elegant form. The paradox of magnetic forces mentioned in Chapter 11 is resolved when the relativistic laws of electricity and magnetism are used.

13.11 SOME DIFFICULTIES WITH THE THEORY OF RELATIVITY. We have learned how to predict correctly the motion of an uncharged particle moving with great speed with respect to a gravitation-free inertial reference frame. If we try to extend this analysis to a reference frame in which a static gravitational field exists, we observe that light will not always travel in a straight line in this frame but will be bent by the gravitational field. Since all of our analysis of the motion of objects involved straight line communication by means of light, the theory will have to be done over for the cases of reference frames in which static gravitational fields exist.

We know perfectly well how to set up an inertial reference frame in a uniform gravitational field. An elevator car which is in free fall in this gravitational field constitutes such an inertial frame. With respect to this elevator car, light will travel in a straight line and all the classical and relativistic laws of mechanics derived in this book will be valid. Indeed, the so-called *principle of equivalence* (see Sec. 9.2) implies that *all* the laws of physics are the same in this inertial frame as they are in inertial frames far from gravitating masses. Thus every mechanics problem in a uniform gravitational field could be solved with respect to an elevator car freely falling in that field. The motion predicted in the falling elevator car could then be described in the laboratory frame by an appropriate transformation of coordinates.

In nature, unfortunately, gravitational fields are not everywhere uniform. Consider the problem of predicting the path taken by a beam of light which passes through the gravitational field of the sun. At every point in this path we can predict its motion—it will be a straight line with respect to an elevator car in free fall at that point. But at different points on the path the gravitational field will be different both in magnitude and in direction. This means that the transformations which relate the falling elevator cars to the laboratory (or "sun") frame will be different at different points. It is the purpose of the theory of gravitation (sometimes called the general theory of relativity) to "patch" between local inertial frames which may be set up at any point of a gravitational field.

Thus the theory of gravitation has as its goal the rigorous formulation of the laws of physics in the presence of gravitational fields. In the limit of weak gravitational fields the theory of gravitation becomes the theory of relativity, which we have been studying in the last few chapters. In the limit of weak gravitational fields *and* low particle velocities the theory of gravitation becomes classical mechanics and electromagnetic theory. Hence the theory of gravitation contains, as special cases, all the physical theory developed in this book.

As the discussion above shows, the theory of gravitation is founded upon the principle of equivalence. One prediction of this principle has recently received experimental support of high sensitivity.* Nevertheless some aspects of the principle of equivalence are not supported by this or by any other laboratory experiments, so that parts of the experimental foundation under the theory of gravitation remain to be put in place.

It is interesting and not a little surprising that the gravitational force, which is the single force of which we are the most aware in our everyday lives, is analyzed rigorously only in the most mathematically sophisticated of the theories of physics. But then, this is only one of life's great surprises.

EXERCISES

13-1 Show that if we define the *relativistic mass* m_r by the equation

$$m_r = \frac{m}{\sqrt{1 - v^2/c^2}} \tag{13-34}$$

then Eq. (13-31) has the same form as in classical mechanics.

$$f^i = \frac{d}{dt}(m_r v^i) \qquad i = 1, 2, \text{or } 3 \tag{13-35}$$

How does the relativistic mass of a particle vary with the speed of the particle? What is the total relativistic energy of a particle expressed in terms of the relativistic mass of the particle?

13-2 Suppose that a particle moving in the x-direction is acted on by a force in the x-direction so that this force changes the speed v of the particle. Carry out the differentiation of Eq. (13-35) for the x-component. Show that the resulting equation can be reduced to the classical form $f^1 = m_l\, d^2(x^1)/dt^2$ if we define a *longitudinal mass* m_l by the equation

$$m_l = \frac{m}{(1 - v^2/c^2)^{3/2}} \tag{13-36}$$

13-3 Suppose that a particle moving in the x-direction is acted on by a force in the y-direction so that this force does not initially change the

* R. H. Dicke, "The Eötvös Experiment," *Scientific American*, **205**, 84 (December 1961).

speed v of the particle. Carry out the differentiation of Eq. (13-35) for the initial acceleration in the y-direction. Show that the resulting equation can be reduced to the classical form $f^2 = m_t\, d^2(x^2)/dt^2$ if we define a *transverse mass* m_t by the equation

$$m_t = \frac{m}{\sqrt{1 - v^2/c^2}} \tag{13-37}$$

13-4 Suppose that in the previous exercise the force continues to act on the particle in the y-direction. By setting $(v)^2 = (v^1)^2 + (v^2)^2$ in Eqs. (13-35), show that in this case the proper force is not parallel to the spatial acceleration.

Comment. The material structure of a particle does not depend on its uniform velocity. If it did, we could distinguish between inertial coordinate systems by looking at the structure of particles at rest in them. The concepts of relativistic, longitudinal, and transverse mass allow us to consider the motion of particles in a few simple cases in terms of the familiar equations of classical mechanics. The apparent "increase in mass" of a particle moving at a great velocity is due to the breakdown of the classical concepts of length and time, and not to any change in structure of the particle. There is some controversy among physicists about whether the relativistic masses are useful concepts or whether they conceal more than they reveal. If you find it convenient to think classically about particles *as if* their masses depend on velocity, do so; but do not attribute any profound property of matter to this concept of mass.

13-5 The speed of a particle moving in the positive x-direction of frame S is given by the equation

$$\frac{v}{c} = \frac{1}{1 + t_1/t}$$

where t_1 is a constant. Find an expression for the proper force exerted on the particle as a function of time t. Find expressions for all four components of the world force exerted on the particle as functions of time t. Set up an equation whose solution would enable you to express the components of the world force as functions of proper time. You do not need to solve these equations.

PROJECT XI. RELATIVISTIC COLLISIONS

The collisions of particles with high velocities can be analyzed by using the laws of conservation of momentum and mass-energy (Eqs. 13-24). We cannot analyze yet the details of interaction between the particles during the collision, since we have not treated electric or magnetic or gravitational interactions relativistically. Therefore we shall apply the conservation laws to initial and final states of the system before and after the particles have interacted and say nothing about the system during the interaction.

At the present time the analysis of relativistic collisions is used principally in studying collisions of elementary and nuclear particles. Such collisions are studied in order to learn about the properties of elementary particles and nuclear matter. The sources of projectiles for these collisions are cosmic rays, radioactive decays, and man-made accelerators. It is necessary to caution once again that elementary particles and nuclei are not "particles" according to the meaning of the word in classical mechanics, because they cannot be seen directly by the human eye. In what follows we shall apply the analysis of relativistic collisions of particles to some examples of collisions involving elementary and nuclear particles. A more careful analysis using quantum mechanics gives the same results for the examples treated here.

The important variables in the analysis of relativistic collisions are the components of world momentum (which include mass-energy). The spatial velocities of particles are rarely used in such an analysis because, in the first place, velocity does not have the simple relation to a conserved quantity (the momentum) that it does in non-relativistic collisions and, in the second place, the particles in relativistic collisions may be moving nearly at the speed of light. Under such circumstances very large changes in the components of world momentum may correspond to very small changes in speed.

Question

XI-1 The speed of a particle will be $0.99c$ when the kinetic energy is how many times its rest energy? For energies greater than this the speed will change by less than one percent!

We shall call the vector $\boldsymbol{P}$ with x, y, and z components given by P^1, P^2, and P^3 respectively the *spatial world momentum* of a particle. Thus the square of the magnitude of the spatial world momentum is given by $(P)^2 = (P^1)^2 + (P^2)^2 + (P^3)^2$. From Eq. (13-23) this magnitude of the spatial world momentum is related to the energy of the particle by the equations

$$(P^0)^2 = (P)^2 + m^2c^2$$

or (XI-1)

$$W^2 = (P)^2c^2 + m^2c^4$$

Question

XI-2 Show that the spatial world momentum vector of a particle points in the same direction as its spatial velocity vector.

ELASTIC COLLISIONS. Collisions are of two types: elastic and inelastic. Elastic collisions have the following characteristics: (*a*) the same number of particles and particles of the same individual rest masses leave the collision as approach the collision, and (*b*) no electromagnetic radiation is given off, or absorbed, by the system of particles.

Consider the following simple elastic collision (see Fig. XI-1). Two particles approach each other along the x-axis with equal but opposite x components of world momentum. Notice that, since the masses of the two particles may not be equal, their spatial speeds may not be equal either.

Class Discussion Question

XI-3 Show that as the two particles approach or recede there will be some disagreement between observers in different S-frames about whether or not the motion is being analyzed "simultaneously" for the two particles. Show that, as long as the particles do not interact with each other or with other particles, this difference in simultaneity creates no difficulty in comparing the analysis between S-frames.

Since the spatial world momenta of the two particles are equal and opposite, the total spatial world momentum of the system is equal to zero

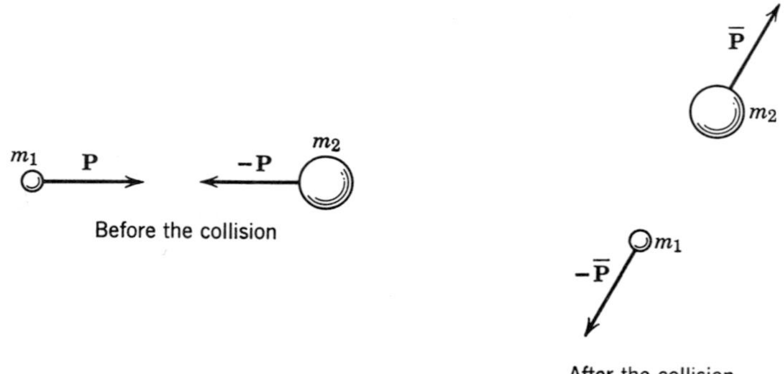

Fig. XI-1. Elastic collision observed in the center of mass frame.

before the collision. From the conservation equations, every component of the total world momentum must be conserved in the collision. Hence the spatial components must be conserved, so that the total spatial world momentum of the system must be equal to zero after the collision.

Since we have assumed that this is an elastic collision, two particles will leave the collision. This means that the spatial world momenta of the two particles must be oppositely directed. If they were not, there would be a non-zero component of the total spatial world momentum perpendicular to the spatial world momentum of either particle after the collision. In addition, the spatial world momenta of the two particles must be equal in magnitude. If they were not, the resultant component of spatial world momentum along their common line of motion would not be equal to zero.

We have shown that after the collision the spatial world momenta of the two particles are equal in magnitude and opposite in direction. Using the conservation of the zeroth component of world momentum (the conservation of mass-energy), we shall now show that the magnitude of the spatial world momentum of each particle after the collision is equal to the magnitude of its spatial world momentum before the collision. If we use bars over the symbols to represent quantities after the collision and subscripts which refer to the particle, the law of conservation of mass-energy reads

$$P_1^{\,0} + P_2^{\,0} = \bar{P}_1^{\,0} + \bar{P}_2^{\,0} \tag{XI-2}$$

Since the zeroth component of world momentum of a particle always has a value greater than zero, we may substitute the positive square root of both sides of Eq. (XI-1) for each term in Eq. (XI-2).

$$\sqrt{(P)^2 + m_1^{\,2}c^2} + \sqrt{(P)^2 + m_2^{\,2}c^2} = \sqrt{(\bar{P})^2 + m_1^{\,2}c^2} + \sqrt{(\bar{P})^2 + m_2^{\,2}c^2}$$

In this equation we have used the results found above that $(P_1)^2 = (P_2)^2 = (P)^2$ and $(\bar{P}_1)^2 = (\bar{P}_2)^2 = (\bar{P})^2$ and the added condition for an elastic collision that $\bar{m}_1 = m_1$ and $\bar{m}_2 = m_2$. This equation can be satisfied only if $(\bar{P})^2 = (P)^2$. In other words, the magnitude of the spatial world momentum of each particle after the collision is equal to the magnitude of its spatial world momentum before the collision.

We have shown that, in an elastic collision between two particles which approach each other with equal and opposite spatial world momenta, the final spatial world momenta are also equal and opposite and are equal in magnitude to the spatial world momenta of the particles before the collision. *The angle between the lines along which the initial and final spatial world momenta lie is irrelevant to these conclusions and may be different for different collisions.*

A more common experimental situation using cosmic rays or particles from an accelerator is one in which a high energy particle collides with

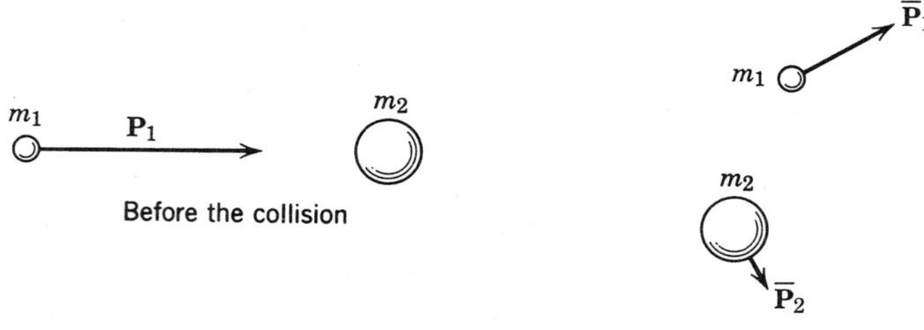

Fig. XI-2. Elastic collision observed in the laboratory frame.

another particle which is initially at rest (Fig. XI-2). Choose the x-axis parallel to the spatial world momentum of the incoming particle and the y-axis so that both final spatial world momenta lie in the xy plane. Once again, let superscripts refer to components and subscripts refer to the particle. Then the conservation laws become

$$\begin{aligned} P_1{}^0 + P_2{}^0 &= \bar{P}_1{}^0 + \bar{P}_2{}^0 \\ P_1{}^1 &= \bar{P}_1{}^1 + \bar{P}_2{}^1 \\ 0 &= \bar{P}_1{}^2 + \bar{P}_2{}^2 \end{aligned}$$

There are thus three equations in the six unknowns on the right sides of these equations. Equation (XI-1) provides two more equations,

$$\begin{aligned} (\bar{P}_1{}^0)^2 &= (\bar{P}_1)^2 + m_1{}^2c^2 \\ (\bar{P}_2{}^0)^2 &= (\bar{P}_2)^2 + m_2{}^2c^2 \end{aligned}$$

Thus we have five equations in six unknowns. One more condition is required to solve the equations. This added condition might be the direction of motion of one of the particles after the collision or the energy or spatial world momentum of one of the particles after the collision. This gives the sixth equation in the six unknowns $\bar{P}_1{}^0, \bar{P}_1{}^1, \bar{P}_1{}^2, \bar{P}_2{}^0, \bar{P}_2{}^1, \bar{P}_2{}^2$. The solution of such a set of equations is complicated, to say the least, compared with the ease with which the elastic collision problem was solved in a reference frame in which the net spatial world momentum of the system was zero.

Let the S-frame in which the x, y, and z components of the total world momentum of a system of particles is equal to zero be called the *center of mass frame*. We shall see later that this name is a misnomer, but because it is in common use we shall adopt it. Let the S-frame in which observations are carried out experimentally be called the *laboratory frame*. One way to solve collision problems is to transform the initial conditions into the center of mass frame, solve the problem in this frame, and then transform the solutions to the laboratory frame again. But what is the velocity of the center of mass frame with respect to the laboratory frame for a given system of particles? The following problem will lead toward an answer to this question.

Question

XI-4 Suppose that a single particle moves along the x-axis. Suppose also that we do not know either its rest mass or its spatial speed, but we do know that the zeroth and first components of its world momentum have the values P^0 and P^1 respectively. Show that the speed v of this particle (i.e., the speed of the frame in which the x, y, and z components of its world momentum are all equal to zero) is given by the equation

$$v/c = P^1/P^0 \tag{XI-3}$$

Now return to the case of a particle of high energy colliding with another particle which is initially either at rest or moving along the x-axis. Let the components of the total world momentum of the two particles in the laboratory frame have the symbols P^0, P^1, P^2, and P^3. Then

$$P^0 = P_1{}^0 + P_2{}^0$$
$$P^1 = P_1{}^1 + P_2{}^1$$
$$P^2 = P^3 = 0$$

where subscripts refer to the particles, superscripts refer to the components. We know the components of total world momentum of a system of particles, and we want to find the speed v_{cm} of an S-frame in which the x, y, and z components of total world momentum are equal to zero. This is, by definition, the speed of the center of mass frame. This is formally the same problem that you answered in Question XI-4, and the answer is the same.

$$\beta_{\text{cm}} = \frac{v_{\text{cm}}}{c} = \frac{P^1}{P^0} = \frac{P_1{}^1 + P_2{}^1}{P_1{}^0 + P_2{}^0}$$

Notice that this can be written

$$\beta_{\text{cm}} = \frac{v_{\text{cm}}}{c} = \frac{(P_1{}^1 + P_2{}^1)c}{W_1 + W_2} \tag{XI-4}$$

where W_1 and W_2 are the total relativistic energies of particles one and two respectively in the laboratory frame. For a larger system of particles which have velocity components not only along the x-axis of the laboratory frame the generalization of Eq. (XI-4) is

$$\frac{v_{\text{cm}}{}^i}{c} = \frac{\sum_k P_k{}^i c}{\sum_k W_k} \qquad i = 1, 2, \text{ or } 3 \tag{XI-5}$$

In this equation $v_{\text{cm}}{}^i$ is the ith component of the spatial velocity of the center of mass frame with respect to the laboratory frame in which the kth particle has spatial world momentum components $P_k{}^i$ ($i = 1, 2,$ or 3) and total relativistic energy W_k.

Question

XI-5 Show that the center of mass system defined above is not the same as an S-frame at rest with respect to the center of mass as defined in Chapter 7. Show that a better label might be "center of momentum system."

We have shown how to find the spatial velocity of the center of mass the positive x-axis of the laboratory frame for a system of particles. If the positive x-axis of the laboratory frame is chosen to coincide with the direction of this velocity, Eqs. (13-17) and their inverse can be used to transform the components of initial world momentum into the center of mass frame and the components of final world momentum back into the laboratory frame. Elastic relativistic collision problems can be solved by this procedure.

Questions

XI-6 A particle of initial spatial world momentum $\mathbf{P}_1$ collides elastically with a particle of equal rest mass which is initially at rest. After the collision one of the particles moves forward in the same direction as the incident particle. Find the direction of motion of the other particle and the spatial world momenta of both particles after the collision.

XI-7* Particle one of mass m_1 and total relativistic energy W_1 rebounds elastically from particle two of mass m_2 which is initially at rest. The final velocity of particle one is opposite to its initial velocity. Using Eqs. (XI-4) and (XI-1), show that the speed of the center of mass is

$$v_{\text{cm}} = \frac{c\sqrt{W_1{}^2 - m_1{}^2c^4}}{W_1 + m_2c^2} \tag{XI-10}$$

Show that the total relativistic energy of particle two both before and after the collision in the center of mass frame (indicated by primes) is

$$W_2' = \overline{W}_2' = \frac{m_2c^2}{\sqrt{1 - v_{\text{cm}}{}^2/c^2}}$$

Use the inverse of Eq. (13-17), namely,

$$P^0 = \gamma(P^{0'} + \beta P^{1'})$$

* For the treatment of more general cases and a discussion of these results, see L. Landau and E. Lifshitz, *The Classical Theory of Fields*, Addison-Wesley Press Inc., Cambridge, Mass., 1962, Sec. 13.

to show that the energy $\overline{W}_2$ of particle two after the collision in the laboratory frame is

$$\overline{W}_2 = m_2c^2 + \frac{2m_2(W_1^{\,2} - m_1^{\,2}c^4)}{m_1^{\,2}c^2 + m_2^{\,2}c^2 + 2m_2W_1} \tag{XI-11}$$

where the second term on the right side of the equation is the kinetic energy of particle two obtained during the collision. From the conservation of energy, show that the energy $\overline{W}_1$ of particle one after the collision is given by

$$\overline{W}_1 = W_1 - \frac{2m_2(W_1^{\,2} - m_1^{\,2}c^4)}{m_1^{\,2}c^2 + m_2^{\,2}c^2 + 2m_2W_1} \tag{XI-12}$$

XI-8 A 30-GeV electron rebounds elastically from a proton which is initially at rest. The final velocity of the electron is opposite to its initial velocity. Find the approximate kinetic energy of each particle after the collision. Approximate the rest energy of the electron by $m_1c^2 = \frac{1}{2} \times 10^{-3}$ GeV and of the proton by $m_2c^2 = 1$ GeV.

INELASTIC COLLISIONS. Inelastic collisions are collisions which are not elastic: that is, particles which leave an inelastic collision may have individual rest masses or a total rest mass different from those which approach the collision, or particles may be created or annihilated during the collision, or electromagnetic radiation may be given off, or absorbed, by the system of particles, or some combination of these effects may occur. We have already presented the experimental result that the conservation laws (Eqs. 13-24) hold true for inelastic collisions as well as elastic ones. Because of this experimental result, the analysis of collisions in the center of mass system is simplified for inelastic collisions, just as it is for elastic collisions.

Questions

XI-9 In a center of mass system, two particles of equal rest mass approach each other with equal and opposite spatial velocities. They collide and stick together after the collision. Find the final velocity of the combined particle in this frame. Show that the rest mass of the combined particle is greater than the sum of the rest masses of the original particles. This increase in rest mass corresponds to an increase in some form of energy of the combined particle; for instance, heat energy if the particles are made of clay, or an excited nuclear state or if the particles are nuclei.

XI-10 Two particles of rest mass m_1 and m_2 approach each other with spatial momenta P_1 and P_2 in the center of mass frame. Two new particles of equal rest mass M, and only these two new particles, emerge from the collision. With what spatial momenta do these new particles move?

Collisions involving photons. Inelastic collisions may involve the emission or absorption of electromagnetic radiation. In the study of mechanics in Chapters 1 through 9 we neglected the energy and momentum which light carries into or away from an interaction between visible particles. Such treatment is usually justified in dealing with visible particles (but not always: remember the effects of solar light pressure on the orbiting astronomical observatory). In collisions involving elementary and nuclear particles, on the other hand, the emission and absorption of electromagnetic radiation (usually so-called gamma rays, which are photons with very short wavelength) can involve significant quantities of energy and momentum. Two-particle collisions often involve the emission or absorption of one or a few photons (see Sec. 11.2). How can the effect of photons on a collision be predicted? An analysis using relativistic quantum electromagnetic theory shows that correct answers to collision problems will be obtained if a photon of frequency ν is treated as a particle of zero rest mass and total relativistic energy $h\nu$ (where h is Planck's constant), and with a magnitude of the spatial world momentum equal to

$$P = \sqrt{(P^1)^2 + (P^2)^2 + (P^3)^2} = \frac{h\nu}{c} \tag{XI-6}$$

For instance, suppose that we choose the direction of the y-axis so that a given photon moves in the xy plane in a direction which makes an angle θ with the positive x-axis. Then our assumption says that the four components of world momentum of the photon are

$$\begin{aligned} P^0 &= \frac{W}{c} = \frac{h\nu}{c} \\ P^1 &= \frac{h\nu}{c}\cos\theta \\ P^2 &= \frac{h\nu}{c}\sin\theta \\ P^3 &= 0 \end{aligned} \tag{XI-7}$$

If we treat the photon as a particle with these characteristics, several important results follow.

1. For a conventional particle the summation $P_\alpha P^\alpha = m^2c^2$. For the photon, Eqs. (XI-7) give $P_\alpha P^\alpha = 0$. This is consistent with the assumption that the photon has zero rest mass.
2. Since all photons move with a speed c in every S-frame, there is no "rest frame" for photons as there is for ordinary particles.
3. In different S-frames a given photon will be observed to have different frequencies. Suppose that a photon is observed to have a

frequency ν and to be moving at an angle θ with respect to the positive x-axis of some frame S. Then we can use transformation equations (13-17) and Eq. (XI-7) to find its frequency ν' and angle θ' in frame S', which moves in the positive x-direction with velocity v with respect to frame S. The results are

$$\nu' = \nu\gamma(1 - \beta \cos \theta)$$

$$\cos \theta' = \frac{\cos \theta - \beta}{1 - \beta \cos \theta} \qquad \text{(XI-8}a\text{)}$$

This change in observed frequency is called the *relativistic Doppler shift.*

Questions

XI-11 Carry out the derivation of Eq. (XI-8*a*). Show that the inverse transformations are

$$\nu = \frac{\nu'}{\gamma(1 + \beta \cos \theta')}$$

$$\cos \theta = \frac{\cos \theta' + \beta}{1 + \beta \cos \theta'} \qquad \text{(XI-8}b\text{)}$$

XI-12 A flasher at rest in frame S' emits photons uniformly in all directions with respect to that frame. Using Eqs. (XI-8*a*) and (XI-8*b*), show that, in a frame S in which the flasher is moving with speed v in the positive x-direction, the photons will not appear to be emitted uniformly in all directions but rather will be concentrated toward the forward direction. This is called the *headlight effect.*

XI-13 At the distance of the earth from the sun but outside the earth's atmosphere, the flux of photons from the sun carries an energy of about 1.40×10^3 joules every second through an area of 1 m^2 perpendicular to this flux. Find the pressure due to this light on a perfectly absorbing surface placed perpendicular to the direction of incoming photons. Verify the approximate pressure of this light on a smooth perfectly reflecting surface given as 9×10^{-6} N/m^2 in Project VIII at the end of Chapter 8. If the angle of incidence of photons is equal to the angle of reflection, how would you calculate the pressure of this light on a smooth perfectly reflecting surface whose normal is inclined at an angle θ with respect to the incident photons? What pressure would you expect on a *rough* perfectly reflecting surface perpendicular to the incident photons? on a *real* surface (i.e., a rough partially reflecting surface)?

In 1922 Arthur H. Compton discovered that, if X-rays are scattered by electrons, the scattered X-rays have a frequency different from the incident X-rays and that the frequency of the scattered X-rays depends on the angle through which they are scattered. Such a process is called *Compton*

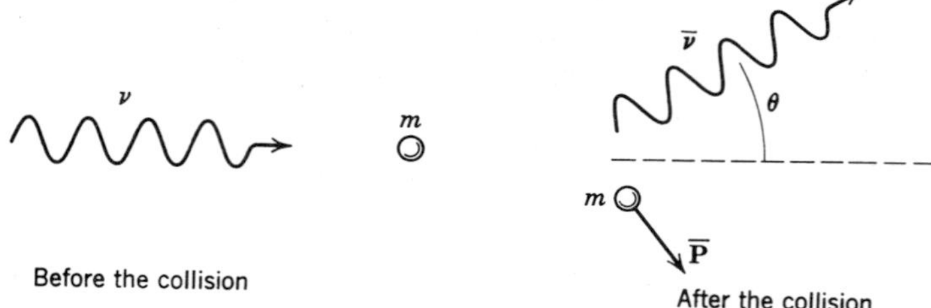

Fig. XI-3. Compton scattering.

scattering. This phenomenon may be described as a relativistic collision.

In Fig. XI-3 a photon of initial frequency ν "collides" with an electron of rest mass m. After the collision the photon has a frequency $\bar{\nu}$ and moves along a line which makes an angle θ with the direction of the incident photon. Let the y-axis be chosen so that the path of the scattered photon lies in the xy plane. Let the components of world momentum of the electron after the collision have the symbols $\bar{P}^0 = \bar{W}/c$, $\bar{P}^1$, $\bar{P}^2$, and $\bar{P}^3$. Then, from the conservation laws,

$$\frac{h\nu}{c} + mc = \frac{h\bar{\nu}}{c} + \frac{\bar{W}}{c}$$

$$\frac{h\nu}{c} = \frac{h\bar{\nu}}{c}\cos\theta + \bar{P}^1$$

$$0 = \frac{h\bar{\nu}}{c}\sin\theta + \bar{P}^2$$

$$0 = \bar{P}^3$$

Solve these equations for $\bar{W}$, $\bar{P}^1$, and $\bar{P}^2$ and substitute into Eq. (XI-1).

$$\bar{W}^2 = (\bar{P})^2c^2 + m^2c^4 \tag{XI-1}$$

where $(\bar{P})^2 = (\bar{P}^1)^2 + (\bar{P}^2)^2 + (\bar{P}^3)^2$. The resulting expression can be solved for $\bar{\nu}$, the frequency of the photon after scattering.

$$\bar{\nu} = \frac{\nu}{1 + (h\nu/mc^2)(1 - \cos\theta)} \tag{XI-9}$$

Question

XI-14 Complete the derivation of Eq. (XI-9). Show that, if the energy of the incoming photon is very much less than the rest energy of the electron, the incident and scattered photons have the same frequency.

Now you have sufficient background material to solve most relativistic collision problems. The question whether or not a given nuclear reaction will occur during a collision is part of the study of nuclear physics. However, given the products of a real or possible reaction and the initial conditions, you can analyze the final state of the system after the collision. In addition you can show that some reactions cannot occur because they would violate the conservation laws.

TABLE XI-1

Rest Masses and Rest Energies of Some Particles

Particle	Rest Mass in units of the electron mass	mc^2, in units of MeV
Electron and positron	1	0.511
μ^+ meson and μ^- meson	206.8	105.7
π^0 meson	264.4	135.1
π^+ meson and π^- meson	273.2	139.6
Proton and anti-proton	1836.1	938.21
Neutron	1838.7	939.50
Deuteron	3671.3	1875.41
Alpha-particle	7296.1	3727.07

The initial conditions of a collision problem are often specified in terms of the energies of the particles involved. In solving such problems it is convenient to have values for the rest energies mc^2 of particles. Values of mc^2 for several elementary particles are presented in Table XI-1 in units of million electron volts (MeV).

Questions

XI-15 When the kinetic energy of a moving particle is what fraction of its rest energy will its speed be equal to one-tenth the speed of light? Note that this kinetic energy can be calculated approximately by using classical mechanics. We have used this speed as an approximate dividing line between classical and relativistic mechanics. From Table XI-1 find the values for this kinetic energy for the electron and the proton in units of MeV.

XI-16 When two or more elementary particles fuse to form a nucleus, energy is given off in the form of photons or kinetic energy or both. The energy given off in this way results in a decrease of the rest mass of the resulting nucleus. This energy is called the *binding energy* of the nucleus because the same amount of energy must be supplied in order to break the nucleus apart again into the elementary particles of which it is composed. The deuteron is made up of a proton and a neutron. From Table XI-1 find the binding energy of the deuteron in MeV. The alpha particle (which is the same as the helium nucleus) is made up of two protons and two neutrons. From the table find the binding energy of the alpha-particle in MeV.

XI-17 In a center of mass frame a proton and an anti-proton approach each other with equal kinetic energy T. They collide and annihilate each other. Only two photons are given off. What are the relative directions of emission of the two photons in the center of mass frame? What is the frequency of each photon in this frame?

XI-18 A π^0 meson decays into two photons. In the rest S-frame of the π^0 meson these photons are emitted in the positive and negative y-directions. In a laboratory S-frame the π^0 meson is moving along the positive x-axis with $\beta = 0.99$ when decay occurs. In the laboratory frame what is the energy of each photon and what angles do the paths of the photons make with the x-axis? You may express energy in MeV if you wish.

XI-19 Modify Eq. (XI-5) for the components of velocity of the center of mass frame (i.e., the frame in which the x, y, and z components of total world momentum are equal to zero) to include a system containing photons. Give examples of systems containing *only* photons in which the velocity of the center of mass frame cannot be found. Are there systems containing only photons for which the velocity of the center of mass frame *can* be found?

XI-20 Consider the following hypothetical collision. A free electron originally at rest absorbs a photon without re-emitting it. Show that the conservation laws cannot be satisfied by this collision, i.e., that it is not physically possible. Can the conservation laws be satisfied if a free particle *emits* only a single photon? two photons? Can the conservation laws be satisfied if an electron attached to a nucleus absorbs a photon so that the electron and the nucleus recoil separately from the collision?

XI-21 An electron and a positron approach each other with spatial world momenta which are equal in magnitude but opposite in direction. They collide and annihilate each other near a nucleus. After the collision a single photon is emitted. Set up equations whose solutions would give the frequency of the photon emitted and the recoil spatial world momentum of the nucleus.

XI-22 Show that the conservation laws would not be violated in the center of mass frame if all the kinetic and photon energy of a system were turned into rest mass (for instance, by the creation of new particles) so that all particles would remain at rest in this frame after the interaction. Show that in a frame other than the center of mass frame the conservation laws would not be satisfied by such a total conversion of kinetic and electromagnetic energy to rest mass.

XI-23 Consider the following problem. In a given interaction what is the maximum amount of energy available for the production of new particles? Show that in the center of mass frame this maximum amount of energy is equal to the total relativistic energy of the system. Using the Lorentz invariance of rest mass, show that in a given interaction the maximum amount of energy available for the production of new particles *in any frame* is equal to the total relativistic energy of the system in the center of mass frame. Using the equivalence of energy and rest mass, show that *in any interaction the maximum amount of energy which is available for any purpose* (such as the creation of particles, production of photons, increase of total kinetic energy) *is equal to the total relativistic energy of the system in the center of mass frame.* This important result will be useful in some of the following questions.

XI-24 A very energetic gamma ray (photon of very high frequency) produces an electron-positron pair. Show that this conversion of energy to mass will not satisfy the conservation laws (i.e., it cannot occur) if no other particles and no other incident photons are involved in the interaction.

XI-25 Suppose that a gamma ray produces an electron-positron pair in the presence of another nuclear particle of mass M which is initially at rest. Find the lowest energy gamma ray which can cause this reaction. [*Hint*: Proceed as follows: In the center of mass system the x component of the world momentum of the photon is equal and opposite to the x component of the world momentum of the particle of mass M. From Questions XI-22 and XI-23, if all the available kinetic and electromagnetic energy is turned into rest mass, the resulting particles will be at rest in the center of mass frame. Therefore the result in *any S-frame* is that, when a maximum amount of kinetic and electromagnetic radiation is turned into rest mass, the resulting particles will all move with the same velocity after the collision. Applying this result to the gamma ray incident upon a particle of mass M initially at rest, we see that the maximum amount of rest mass will result if the interaction looks as depicted in Fig. XI-4. Set up the conservation laws for this interaction and derive a relation containing only $h\nu$, c, M, and m, where m is the mass of an electron or a positron. Now let M become very large and show that for this case $h\nu = 2mc^2$. Gamma

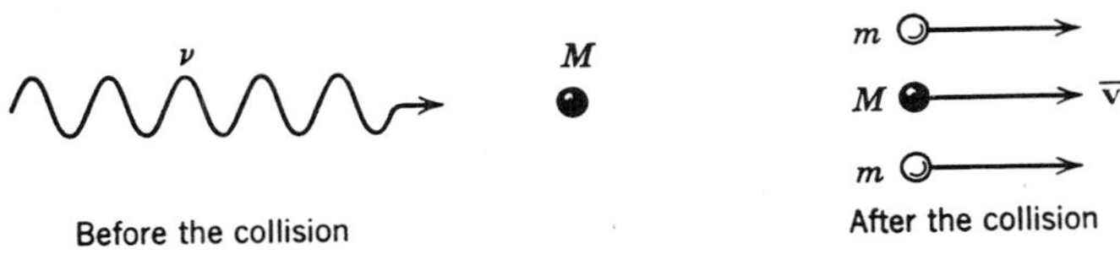

Fig. XI-4. Creation of maximum rest mass by a photon.

rays must have this frequency or a higher frequency in order to be able to produce an electron-positron pair in the presence of matter.]

XI-26 For particle one of mass m_1 and energy W_1 incident on particle two of mass m_2 initially at rest, use Eq. (XI-1), the transformation equations (13-17), and the results of Question XI-7 to show that the total energy $W_1' + W_2'$ of the two particles in the center of mass frame available for, say, the production of new particles is given by the equation

$$W_1' + W_2' = [2W_1m_2c^2 + m_2^2c^4 + m_1^2c^4]^{1/2} \qquad \text{(XI-13)}$$

For the extreme relativistic case in which $W_1 \gg m_1c^2$ and $W_1 \gg m_2c^2$ this equation becomes

$$W_1' + W_2' \simeq (2W_1m_2c^2)^{1/2} \qquad \text{extreme relativistic case} \quad \text{(XI-14)}$$

The result of Question XI-23 shows that the same amount of energy is available in any S-frame for the production of new particles. If 25-GeV protons are incident on protons initially at rest, how much energy is available in each collision for the production of new particles?

XI-27 A *colliding beam accelerator* consists of two accelerators which produce colliding beams of particles moving in opposite directions. If the colliding beams are made up of particles of the same rest mass and the same kinetic energy, then for collisions which take place between particles in the two beams the laboratory frame will also be the center of mass frame. Show that in the extreme relativistic case the energy available for, say, the production of new particles in each collision is approximately $2T$, where T is the kinetic energy of the particles in either beam. Thus two 30-GeV proton beams in such a colliding beam accelerator would provide an available energy of approximately 60 GeV. From the result of Question XI-26, what would be the necessary kinetic energy of protons from a single accelerator incident on protons initially at rest in order to have an energy of 60 GeV available for the production of new particles? The outstanding experimental problem in building a colliding beam accelerator is the difficulty in obtaining two beams intense enough that a useful number of collisions will occur.

appendix I

The ephemeris second

The derivation of the ephemeris second from astronomical observations will be explained first without corrections in order to convey the idea; then the corrections will be outlined.

If we are interested only in the *directions* of celestial bodies from the earth, the heavens can be replaced in thought by a very large sphere in which the stars, sun, and planets are embedded. This imaginary sphere must be large enough that relative to it the size of the earth is negligible. In this way the position of a given star on the imaginary sphere relative to other stars will be the same from every point on earth. This imaginary sphere is called the *celestial sphere*. The earth rotates on its axis at the center of the celestial sphere. In what follows shall be concerned mainly with the *relative* position of sun and stars on the celestial sphere with respect to one another, which will not depend on the rotation of the earth.

Along with the stars, the sun has a position on the celestial sphere. This position is hard to determine directly because we cannot see the stars when the sun is shining, but by noticing which stars appear in the east just before sunrise or disappear in the west just after sunset the location of the sun on the celestial sphere can be determined. This position can be determined more accurately by using planets visible during the daytime.

As the earth revolves around the sun, the background of stars against which we see the sun changes. This is equivalent to saying that the sun appears to move around the celestial sphere. The interval of one year is related to one complete circuit of the sun about the celestial sphere (corresponding to one revolution of the earth about the sun). We must now show how points of reference on the celestial sphere by which to measure one circuit of the sun are chosen.

The axis of rotation of the earth remains more or less fixed with respect to the fixed stars. The point on the celestial sphere at which the north pole of the earth points is called the *north celestial pole*. Right now the north celestial pole is near the star polaris. For the minute ignore the very slow motion of the north celestial pole among the stars; it will be considered later. In other words, suppose that the north celestial pole is fixed on the celestial sphere. Consider an imaginary circle drawn on the celestial sphere in such a way that it is overhead at every point on the equator of the earth. This circle is called the *celestial equator*. The celestial hemisphere which is on the same side of the celestial equator as the north pole of the earth is called the *north celestial hemisphere*.

Since the axis of the earth is inclined with respect to the plane of its orbit around the sun, the apparent motion of the sun on the celestial sphere is half in the northern celestial hemisphere and half in the southern celestial hemisphere. The line which the sun traces out on its path around the celestial sphere is called the *ecliptic*. The ecliptic is inclined with respect to the celestial equator and crosses it at two points at opposite sides of the celestial sphere. These points of intersection are called the *equinoxes*. The equinox at which the sun crosses the celestial equator in going from the southern celestial hemisphere toward the northern hemisphere is called the *vernal equinox*. The term vernal equinox is applied also to the time when the sun makes this crossing. (Equinox means "equal night" because when the sun is at either equinox the night and the day are of equal length. *Vernal* means spring since the summer in the northern hemisphere on earth occurs when the sun is most nearly overhead, i.e., after the vernal equinox.) No conspicuous star marks the position of the vernal equinox on the celestial sphere at present.

The length of time which it takes for the sun to traverse the celestial sphere once from vernal equinox to vernal equinox is called the *tropical year*. For reasons which will be discussed below, the length of the tropical year varies from year to year. This variation of the length of a tropical year can be predicted quite accurately. In fact, it is possible to determine by interpolation methods the length of a given tropical year which begins at some calendar date other than the vernal equinox. This fact is important in what follows.

The position of the sun on the ecliptic can be expressed in degrees, the whole circle of the ecliptic being divided into 360 equal degrees. By definition, zero angle is taken to be at the vernal equinox and the angle is measured toward the east from the vernal equinox. The position of the sun as specified by this angle is called the *longitude of the sun*.

By definition, the year 1900 began at the instant near January first of that year when the longitude of the sun was 279 deg 41 min 48.04 sec of arc. The *ephemeris second* is, by definition, 1/31556925.9747 of the tropical year which began at this instant. This definition of the ephemeris second is not exact, and it will be modified by the corrections which follow.

Several corrections need to be made. In the first place, the earth moves in an ellipse around the sun and with different speeds at different places in its orbit. This means that the sun will appear to move at different angular rates on different parts of its path around the ecliptic. In order to simplify calculations, astronomers have devised a fiction called the *geometric mean sun* which moves each day through equal geometric angles on the ecliptic. The geometric mean sun is so defined as to coincide with the position of the real sun when the earth is nearest to and farthest from the sun in its orbit. Neither of these points of coincidence is at the vernal equinox.

The vernal equinox is defined as one of the points of intersection of the celestial equator and the ecliptic. Careful observation shows that the position of the vernal equinox moves about slowly on the celestial sphere from year to year. This motion is due to the fact that the axis of the earth is not perfectly fixed in space but "wobbles" around an average direction while the average direction itself changes with time. The physical reasons for these motions are understood, but an explanation is too lengthy and too advanced to undertake here.* The result of these motions is that the vernal equinox oscillates about a mean position which itself moves. The mean position of the vernal equinox at any time is called the *mean vernal equinox of date*.

The definition of the *ephemeris second* is expressed in terms of the geometric mean sun and the mean vernal equinox of date. Carefully defined, the ephemeris second is the fractional part 1/31556925.9747 of the tropical year 1900. The tropical year is defined as the interval of time between subsequent arrivals of the geometric mean sun at the mean vernal equinox of date. The year 1900 began when the longitude of the geometric mean sun with respect to the mean vernal equinox of date was 279 deg 41 min 48.04 sec.

* See Herbert Goldstein, *Classical Mechanics*, Addison-Wesley Publishing Co., Cambridge, Mass., 1953, p. 163.

appendix II

The English system of units*

There are important differences between some of the standards used in Great Britain and the system in common use in the United States. This is particularly true of the units of liquid measure and the definition of the ton. However, the second, yard, pound mass, slug, and pound force are defined identically in the two countries. These definitions follow.

The second is defined in the English system in the same way as in the metric system. See Appendix I.

The yard is defined to be equal to exactly 0.9144 m. Other units of length of the system are fractions or multiples of the yard.

$$1 \text{ in.} = 1/36 \text{ yd} = \text{exactly } 2.54 \text{ cm}$$
$$1 \text{ ft} = 1/3 \text{ yd} = \text{exactly } 0.3048 \text{ m}$$
$$1 \text{ mile} = 1760 \text{ yd} = 5280 \text{ ft} = \text{exactly } 1.609344 \text{ km}$$

Before we can understand the English units of force and mass, we must introduce the *standard acceleration of gravity*. The standard acceleration of gravity is approximately equal to the measured acceleration of gravity at 45 degrees north latitude on the surface of the earth. Since the exact acceleration of gravity at 45 degrees latitude varies from place to place because of local geological structures, the standard acceleration of gravity is defined to be equal to 9.80665 m/sec^2, which is equal to 32.1740 ft/sec.^{2}

There are two principal English units of mass and one principal unit of force. The first unit of mass is the pound mass, sometimes called the avoirdupois pound (abbreviation: lb mass or lb av.). The pound mass is, by definition, equal to exactly 0.45359237 kg. The unit of force is the pound

* See U.S. Department of Commerce, *National Bureau of Standards Letter Circular* 1035 or replacement.

of force (abbreviation: lb force). By definition, the pound of force is equal to the force necessary to accelerate a pound mass with the standard acceleration of gravity. The second unit of mass is the slug, which is equal to the mass of a body accelerated at 1 ft/sec^2 when acted on by 1 lb of force. Other units of mass are fractions or multiples of the pound mass:

1 ounce = $\frac{1}{16}$ pound mass = exactly 28.349523 g
one ton (one "short ton") = 2000 pounds mass = exactly 907.18474 kg

Questions

1 Consider a location at which the acceleration of gravity is equal to the standard acceleration of gravity. At this location how much does the standard pound mass weigh? How much does the standard slug weigh?

2 Show that one slug is equal to 32.1740 pounds mass.

3 Show how in principle the National Bureau of Standards can reproduce the pound mass, the pound of force, and the slug, using metric standards of mass, length, and time.

appendix III

Answers to selected exercises

Chapter 3

3-2 2.5×10^{-3} sec, 3.2×10^{3} m/sec, 32 newtons.

3-5 No collision, 20 meters minimum distance.

3-6 3×10^{6} sec, 46×10^{12} m, 4.8×10^{-3} light-year.

3-7 24 sec, $F = 8mg$.

Chapter 4

4-8

$$\int_{m_1}^{m_2} dm = m \Big|_{m_1}^{m_2} = m_2 - m_1$$

$$\int_{m_1}^{m_2} m\,dm = \frac{m^2}{2}\Big|_{m_1}^{m_2} = \tfrac{1}{2}(m_2^{\,2} - m_1^{\,2})$$

$$\int_{r_1}^{r_2} \frac{dr}{r^2} = -\frac{1}{r}\Big|_{r_1}^{r_2} = \frac{1}{r_1} - \frac{1}{r_2}$$

$$\int_{m_1}^{m_2} \frac{dm}{m} = \ln m \Big|_{m_1}^{m_2} = \ln m_2 - \ln m_1$$

$$\int_{t_1}^{t_2} \frac{d\mathbf{p}}{dt}\,dt = \mathbf{p}\Big|_{t_1}^{t_2} = \mathbf{p}_2 - \mathbf{p}_1$$

$$\int_{t_1}^{t_2} \mathbf{v}\cdot\frac{d\mathbf{v}}{dt}\,dt = \frac{1}{2}\int_{t_1}^{t_2} \frac{d(\mathbf{v}\cdot\mathbf{v})}{dt} = \frac{v^2}{2}\Big|_{t_1}^{t_2} = \frac{v_2^{\,2}}{2} - \frac{v_1^{\,2}}{2}$$

4-10 $\mathbf{v} = \frac{1}{2}t^2\hat{\imath} + \frac{1}{3}t^3\hat{\jmath} + \frac{1}{4}t^4\hat{k}$ m/sec

$\mathbf{r} = \frac{1}{6}t^3\hat{\imath} + \frac{1}{12}t^4\hat{\jmath} + \frac{1}{20}t^5\hat{k}$ m

4-12 $\mathbf{v} = t\hat{\imath} + (\frac{1}{3}t^3 + \frac{1}{2}t^2 + 3)\hat{\jmath} - 3t\hat{k}$ m/sec

$\mathbf{r} = \frac{1}{2}t^2\hat{\imath} + (\frac{1}{12}t^4 + \frac{1}{6}t^3 + 3t)\hat{\jmath} - (\frac{3}{2}t^2 - 2)\hat{k}$ m

4-14 42 km.

Chapter 5

5-1 $M/(m + M)$, where m is the mass of the incident particle and M is the mass of the particle initially at rest.

5-3 It depends on the velocity with which George can throw the empty oxygen tank. New question: What must this minimum velocity be?

5-5 $s = v_1^2/(2\mu_K g)$.

5-7 100 sec. The engineer will follow shortly thereafter.

5-9 $h = GM/(gR)$, where M is mass of the asteroid and R is its radius. Assumes that the velocity at takeoff is the same in the two environments. Is it? $v = (2GM/R)^{1/2}$.

Chapter 6

6-2 96,500 years.

6-4 2.3, 2.14, 24.4; 4.5×10^7 sec (about 1.4 years).

6-6 $d = GM/(aR)$, $P_{max} = ma(2GM/R)^{1/2}$, where d is the length of track, M and R are the mass and radius of the moon, a is the acceleration, P_{max} is the maximum power, and m is the mass of the payload.

Chapter 7

7-3 Only the center of mass.

7-5 Possible ultimate result is the earth and moon farther apart than at present revolving with the same faces always toward each other.

Chapter 8

8-1 $$\omega_{\text{final}} = \frac{I_1\omega_1 + I_2\omega_2}{I_1 + I_2}, \quad \frac{\Delta T}{T_{\text{initial}}} = \frac{I_1 I_2(\omega_1 - \omega_2)^2}{(I_1 + I_2)(I_1\omega_1^2 + I_2\omega_2^2)}$$

where ω_1 and ω_2 have the same sign if the initial rotations are in the same sense and opposite signs if in opposite sense.

8-3 2.6×10^6 newtons (over half a million pounds of force!).

8-5 40 hours, 2/5.

8-7 $\omega_f = \omega_1[2 + (L/R)^2 + 6mL^2/(MR^2)]^{-1}$, where ω_f is the final angular velocity of the beam, ω_1 is the initial angular velocity of the disk, L is the length of the beam, R is the radius of either disk, m is the mass of the beam, and M is the mass of each disk.

8-9 $a/g = [1 + M/(2m)]^{-1}$, where M is the mass of the disk and m is the mass of the particle.

8-11 $a/g = [1 + R^2/(2r^2)]^{-1}$, where R is the radius of the larger disks, r is the radius of the connecting disk.

8-13 $h_2 = \frac{2}{3}h_1$, where h_1 is the initial height of the center of the cylinder above its height at the lowest point of the trough and h_2 is the corresponding maximum final height. The sphere will go higher.

8-15 $s = (12/49)v_1^2/(\mu_K g)$, 3.1 meters.

8-20 $\cos\theta = 10/17$ or $\theta \approx 54°$, where θ is the angle between the vertical and the radius vector from the center of the large sphere to the center of the small sphere.

Chapter 9

9-2 0.2 m/sec^2.

9-5 $a = g\tan\theta$, where θ is the angle of the wedge. Compare this to Exercise 9–2.

9-6 $\mu_S < 1$, $\omega = \sqrt{\mu_S g/r}$, where r is the radial distance of the block from the center of the turntable.

9-8
$$v_r^2 = \frac{r_1^2\omega_1^2}{[1 + M/(3m)]}\left[1 + \left(\frac{M}{3m}\right)\left(\frac{r^2}{r_1^2} - 1\right) - \frac{r_1^2}{r^2}\right]$$

where r is the length of the rod, M is the mass of the rod, m is the mass of the particle, r_1 is the initial radius of the particle, and ω_1 is the initial angular velocity of the rod.

Chapter 11

11-2 1 sec, 1.03 sec.

Chapter 12

12-1 (2) $x' = -2.33 \times 10^8$ m

$t' = 1.2$ sec

$\tau = 0.94$ sec

(6) $x' = 5.8 \times 10^9$ m

$t' = 0$

(8) $x' = 0$

$t' = \tau = 0.6$ sec

12-2 12×10^8 m.

12-7 4×10^{-4} sec.

Index